3rd

NUMERICAL SOLUTIONS OF DIFFERENTIAL EQUATIONS

NUMERICAL SOLUTIONS
OF DIFFERENTIAL
EQUATIONS

H. LEVY
M.A., D.SC., F.R.S.E.

PROFESSOR OF MATHEMATICS AT THE IMPERIAL
COLLEGE OF SCIENCE, UNIVERSITY OF LONDON

AND

E. A. BAGGOTT
M.SC., A.R.C.S., D.I.C.

LECTURER IN MATHEMATICS, THE POLYTECHNIC,
REGENT STREET, LONDON

DOVER PUBLICATIONS, INC.

FIRST AMERICAN EDITION, 1950

DOVER PUBLICATIONS, INC.
1780 BROADWAY, NEW YORK 19, N. Y.

Published in England under the title

"Numerical Studies in Differential Equations"

PRINTED AND BOUND IN THE UNITED STATES OF AMERICA

PREFACE

THE methods described in this volume have been developed and tried out in practice during more than ten years in the Mathematical Laboratory at the Imperial College of Science and Technology. Although a great deal of it is here published for the first time, much of it has formed part of the systematic instruction of the many hundreds of students who have passed through the Department of Mathematics of that college during these years.

This, the first volume, concerns itself only with the actual solution of ordinary differential equations and the numerical examination of many of their properties. The determination of Characteristic Numbers (*Eigenwerte*) and the investigation of Orthogonal Properties in general are, however, omitted. These will be included in Vol. II, since such properties are primarily of importance in connection with the practical solution of partial differential equations. It is for this reason also that no attempt has been made to examine in detail the special properties of well-known equations (Legendre, Emden, Mathieu, etc.), except where these have illustrated general methods applicable to classes of equations of similar types.

Although frequent use has been made of Finite Difference methods, little knowledge of that subject is here required, and as far as possible such use has been accompanied by full explanations of the meaning, and sometimes of the derivation of the formulæ. The authors desire to express their appreciation of the typing assistance so generously given by Miss R. E. Taylor and the help in sketching some of the integral curves by Mr. A. W. King.

August, 1934.

CONTENTS

CHAPTER I

CHAPTER II

CHAPTER III

CHAPTER IV

CHAPTER V

CHAPTER VI

GRAPHICAL INTEGRATION OF DIFFERENTIAL EQUATIONS

Descriptive Process for First Order Equations

1. General remarks.

If x is an independent variable, y a dependent variable, $\frac{dy}{dx}, \frac{d^2y}{dx^2}, \cdots \frac{d^ny}{dx^n}$, the first n differential coefficients of y with respect to x, then a differential equation is a relation between all or some of the numbers

$$x, y, \frac{dy}{dx}, \cdots \frac{d^ny}{dx^n},$$

in which one differential coefficient at least occurs.

Thus
$$\frac{dy}{dx} = x^2 + y^2$$

$$(1 - x^2)\frac{d^2y}{dx^2} - x\frac{dy}{dx} + y + 1 = 0$$

are examples of differential equations.

The order of such an equation is defined as the order of the highest differential coefficient present in it. The two cases cited above, for example, are of orders *one* and *two* respectively.

By a solution of the differential equation is here to be understood, a function of x denoted y, such that if the differential coefficients $\dfrac{dy}{dx}$, $\dfrac{d^2y}{dx^2}$, etc., are found and the values inserted in the differential equation, the latter (now a function of x alone) is identically satisfied.

For example, in the second equation written above

$$(1 - x^2)\frac{d^2y}{dx^2} - x\frac{dy}{dx} + y + 1 = 0,$$

a solution is $y = x - 1$, since

$$\frac{dy}{dx} = 1 \quad \text{and} \quad \frac{d^2y}{dx^2} = 0,$$

and the equation becomes, when these values are inserted,

$$0 - x \times 1 + x - 1 + 1 \equiv 0.$$

In the present chapter it is proposed to regard the function y, given, not as an explicit expression written in terms of powers of x, or literal functions of x such as $\sin x$ or $\log x$, but by a graph in the plane of the two rectangular axes OX and OY. Remembering that $\dfrac{dy}{dx}$ from this point of view is the slope of the tangent to the curve at any point (x, y), we may suppose that from such a curve of y against x, another curve of $\dfrac{dy}{dx}$ against x may be drawn.

What is the most accurate and convenient method of determining such a derived graph need not for the moment be considered. It will be dealt with in a later chapter. It suffices merely here to assert that if the original curve is everywhere continuous, then the curve for $\dfrac{dy}{dx}$ can certainly be found. Similarly, the curves representing $\dfrac{d^2y}{dx^2}$, $\dfrac{d^3y}{dx^3}$, etc., may also be derived and plotted to the same base x.

On this view of the functional form of y, it can now be stated that a solution of the differential equation is found for a range of values of x when a graph has been obtained for that range, such that when its ordinate is taken to represent y, and all the necessary derived curves for $\dfrac{dy}{dx}, \dfrac{d^2y}{dx^2} \ldots$ are obtained, and these values are inserted in the differential equation, the latter is zero at each value of x in the range.

A few matters immediately call for comment. In the first place, be it noted that the final verification of the solution is not, as in the previous case, that terms in the final form of the differential equation are explicit expressions in x, which reduce to zero in the aggregate, but are mere numbers which when collected together sum up to zero. The verification, therefore, in this case is of an arithmetic rather than of an algebraic nature.

In the second place, and as a consequence, another distinction is apparent between the two types of solution in their verification. In the case of the graphical form of the solution it is evident that a graph can at best represent a function to a restricted degree of accuracy. The limitation arises in the last resort from the severely practical difficulty of placing two points on a chart, closer together than a certain minimum distance. This implies a degree of indefiniteness in the graphical solution which may conveniently be represented as a margin of error in that function. At least a corresponding margin of error will be present in each of the graphs for $\dfrac{dy}{dx}, \dfrac{d^2y}{dx^2}$ derived from this necessarily approximate form for y. In point of fact the errors in the derived curves may be much greater, the magnitude depending especially on the particular method that is adopted in estimating the values of the differential coefficients. This will be discussed later. For the moment it suffices to remark that when these values of y and its differential coefficients are inserted in the equation the terms may not sum up to zero at each value of x, but reduce to a number which is small in comparison with the individual terms that go to make up the sum.

These considerations suggest that, for precision, a modification in our definition of a solution of the differential equation must be made.

Suppose y is graphed as a function of x and suppose, at each value of x, a small possible margin of error $\epsilon(x)$ is attached. This will specify in the $x - y$ plane not really an individual curve but a region within which the curve lies. If then within this narrow region there exists a curve such that when the values of y and $\dfrac{dy}{dx}, \dfrac{d^2y}{dx^2}$, etc. derived from it are inserted in the equation, the latter is accurately satisfied, we shall say that the original graph about which the region was defined is a solution of the differential equation, with a margin of error $\epsilon(x)$.

On this definition it is evident that in practice three things are required :

(i) A method of determining the approximate solution as a graph of y.

(ii) An estimate of the margin of error $\epsilon(x)$ at each value of x.

(iii) An assurance that somewhere within the band defined by y and $\epsilon(x)$ an accurate solution of the differential equation exists.

The first step in the determination of the solution of the differential equation is, if possible, to find a rough approximation to its solution and some idea of the accuracy of that approximation. This will in general be carried out by finding upper and lower limits within which the solution must lie. Whether any further examination is necessary will, of course, depend on the accuracy to which the solution is desired. The second step, therefore, consists in refining this approximate estimate, and for this purpose, as for the initial step itself, many methods are available, but the particular method that should be chosen will depend on certain factors. In the first place, the range of the independent variable for which the solution is required will affect the selection; but even more than this, the degree of accuracy with which the solution is desired over that range will exercise a predominating influence in the choice. In addition to this there are such factors as the labour involved in the actual computation by any method, whether a computing machine is or is not available, and whether the method is suitable for mechanical computation; and finally, the number of intermediate positions along the range of the independent variable for which the solution is desired. All these factors, and others more intimately connected with the exact nature of the differential equation itself, enter into the choice.

As the subject develops and alternative methods are offered for the determination of a solution these points will require to be specially noted. We proceed, therefore, to the first step, to determine a rough approximation to the solution and upper and lower bounds to its accuracy. For this purpose it is simpler to bear in mind a geometrical or a graphical interpretation of the variables and of the relationship involved in the equation.

2. Propositions relating to the integration of $\dfrac{dy}{dx} = f(x, y)$.

If (x, y) be the co-ordinates of a point lying on a curve in a plane, then $p \equiv \dfrac{dy}{dx}$ represents the slope of the tangent at (x, y) to that curve.

A differential equation of the first order

$$p = f(x, y) \quad \cdot \quad \cdot \quad \cdot \quad \cdot \quad (1)$$

attaches a certain direction to every point in the plane.

If a family of curves can be found such that at every point of every member, condition (1) is satisfied, then that family is called the integral family of curves of the differential equation.

Since a relation of the form

$$\phi(x, y, p) = 0 \quad \cdot \quad \cdot \quad \cdot \quad \cdot \quad (2)$$

can be reduced to a set of equations of type (1) merely by

solving algebraically for p in (2), we may refer to the integral curves of (2) in the same sense.

If equation (2) is algebraic in p of order n, then at any point (x, y) there are n values of the slope, and n branches of the integral curves pass through that point. No two integral curves formed by pursuing corresponding branches across the field can meet. For such branches correspond because they are solutions of the same differential equation (1), and p is then uniquely determined at each point. It follows that through a given point there can be one and only one solution of the equation (1).

Some useful consequences follow immediately from these considerations.

(i) In the two equations

$$\frac{dy}{dx} = F(x, y) \quad \text{and} \quad \frac{dz}{dx} = F(x, z)$$

if $y_0 = z_0$ at $x = x_0$, then $y \equiv z$, since the solutions are unique.

Hence if at $x = x_0$, $y_0 > z_0$, then everywhere $y > z$, since they cannot cross.

(ii) In the equations

$$\frac{dy}{dx} = F(x, y) \quad \text{and} \quad \frac{dz}{dx} = \lambda F(x, z)$$

if $\lambda > 1$ and $y_0 = z_0$ at $x = x_0$, then $z > y$ from there onwards.

The two solutions have only one point in common, viz. the starting-point $x = x_0$, $y = y_0$, $z = z_0$.

(iii) In the equations

$$\frac{dy}{dx} = F(x, y) \quad \text{and} \quad \frac{dz}{dx} = \phi(x) \cdot F(x, z)$$

where

$$\phi(x) > \lambda > 1$$

then if y and z start at a common point, from there onwards $z > y$ and they never meet again.

(iv) Throughout a region of the (x, y) plane which includes a point through which the solution of

$$\frac{dy}{dx} = f(x, y)$$

is required, if

$$M(x, y) > f(x, y) > m(x, y),$$

then the required solution lies intermediately between that of

$$\frac{dy}{dx} = M(x, y)$$

and

$$\frac{dy}{dx} = m(x, y).$$

Example 1.—The solution of

$$\frac{dy}{dx} = (x + ye^{-y})$$

which passes through $(0, 0)$ and lies in the first quadrant, between $y = 0$ and $y = 0{\cdot}5$ is intermediate between that of

$$\frac{dy}{dx} = x + y$$

and

$$\frac{dy}{dx} = x + ye^{-0{\cdot}5}.$$

The solutions of these linear equations are respectively

$$y = -1 - x + e^x$$

and

$$y = e[e^{xe^{-0{\cdot}5}} - 1] - xe^{0{\cdot}5}$$

At the limits of the range, viz. at $x = 0{\cdot}5$, these, therefore, provide as upper and lower limits to the value of y, the two numbers $0{\cdot}1487$ and $0{\cdot}1390$, whose mean, $0{\cdot}1438$ is certainly less than $3{\cdot}5$ per cent. in error.

Example 2.—The solution of

$$\frac{dy}{dx} = \frac{x^2 + y^2}{x^2 + a^2} \equiv \frac{x^2}{x^2 + a^2}\left(1 + \frac{y^2}{x^2}\right)$$

for the range a to λa lies between

$$\frac{dy}{dx} = M\left(1 + \frac{y^2}{x^2}\right) \quad \text{and} \quad \frac{dy}{dx} = m\left(1 + \frac{y^2}{x^2}\right),$$

which are both soluble equations, since

$$\tfrac{1}{2} = m < \frac{x^2}{x^2 + a^2} < M = \frac{\lambda^2}{1 + \lambda^2}.$$

(v) In the two equations

$$\frac{dy}{dx} = F(x, y) \quad \text{and} \quad \frac{dz}{dx} = F(x, z) + \lambda$$

where $\lambda > 0$, if at $x = x_0$, $y = y_0$, $z = z_0$, then $z > y$ and always remains so, since where they would meet again $\frac{dz}{dx}$ would be again greater than $\frac{dy}{dx}$.

(vi) In the equation

$$\frac{dy}{dx} = F(x, y) + \psi(x)$$

if $$M > \psi(x) > m > 0,$$

then the solution of the equation lies between that of

$$\frac{dy}{dx} = F(x, y) + m \quad \text{and} \quad \frac{dy}{dx} = F(x, y) + M.$$

Example 3.—In the equation

$$\frac{dy}{dx} = \frac{x^2 + y^2}{x^2 + a^2} = \frac{x^2}{x^2 + a^2} + \frac{y^2}{x^2 + a^2}$$

the solution lies between those of

$$\frac{dy}{dx} = \frac{y^2}{x^2 + a^2} \quad \text{and} \quad \frac{dy}{dx} = 1 + \frac{y^2}{x^2 + a^2}$$

taking the range of x to be 0 to ∞.

The simple methods just outlined may suffice to indicate roughly the general trend of any particular solution, although they are not necessarily very useful in practice. This arises from the fact that in effect we have made the determination of the upper and lower bounds of the solution dependent on the solution of two other equations generally of simpler type. Where these are themselves not directly capable of solution the process does not assist us much, if at all. We turn, therefore, to a consideration of yet another method, in this case of a graphical nature, which will provide us not only with a knowledge, detailed up to a certain degree, of any one particular solution of the equation, but with a picture of the general trend of all the solutions of the equation. For many purposes it is precisely this general knowledge that is required rather than detailed information about any one special solution passing through a particular point.

3. Isoclinals of a differential equation of the first order.

It is necessary that the conclusions, which will presently be drawn in the general discussion of the equation $\phi(x, y, p) = 0$ from a geometrical standpoint, should be expressed in concise mathematical form, and for this purpose the two following paragraphs are required.

3.1. *Singular points on the curve $f(x, y) = 0$.*

Consider the equation $f(x, y) = 0$.
If this be solved for y in terms of x and this value of y be substituted in the equation

$$u = f(x, y),$$

u will vanish identically. It follows, therefore, that the derivatives of u with regard to x will also vanish.
Thus

$$\frac{\partial f}{\partial x} + \frac{\partial f}{\partial y} \cdot \frac{dy}{dx} = 0 \quad . \quad . \quad . \quad . \quad . \quad (3)$$

or

$$f_x + f_y \cdot y' = 0,$$

i.e.

$$y' = -f_x/f_y \quad . \quad . \quad . \quad . \quad . \quad (3.1)$$

For any curve $f(x, y) = 0$, (3.1) in general determines the value of the gradient y'.
Differentiating (3) again,

$$f_{xx} + 2f_{xy} \cdot y' + f_{yy} \cdot y'^2 + f_y \cdot y'' = 0 \quad . \quad . \quad . \quad (4)$$

Now (3.1) fails to determine y' when $f_x = f_y = 0$; in which case

$$f_{xx} + 2f_{xy} y' + f_{yy} y'^2 = 0 \quad . \quad . \quad . \quad (4.1)$$

and this equation in general determines the two possible slopes at a double point.
In these circumstances there are three equations

$$\left. \begin{array}{l} f_x = 0 \\ f_y = 0 \\ f(x, y) = 0 \end{array} \right\} \quad . \quad . \quad . \quad . \quad . \quad (5)$$

to be satisfied, and since two equations only are necessary to determine x and y, it is clear that any points which satisfy equations (5) are necessarily singular to the curve.

3.2. *The Envelope locus of* $f(x, y, c) = 0$.

If $f(x, y, c) = 0$ represent a system of curves obtained by giving real values to c, then

$$\left.\begin{array}{r} f(x, y, c) = 0 \\ \dfrac{\partial f}{\partial c} = 0 \end{array}\right\} \quad \cdots \quad \cdots \quad (6)$$

represents the envelope of the system $f(x, y, c) = 0$.

Consider the intersections of the curves

$$f(x, y, c) = 0 \text{ and } f(x, y, c + \delta c) = 0.$$

$$0 = f(x, y, c + \delta c) = f(x, y, c) + \frac{\partial}{\partial c}\left[f(x, y, c)\right] . \, \delta c + \lambda \delta c^2.$$

where λ is finite in general.

Thus when δc tends to zero

$$\frac{\partial}{\partial c} . f(x, y, c) = 0.$$

It follows that equations (6) determine the locus of the ultimate intersections of each member of the system with the neighbouring member.

Every member of the system $f(x, y, c) = 0$ touches this locus.

For the slope at a point (x_1, y_1) on c_1 is given by

$$f_x(x_1, y_1, c_1) + f_y(x_1, y_1, c_1)\frac{dy}{dx} = 0 \quad \cdots \quad (7)$$

The slope at the same point on the locus (6) is determined from

$$f_x(x_1, y_1, c_1) + f_y(x_1, y_1, c_1)\frac{dy}{dx} + f_c(x_1, y_1, c_1)\frac{dc}{dx_1} = 0 . \quad (8)$$

But from equations (6), $f_c = 0$.

Hence (7) and (8) determine identical values for $\dfrac{dy}{dx}$.

3.3. General discussion of the integral curves and isoclinals of a differential equation of the first order.

A first order differential equation

$$\phi(x, y, p) = 0 \quad \cdots \quad \cdots \quad (9)$$

besides defining an integral system also determines a system of curves

$$\phi(x, y, c) = 0 \quad \cdots \quad \cdots \quad (9.1)$$

This may be regarded as a system which includes the loci of successive points on the integral curves for which $\dfrac{dy}{dx}$

has the constant value c. Thus integral curves which intersect any one of the isoclinal system, as (9.1) is called, all do so at the same slope. By sketching the isoclinal system (9.1) and by attaching to each member its appropriate value of c, a general survey of the integral solutions of (9) may be rapidly laid out as follows.

We begin at any point on one of the isoclinal curves and imagine an infinitesimal line drawn in the direction specified by the value of c. In general this line will meet a neighbouring isoclinal which specifies a new direction differing infinitesimally from the first direction. From the point where the second isoclinal is met by the first infinitesimal line draw another infinitesimal line in the direction specified by the second isoclinal. If this process is repeated from isoclinal to isoclinal, a curve is obtained having values of p at every point (x, y) on it which approximately satisfy the differential equation (9), *and this curve is therefore a rough approximation to a solution of the differential equation*, i.e. *it is an integral curve of the differential equation.* The curve is, of course, developed on both sides of the isoclinal on which the initial point was chosen. If any line be drawn across a region of the plane in which the equation $\phi(x, y, p) = 0$ determines p at every point uniquely, then from every point of this line one integral curve will start out and traverse the region. There will, in fact, be a one-fold infinity of integral curves of the equation $\phi(x, y, p) = 0$ and the solution of the latter must be of the type $\psi(x, y,) = c$.

The class of solution dealt with so far does not exhaust the possible solutions of a differential equation of the type considered here. If a solution of the equation be regarded as any curve whose co-ordinates and slope at each point satisfy the differential equation at each point, then there may exist solutions which do not appear as members of the one-fold infinity of curves mentioned above. Such *singular solutions* will be dealt with in due course.

In general the direction specified by an isoclinal differs from that of the isoclinal itself and the integral curve is continuous on both sides of the isoclinal at the point of crossing. *This is not the case, however, when neighbouring isoclinal curves intersect.* Consider a point in the neighbourhood of the envelope of $\phi(x, y, c) = 0$. Members of the family of curves $\phi(x, y, c) = 0$ do not in general cross the envelope of the family in the neighbourhood of its point of contact with the envelope. Thus the contiguous curves $c - dc$, c and $c + dc$ all lie on the same side of the envelope and all touch it. Since the slope p is not in general that of the envelope (which is that of the isoclinal itself), the integral curve should cut across the envelope. There is, however, now no contiguous isoclinal on the other side of the envelope and consequently the integral curve has either a cusp or a stop point.

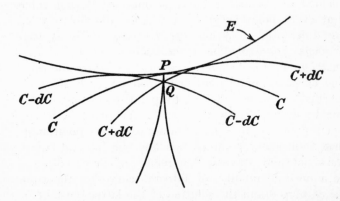

If the envelope is the curve E and the isoclinal touches it at P and PQ be an infinitesimal part of the integral curve at P, then in general two contiguous isoclinals may be found to pass through Q and they touch the envelope on opposite sides of P. Hence, beginning at P to draw the integral curve, on reaching Q there are two possible directions for the integral curve each differing infinitesimally from c. Pursuing these two branches of the curve back from P, it appears that an envelope locus of the isoclinals is in general a cusp locus of the integral curves. This envelope locus, the eliminant of $\phi(x, y, c) = 0$ and $\dfrac{\partial \phi}{\partial c} = 0$, is also the p-discriminant of the equation $\phi(x, y, p) = 0$.

The p-discriminant of $\phi(x, y, p) = 0$ is in general a cusp locus of the integral family and conversely *if E is a locus of cusps of the integral family it is part at least of the envelope of the isoclinal family.* Since two neighbouring isoclinals which touch the envelope of the isoclinals cut at one point only, this locus occurs once only in the p-discriminant. If the direction of p is also that of the isoclinal at P, and therefore the direction of the envelope, the direction p *does not cross* the envelope and there is consequently no discontinuity of the integral curve which therefore touches the envelope at P.

Now the direction of the isoclinal family is given by

$$\frac{\partial \phi}{\partial x} + \frac{\partial \phi}{\partial y} \cdot \frac{dy}{dx} = 0.$$

Hence the condition for the p-discriminant being an envelope locus for the integral family is

$$\frac{\partial \phi}{\partial x} + \frac{\partial \phi}{\partial y} \cdot p = 0.$$

This condition is in general both necessary and sufficient, *i.e.* the slope of the integral curves as defined by $\phi(x, y, p) = 0$ must be the slope of the isoclinal family along the envelope locus. As before, this envelope locus of the integral curves *occurs once only in the p-discriminant.*

The p-discriminant has been shown to be simultaneously the envelope locus of the isoclinals and a cusp locus of the integral curves; but the p-discriminant may also include a locus of double points of the isoclinal family—in general a node locus; for at such points the same value of p is obtained twice where the isoclinal crosses itself. In general the isoclinals and the integral curves will again cross the p-discriminant.

If P and Q have meanings as before at Q there will again be two possible directions for the integral curve. There is also a corresponding point Q' on the other side of the p-discriminant where two neighbouring curves now give Q'. Hence at Q' also there are two possible directions for the integral curve. The integral curve has therefore two

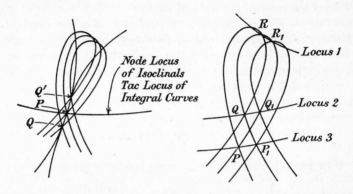

branches which touch at P, i.e. P is a *tac-point* for the integral curve. Hence a *node locus* of the isoclinal family is in general a *tac locus* of the integral family.

The slope of the isoclinals is given by

$$\frac{\partial \phi}{\partial x} + \frac{\partial \phi}{\partial y} \cdot \frac{dy}{dx} = 0.$$

In order that this shall be satisfied by two different values of $\frac{dy}{dx}$,

$$\left.\begin{array}{c} \dfrac{\partial \phi}{\partial x} = 0 \\[2mm] \dfrac{\partial \phi}{\partial y} = 0 \end{array}\right\} \quad \cdots \cdots \cdot (10)$$

and

for $\frac{\partial \phi}{\partial x}$ and $\frac{\partial \phi}{\partial y}$ are single valued functions of x and y.

This is the condition that there should be a node locus of the isoclinal family and a tac locus therefore of the integral family. In addition to the equations (10), of course $\phi(x, y, p) = 0$ and $\frac{\partial \phi}{\partial p} = 0$. Now *in general* if an isoclinal pass through P, there is one and only one curve contiguous to it which passes through a given point which is contiguous to P, but *if P is a tac-point* of the integral family and Q is a contiguous point on both the integral curves which touch at P, then because the rate of variation of p is in general different for the two integral curves, *two contiguous isoclinals* must pass through Q, and similarly for Q' on the other side of P from Q, and the isoclinals which give Q and Q' are therefore branches of the same curves.

In the opposite figure P, Q, R and P_1, Q_1, R_1 are two sets of three points in which the central loop cuts its neighbours.

The points R, R_1, etc. ultimately form an envelope locus of the isoclinal family, and therefore in general the integral curves have this locus as a cusp locus. These loci occur once in the p-discriminant as already indicated. When considering the points P, Q and P_1, Q_1, however, it should be noticed that the locus of the nodes on the isoclinals is the curve obtained when the curves through Q, Q_1, etc. and P, P_1, etc. coincide in the limit. It is to be expected that (since each loop cuts an adjacent loop twice near a node) the node locus will occur twice in the p-discriminant. Thus the node locus of isoclinals or the tac locus of the integral family occur twice in the p-discriminant.

Again, if the loops above be supposed to become smaller and smaller, the case in which the isoclinals fold back along themselves is obtained, giving a cusp locus of the isoclinals. It follows that this degenerate case occurs three times in the p-discriminant, since the three curves then R, R_1, etc., Q, Q_1, etc., P, P_1, etc., coalesce. In this case the tac locus of the integral curves degenerates into a locus of isolated double points while the cusp locus of the integral family remains as a cusp locus.

The branches of the isoclinal curve at a node locus divide the plane into two regions one of which contains the p-discriminant and one does not. There are three kinds of tac loci according as the direction of the integral curves lie in the former or the latter or along an isoclinal.

a. If it lies in the region not containing the p-discriminant the two integral curves have opposite curvature.

b. If it lies in the region containing the p-discriminant the curvature of the two curves is the same.

c. If the direction of the integral curve lies along the isoclinal there is, as will be shown, a point of inflection on one of the branches of the integral curve.

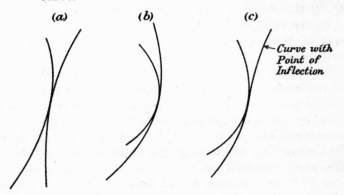

(a)   *(b)*   *(c)*

←*Curve with Point of Inflection*

If the double point is a point of the first order, the directions of the tangents to the isoclinal system are given by q where

$$q^2\frac{\partial^2\phi}{\partial y^2} + 2q\frac{\partial^2\phi}{\partial x\partial y} + \frac{\partial^2\phi}{\partial x^2} = 0.$$

In any particular case it is therefore a simple matter to decide to which species the tac locus belongs. If the roots of the above are equal, *i.e.*

if
$$\left(\frac{\partial^2\phi}{\partial x\partial y}\right)^2 - \frac{\partial^2\phi}{\partial x^2}\frac{\partial^2\phi}{\partial y^2} = 0,$$

the p-discriminant is a cusp locus for the isoclinal family, and similar reasoning to the above shows that it is also a cusp locus for the integral family. In every case except when the direction of both families is the same, the curves contiguous to p passing through Q both lie on the same side, and therefore the curvature of both branches is in the same direction, *i.e.* the cusp is a ramphoid cusp (see opposite page).

If, however, at any point the direction of the integral curve is the same as that of the cusp locus there is in general a tac-point on the integral family, the contact being of higher order than the first. If the roots are imaginary, the p-discriminant is a locus of conjugate points for both families.

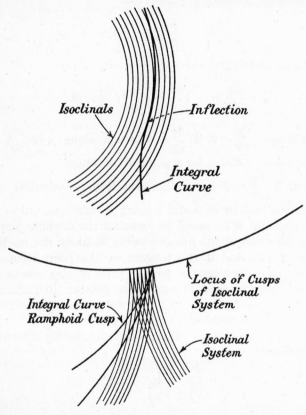

If at any point P, which is *not on the envelope locus* of the isoclinal family, the direction of the integral curve is the same as that of the isoclinal through P, the contiguous points Q and Q' are in general both on the same side of the isoclinal but on opposite sides of the point P; thus the sign of variation of p changes on passing through P, *i.e.* there is in general an inflection on the integral curve.   This demands

that
$$\frac{\partial \phi}{\partial x} + p\frac{\partial \phi}{\partial y} = 0.$$

This is, however, equivalent to the usual condition for an inflection on the integral curve; for

$$\frac{\partial \phi}{\partial x}dx + \frac{\partial \phi}{\partial y}dy + \frac{\partial \phi}{\partial p}dp = 0.$$

but along an integral curve $dy = p \cdot dx$, hence

$$\frac{dp}{dx} = -\left(\frac{\partial \phi}{\partial x} + p\frac{\partial \phi}{\partial y}\right)\Big/\frac{\partial \phi}{\partial p} = 0.$$

Accordingly, $\frac{dp}{dx} = 0$ if $\frac{\partial \phi}{\partial p} \neq 0$, which along with $\frac{d^2p}{dx^2} \neq 0$ is the usual condition for a point of inflection.

Even if $\frac{\partial \phi}{\partial p} = 0$ it can be seen from geometrical considerations that there is still a point of inflection, unless the p-discriminant is an envelope locus for the isoclinal family. If the direction of the integral curve lie along the isoclinal at any point, and if the tangent at the point meet the isoclinal in n contiguous points, then it also meets the integral curve in $(n + 1)$ contiguous points.   In particular *the locus of points of contact of integral curves with isoclinals is a locus of inflections of the integral curves.*

This locus is, of course, obtained by eliminating p between the equations

$$\left.\begin{array}{r} \phi(x, y, p) = 0 \\ \frac{\partial \phi}{\partial x} + p\frac{\partial \phi}{\partial y} = 0 \end{array}\right\}$$

3.4. Application to the practical problem of integration.

It remains, therefore, for us to assemble the information contained in the foregoing paragraphs in order to examine how far it may be of practical assistance in setting forth, with the greatest possible graphical accuracy, the general nature of the solutions.   We may summarise the steps as follows :

$$f\left(x, y, \frac{dy}{dx}\right) = 0.$$

(a) Sketch the isoclinal system

$$f(x, y, c) = 0.$$

(b) Draw a series of small parallel lines across each member of this system at the appropriate slope c.

(c) In particular, examine the curve $f(x, y, 0) = 0$ which will be a locus of maxima or minima on the integral curves.

(d) Find the locus of inflections of the integral curves by eliminating p between

$$f(x, y, p) = 0 \quad \text{and} \quad \frac{\partial f}{\partial x} + p\frac{\partial f}{\partial y} = 0,$$

and verify (i) that the integral curves change the sign of their curvature as they cross this line, (ii) that this locus is also the point of contact of the isoclinals with the integral curves.

(e) Find the envelope locus of the isoclinal system, and by approximating to the integral curves at any point on this envelope, examine the nature of the integral curves there.   (In general this should be a locus of cusps.)

(f) Find approximations to the integral curves at such positions as

(i) The origin of co-ordinates.

(ii) Any point on the X axis.

(ii) Any point on the Y axis.

(g) If any doubt still remains concerning the general trend of the system, find approximations to the integral curves at arbitrary points on any arbitrary straight line through the origin, $y = mx$.

Note 1.—From the foregoing remarks the p-discriminant in general may be written in the form

$$E . C . T^2 = 0$$

where $E = 0$ represents an envelope locus for the integral curves, $C = 0$ a cusp locus and $T = 0$ a tac locus. The form of the p-discriminant may therefore be taken as a guide to its nature.

Note 2.—In the case of the isoclinals of a first order differential equation it has now been shown that in general the loci occur in the c-discriminant in the form

$$E \cdot N^2 \cdot C^3 = 0$$

where $E = 0$ represents the envelope locus of the isoclinals (in general a cusp locus of the integral curves), $N = 0$ a node locus and $C = 0$ a cusp locus.

Drawing the integral curves.

Consider the differential equation,

$$\frac{dy}{dx} = xy$$

Isoclinals and Integral curves of $\dfrac{dy}{dx} = xy$.

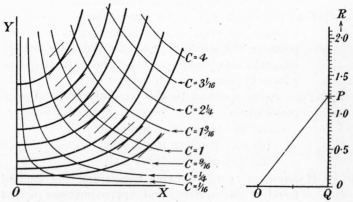

The isoclinals of this equation are given by

$$xy = c$$

and are therefore hyperbolas in the first and third quadrants of the $x - y$ plane. Consider those in the first quadrant, and suppose that they are drawn from $C = 0$ to $C = 4$.

In order to draw the integral curves rapidly it is convenient to draw a line OQ parallel to the positive direction of the axis of x, and taking this as unit length, QR is drawn perpendicular to OQ of length 4 units. QR is graduated in units, and hence any line such as OP has a gradient of PQ units. Using this figure, any gradient is readily transferred to the appropriate isoclinal. Along the isoclinal corresponding to

$$xy = C_1$$

short lines are drawn at a number of points crossing the isoclinal and having the gradient C_1. This process is repeated for the whole field of isoclinals until the region is mapped out as a directional field. Curves are now drawn having the slopes specified by the system of short lines drawn in the above manner. These curves are approximations to the integral curves in the first quadrant.

Example 1.—Consider the equation
$$f(x, y, p) = p^2 + 2(x + y)p + 2xy + y^2 + x^3 = 0,$$
$$\frac{\partial f}{\partial p} = 2p + 2(x + y) = 0.$$

The p-discriminant is $x^2(x - 1) = 0$.

This suggests $x = 1$ as a cusp locus of the integral curves and an envelope locus of the isoclinals. It also suggests that $x = 0$ is a tac locus of the integral curves and a node locus of the isoclinals.

Now if $x = 1$, $(p + y + 1)^2 = 0$, and hence the equation gives two equal values of p at all points along $x = 1$. Also along $x = 1$, $\frac{dy}{dx}$ for the isoclinals is infinite. This confirms the locus $x = 1$.

For a tac locus of the integral curves or node locus of the isoclinals

$$\left.\begin{array}{l} \dfrac{\partial f}{\partial x} = 0 \\[2mm] \dfrac{\partial f}{\partial y} = 0 \end{array}\right\}$$

together with $f(x, y, c) = 0$ along the node locus.

Now $$\frac{\partial f}{\partial x} = 2p + 2y + 3x^2$$

and $$\frac{\partial f}{\partial y} = 2p + 2x + 2y.$$

These in conjunction with $f(x, y, p) = 0$, and $x^2 = 0$ vanish identically and verify the node locus.

Example 2.

$$f(x, y, p) = (p - x)^2 - 2\left(y - \frac{x^2}{2}\right) = 0$$

$$\frac{\partial f}{\partial p} = 2(p - x) \qquad\qquad = 0$$

Hence the p-discriminant is $y - \dfrac{x^2}{2} = 0$.

When $y = \dfrac{x^2}{2}$, $(p - x)^2 = 0$, and this appears to confirm a cusp locus of the integral curves, together with the envelope locus of the isoclinals. It should be noticed, however, that $p = x$ also gives the slope of the envelope locus of the isoclinals, and hence this is the special case in which the envelope locus of the isoclinals is the envelope locus of the integral curves, and this locus is a singular solution of the differential equation.

3.5. Approximations at points of integral curves and isoclinals.

Example 3.—Consider the differential equation

$$\frac{dy}{dx} = x^2 - y^2.$$

The integral curves cross $y = \pm x$ horizontally. Remove the origin to (h, h) so that

$$x = h + \xi \qquad y = h + \eta$$

The equation becomes

$$\frac{d\eta}{d\xi} = (h + \xi)^2 - (h + \eta)^2 = 2h(\xi - \eta) + \xi^2 - \eta^2.$$

Let $\eta = A\xi^n$ be the first approximation at the point.

$$An\xi^{n-1} = 2h\xi - 2hA\xi^n + \xi^2 - A^2\xi^{2n}.$$

The term ξ^2 may be neglected in comparison with ξ.

,, ξ^{2n} ,,   ,,   ,,   ,, ξ^n.

,, ξ^n ,,   ,,   ,,   ,, ξ^{n-1}.

Thus to the first order of small quantities the equation will be satisfied if

$$An\xi^{n-1} = 2h\xi$$

i.e. $\qquad\qquad n - 1 = 1,\ An = 2h$

giving as the required approximation at $(h,\ h)$

$$\eta = h\xi^2.$$

Hence along $y = x$ the integral curves have a series of minima in the first quadrant and a series of maxima in the third.• The maxima and minima become flatter and flatter as they approach the origin at which point this approximation becomes invalid. To determine the shape of the integral curve passing through $(0,\ 0)$ as before, let $y = Ax^n$, then, substituting in the original differential equation

$$An\ x^{n-1} = x^2 - 2Ax^{2n}.$$

Equating powers, we have an approximation if

(i) $n - 1 = 2$ provided x^{2n} is of higher order than x^2.

(ii) $n - 1 = 2n$,, x^2 ,,   ,,   ,, x^{n-1}.

(iii) $2 = 2n$,, x^{n-1} ,,   ,,   ,, x^2.

The first gives $n = 3$ and makes $x^{2n} = x^6$, which is of higher order than x^2. The second and third possibilities do not give justifiable approximation.

Thus the equation becomes reduced to

$$An\ x^{n-1} = x^2$$

which with $n = 3$ gives $A = \tfrac{1}{3}$, and the approximation at the origin, instead of being simply parabolic, is

$$y = \frac{x^3}{3}.$$

In precisely the same way the approximations at all points of the line $y = -x$ may be found.

Example 4.

$$\left(\frac{dy}{dx}\right)^2 - 2x\frac{dy}{dx} + y^2 = 0 \quad . \quad . \quad . \quad (11)$$

Nature of the intersections of the integral curves with $y = 0$.

It is to be noticed in the first place that $y = 0$ is actually a solution of the equation, and therefore at each point of the x axis there will be only one other approximation.

Remove the origin to $(h, 0)$, then with reference to this new origin the differential equation becomes

$$\left(\frac{dy}{dx}\right)^2 - 2(x + h)\frac{dy}{dx} + y^2 = 0 \ . \quad . \quad (11.1)$$

At the new origin the slopes of the integrals, obtained by inserting $x = 0 \quad y = 0$ are given by

$$\left(\frac{dy}{dx}\right)^2 - 2h\frac{dy}{dx} = 0,$$

i.e. $\frac{dy}{dx} = 0$ corresponding to the integral $y = 0$, and $\frac{dy}{dx} = 2h$.

A first approximation, therefore, is

$$y = 2hx.$$

As a second approximation let

$$y = 2hx + Ax^n$$

so that $\qquad\qquad \frac{dy}{dx} = 2h + nAx^{n-1}$

then, on inserting in (11.1) we find

$$4h^2 + n^2A^2x^{2n-2} + 4hnAx^{n-1} - 4hx - 2nAx^n - 4h^2$$
$$- 2nAhx^{n-1} + 4h^2x^2 + A^2x^{2n} + 4Ahx^{n+1} = 0.$$

As regards the order of these terms we note :

a. The term x^{2n-2} is negligible in comparison with x^{n-1}, since it is the square of the latter.

b. The terms x^n, x^{n+1} and x^{2n} are all of higher order than x^{n-1}.

c. The term x^2 is negligible in comparison with x.

If therefore we restrict ourselves to terms that may be of lowest order, the equation gives

$$Ax^{n-1} - 2x = 0$$

and this requires $A = 2$, $n = 2$.

Hence the second approximation to the curves that cross the x-axis is

$$y = 2hx + 2x^2.$$

Nature of the intersections of the integral curves with $x = 0$.

Setting $x = 0$ in equation (11), it follows that

$$\left(\frac{dy}{dx}\right)^2 + y^2 = 0.$$

Thus the integral curves do not intersect the axis of y.

Nature of the intersections with the p-discriminant.

The p-discriminant is $y = \pm x$.

Remove the origin to a point (h, h) on $y = x$ and the equation becomes :

$$\left(\frac{dy}{dx}\right)^2 - 2(x + h)\frac{dy}{dx} + (y + h)^2 = 0 \ . \quad . \quad (11.2)$$

At $(0, 0)$ we have :

$$\left(\frac{dy}{dx}\right)^2 - 2h\frac{dy}{dx} + h^2 = 0.$$

Hence the two branches touch at a slope h, and the first approximation at (h, h) is $y = hx$.

Let $y = hx + Ax^n$ be the second approximation and therefore

$$\frac{dy}{dx} = h + nAx^{n-1}.$$

Inserting this into (11.2) we get :

$$h^2 + 2nhAx^{n-1} + n^2A^2x^{2n-2} - 2hx - 2nAx^n - 2h^2$$
$$- 2nAhx^{n-1} + h^2 + 2h^2x + 2Ahx^n + h^2x^2 + 2Ahx^{n+1}$$
$$+ A^2x^{2n} = 0.$$

We note

    a. The term x^{n+1} is of higher order than x^n ;

    b.   ,, x^2 ,,   ,,   ,, x ;

    c.   ,, x^{2n} ,,   ,,   ,, x^{2n-2} ;

    d.   ,, x^n ,,   .,,   ,, x ;

since $y = hx$ is the first approximation.

Hence, retaining only terms that may be of lowest order the equation gives

$$n^2A^2x^{2n-2} - 2h(1 - h)x = 0$$

and therefore

$$2n - 2 = 1, \quad n^2A^2 = 2h(1 - h)$$

or $$n = \tfrac{3}{2}, \quad A = \pm \tfrac{2}{3}\sqrt{2h(1 - h)}.$$

The second approximation is

$$y = hx \pm \tfrac{2}{3}\sqrt{2h(1 - h)} \cdot x^{\frac{3}{2}}.$$

It follows that when h is such that $h(1 - h)$ is positive the integral curve can only lie on positive side of the x-axis at (h, h), and when $h(1 - h)$ is negative x must similarly be negative.

Now $h(1 - h)$ is positive so long as $0 < h < 1$, otherwise it is negative.

Similarly the second approximation to the integral curves at a point $(h, -h)$ on $y = -x$ is

$$y = -hx \pm \tfrac{2}{3}\sqrt{2h(1 - h)} \cdot x^{\frac{3}{2}}.$$

The isoclinals are given by

$$y^2 = 2cx - c^2 = 2c\left(x - \frac{c}{2}\right),$$

a system of parabolas whose axis is the axis of x and whose vertex is at $\dfrac{c}{2}$. The envelope of the isoclinals is $y = \pm x$.

Locus of inflections.

From (11) by differentiation

$$2 \frac{dy}{dx} \cdot \frac{d^2y}{dx^2} - 2x\frac{d^2y}{dx^2} - 2\frac{dy}{dx} + 2y\frac{dy}{dx} = 0$$

and $$\frac{d^2y}{dx^2} = 0, \quad \text{where} \quad y = 1.$$

Locus of maxima and minima.

There is no such locus in this case, other than the integral $y = 0$ itself, unless at $x \to +\infty$, in which case y may be finite.

Approximation at $(0, 0)$.

Let $y = Ax^n$ and insert in (1), then

$$A^2n^2x^{2n-2} - 2Anx^n + A^2x^{2n} = 0.$$

Ignoring the last term, which is of higher order than the others, we have :

$$2n - 2 = n \quad \text{and therefore} \quad n = 2,$$
$$A^2n^2 = 2An \quad \text{and thus} \quad A = 1.$$

The approximation is therefore

$$y = x^2.$$

The isoclinals and integral curves may now be sketched.

Example 5.—To sketch the integral curves of the equation

$$y^2 = x(x^2 - p^2).$$

Isoclinal system.

There is symmetry about the axis of x.

$$f(x, y, c) \equiv y^2 - x(x^2 - c^2) = 0.$$
$$\frac{\partial f}{\partial c} = \qquad\qquad + 2cx = 0.$$

The c-discriminant is therefore $\qquad \underline{y^2 = x^3.}$

The value of p found from $y^2 = x^3$ does not make

$$\frac{\partial f}{\partial x} + p \cdot \frac{\partial f}{\partial y}$$

vanish identically for all values of c, and therefore this is not an envelope locus for the isoclinals. It is the isoclinal corresponding to $c = 0$.

Approximations along $y = 0$.

For $\qquad\qquad y = 0$
$$x = 0, \quad \text{or} \quad x = \pm c.$$

Take c a positive constant then, since

$$y^2 = x(x^2 - c^2).$$
$$y \text{ is imaginary for } 0 < x < c.$$

Transfer the origin to $(c, 0)$ then,

$$y^2 = (x + c)x(x + 2c)$$
$$= x^3 + 3cx^2 + 2c^2x$$

Suppose $y = ax^n$ is a valid approximation at $(c, 0)$

$$a^2x^{2n} = x^3 + 3cx^2 + 2c^2x.$$

For small values of x, $n = \frac{1}{2}$ and $a^2 = 2c^2$ provides a valid approximation,

$$\underline{y^2 = 2c^2x.}$$

For large values of x, $n = \frac{3}{2}$, $a^2 = 1$ provides a valid approximation,

$$\underline{y^2 = x^3.}$$

These facts indicate the nature of the curves in the positive range of values of x.

For x negative, y is real in the region $-c < x < 0$ and imaginary for $x < -c$.

At the origin

$$y^2 = x^3 - c^2x.$$

A valid approximation is therefore

$$\underline{y^2 = -c^2x.}$$

Transferring the origin to $(-c, 0)$,

$$y^2 = (x - c)x(x - 2c)$$
$$= x^3 - 3cx^2 + 2c^2x.$$

A valid approximation at $(-c, 0)$ is therefore

$$\underline{y^2 = 2c^2x,}$$

and there is no valid approximation for x large and negative. Again, writing $y = kx$

$$k^2x^2 = x(x^2 - c^2)$$

and $\qquad\qquad x = 0$

or $\qquad\qquad x = (k^2 \pm \sqrt{k^2 + 4c^2})/2.$

Hence $y = kx$ cuts the isoclinals once in the region x positive and once in the region x negative, in addition to the origin. Thus for x negative the isoclinals are loops which touch the y axis at the origin.

The integral curves.

There are two values of p at all points in the plane except in the region bounded by $y^2 = x^3$ and the y axis.

The p-discriminant is

$$y^2 = x^3$$

and the values of p are given by $p^2 = 0$ along this locus, which is therefore a cusp locus for the integral curves.

For the inflection loci,

$$f(x, y, p) \equiv y^2 - x(x^2 - p^2) = 0$$
$$\frac{\partial f}{\partial x} + p \cdot \frac{\partial f}{\partial y} \equiv -3x^2 + p^2 + 2py = 0$$

Hence eliminating p

$$\left(2x^2 + \frac{y^2}{x}\right)^2 = 4y^2\left(x^2 - \frac{y^2}{x}\right).$$

Since for x positive, y is imaginary, this locus is therefore entirely confined to negative values of x.

Rewriting the locus,

$$y^4(1 + 4x) + y^2(1 - x)4x^3 + 4x^6 = 0$$

a valid approximation at the origin is $\qquad y^2 = -2x^3$

and for large values of x $\qquad y = \pm x.$

The diagram on the following page shows the general trend of the solutions of the equation over the whole plane.

Examples.

Find approximations to the shape of the integral curves of the following differential equations at all points on the axes of x and of y :

1. $\left(\dfrac{dy}{dx}\right)^2 = y - x\dfrac{dy}{dx}.$

2. $\left(\dfrac{dy}{dx}\right)^2 - 2x\dfrac{dy}{dx} = y^2.$

3. $\dfrac{dy}{dx} = y - x\left(\dfrac{dy}{dx}\right)^2.$

4. $\dfrac{dy}{dx} = x^2 + y^2.$

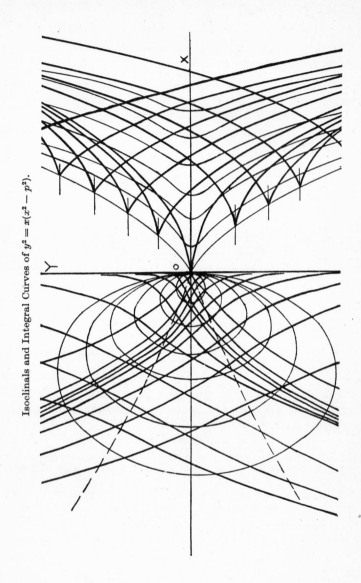

Isoclinals and Integral Curves of $y^2 = x(x^2 - p^2)$.

5. $\left(\dfrac{dy}{dx}\right)^2 = x^2 + y^2.$

6. $\left(\dfrac{dy}{dx}\right)^2 = x^2 - y.$

7. $\left(x^2\dfrac{dy}{dx} - y\right)\left(y^2\dfrac{dy}{dx} - x\right) = 1.$

8. $\left(x^2 - y\dfrac{dy}{dx}\right)\left(y^2 - x\dfrac{dy}{dx}\right) = x^2y^2.$

Isoclinals and Integral Curves of $p^2 = x(x^2 - y^2)$.

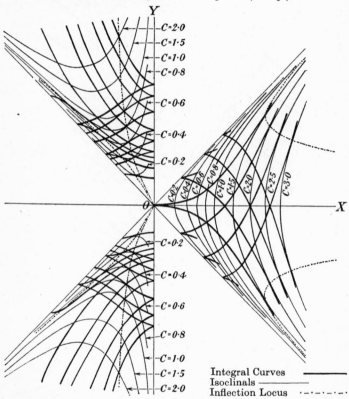

Integral Curves ——————
Isoclinals ——————
Inflection Locus $\cdot — \cdot — \cdot — \cdot$

Approximate to the shape of the integral curves of the following differential equations at all points of the curves indicated.

9. $\left(\dfrac{dy}{dx}\right)^2 = x^2 - y^2$ along $x^2 - y^2 = 1$ and $y = \pm\, x.$

10. $\left(\dfrac{dy}{dx}\right)^2 = x^2 - y$ along $y = x^2.$

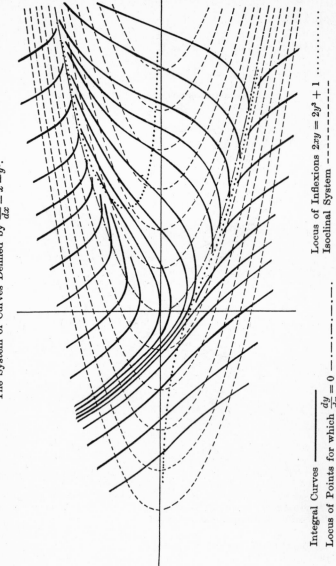

The System of Curves Defined by $\frac{dy}{dx} = x - y^2$.

Integral Curves ————
Locus of Points for which $\frac{dy}{dx} = 0$ — · · — · · — · · —

Locus of Inflexions $2xy = 2y^3 + 1$ · · · · · · · · · ·
Isoclinal System — — — — — — —

11. $\left(\dfrac{dy}{dx}\right)^2 + 2y\dfrac{dy}{dx} + x = 0$ along $y^2 = x$.

12. $\left(\dfrac{dy}{dx}\right)^m = x^m - y^m$ along $y = x$.

13. $\left(\dfrac{dy}{dx}\right)^3 - 3y\dfrac{dy}{dx} + xy = 0$ along $y = 0$ and $x^2 = 4y$.

14. Verify the adjoining sketch of the system of integral curves of the differential equation
$$\left(\frac{dy}{dx}\right)^2 = x^2 - y^2$$
and prove that the p-discriminant is a locus of cusps.

Integral Curves of $\left(\dfrac{dy}{dx}\right)^2 = x^2 - y^2$.

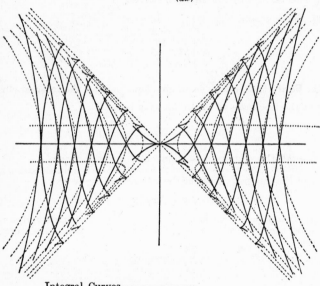

Integral Curves ————————
Locus of Inflexions $y^2(x^2 - y^2) = x^2$ ············
Isoclinal System – – – – – – – – – –

15. Sketch the system of integral curves of the differential equation
$$\frac{dy}{dx} = x^2 + y^2 - 1.$$

16. Sketch the system of integral curves of the differential equation
$$x - \left(\frac{dy}{dx}\right)^2 = y^2.$$

17. Approximate to the shape of the integral curves of the differential equation

$$\left(\frac{dy}{dx}\right)^2 = y^2 - x$$

in the neighbourhood of the lines (i) $x = 0$, (ii) $y = 0$, (iii) $y^2 = x$. Hence roughly sketch the curves.

18. Approximate to the shape of the integral curves of

$$\left(\frac{dy}{dx}\right)^2 - x\frac{dy}{dx} = 4 - y^2.$$

19. Show that the envelope of the isoclinal system of the equation

$$(p - x)^2 + y^2 = 1$$

is a locus of cusps of the integral curves.

20. Solve graphically   (i) $x = p$.
                       (ii) $x + y = p^2$.
                       (iii) $x - yp = p^2$.
                       (iv) $x^2 + y^2 = p^2$.
                       (v) $4px - 4p^2 = y^2$.

21. Verify that $y = \frac{x^2}{2}$ is an envelope locus of the integral curves and of the isoclinals of the differential equation

$$(p - x)^2 - 2\left(y - \frac{x^2}{2}\right) = 0$$

and sketch the system of isoclinals and integral curves.

22. Prove that $x = 0$ is a node locus of the isoclinals and a tac-locus of the integral curves of the differential equation,

$$p^2 + 2(x + y)p + 2xy + y^2 + x^3 = 0.$$

Verify that $x = 1$ is an envelope locus of the isoclinals and a cusp locus of the integral curves. Sketch the isoclinals and integral curves.

CHAPTER II

GRAPHICAL METHODS FOR DETAILED SOLUTION

3.6. Graphical integration of $\frac{dy}{dx} = f(x, y)$.

The foregoing methods should certainly make it possible in almost every case to acquire not only a broad survey of the whole class of ordinary solutions of the differential equation, special singular solutions that may be intimately interwoven with this system (*e.g.* envelope loci, etc.), but should also provide a first *rough* approximation to the particular solution that passes through any given point in the plane. It remains, therefore, to provide a graphical method that will refine such an approximate solution to any prescribed degree of accuracy, consistent with the mechanical materials at our disposal for carrying through this process. In the first instance, therefore, we turn to a graphical method. An alternative method of obtaining a first approximation to the solution through a given point is given below, before proceeding to methods of refining the first approximation.

3.61. First approximation to the solution of $\frac{dy}{dx} = f(x, y)$ subject to $x = x_0, y = y_0$.

By substitution in the equation, determine the gradient $\frac{dy}{dx}$ at (x_0, y_0). From the initial point A_1 draw $A_1 A_2$ gradient y_0' to meet the ordinate at $x_0 + h$, and read off the new values of x and y. Substitute the new values of x and y in the differential equation, and so determine the gradient at A_2. Now proceed as above until the range has been covered. It should be clear that where the gradient is changing more rapidly smaller intervals in x should be taken.

3.62. Sequence method of refining the first approximate solution.

Here a solution is required to a higher degree of accuracy than the more general "class solution" or the first approximation found by the method of the last paragraph.

The integral curves obtained by the methods already described are only first approximations to the solutions. A second approximation may be obtained as follows :

If the differential equation to be solved is written in the form

$$\frac{dy}{dx} = f(x, y)$$

and corresponding values of x and y from the first approximation curve A (Fig. 1) are inserted in the function, a table for $\frac{dy}{dx}$ may be constructed and plotted as in Fig. 2, curve A'. On integrating this curve, by means of a planimeter or otherwise, a corrected set of values of (x, y) is derived and plotted as the second approximation (Fig. 1, curve B). In effect the sequence

$$\frac{dy_{n+1}}{dx} = f(x, y_n)$$

or

$$y_{n+1} = y_0 + \int_{x_0}^{x} f(x, y_n)dx$$

has been used.

If the curve B be treated in exactly the same manner as curve A, a second approximation to $\frac{dy}{dx}$ (viz. curve B', Fig. 2) will be found, and hence again by integration a third approximation (Fig. 1, curve C) is derived.

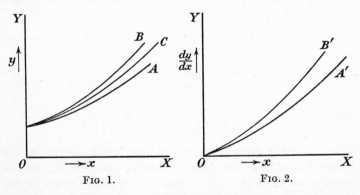

FIG. 1.   FIG. 2.

Example.—Find by the foregoing methods the integral curve of

$$\frac{dy}{dx} = -xy$$

which passes through the point $x = 0$, $y = 1$, proceeding as far as a third approximation. By integrating the equation examine the accuracy of the result.

3.7. The convergence of successive approximations.

Let $\dfrac{dy}{dx} = f(x, y)$ be the differential equation. It is given that $y = Y$ when $x = X$.

Let y_n represent the nth approximation

$$y_{n+1} - Y = \int_X^x f(x, y_n) \, . \, dx \quad . \quad . \quad . \quad (1)$$

where y is defined by the equation

$$y - Y = \int_X^x f(x, y) \, . \, dx. \, . \quad . \quad . \quad . \quad (2)$$

From these equations

$$y_{n+1} - y = \int_X^x [f(x, y_n) - f(x, y)]$$

$$= \int_X^x (y_n - y) \, . \, f_y(x, y)_\lambda \, . \, dx$$

where $f_y(x, y)_\lambda$ is the value of $\dfrac{\partial f}{\partial y}$ at a number intermediate between y_n and y.

Writing $\epsilon_n = y_n - y$ so that ϵ_n will ultimately measure the error of the nth approximation.

$$\epsilon_{n+1} = \int_X^x \epsilon_n f_y(x, y)_\lambda \, . \, dx$$

therefore $\qquad |\epsilon_{n+1}| \leq \int_X^x |\epsilon_n| \, . \, |f_y(x, y)_\lambda| \, . \, dx$

Let ϵ_n' be the greatest value of $|\epsilon_n|$ which occurs in the range during the nth approximation, and let M_n be the greatest value of $|f_y(x, y)_\lambda|$ which occurs in the range during the nth approximation.

Then ϵ_n' and M_n will not be functions of x, and therefore may be removed from under the integral sign.

Thus
$$|\epsilon_{n+1}| < \epsilon_n' . M_n \int_X^x dx$$

or
$$|\epsilon_{n+1}| < \epsilon_n' . M_n(x - X).$$

At some point in the range $|\epsilon_{n+1}|$ will assume its greatest value ϵ_{n+1}', the inequality still being true

$$\epsilon_{n+1}' < \epsilon_n' . M_n(x - X)$$
$$\epsilon_n' < \epsilon_{n-1}' . M_{n-1}(x - X)$$
$$. \quad . \quad . \quad . \quad . \quad . \quad . \quad . \quad .$$
$$\epsilon_2' < \epsilon_1' . M_1(x - X)$$

Since the numbers are all $+ve$ quantities,

$$\epsilon_{n+1}' . \epsilon_n' \ldots \epsilon_2' < \epsilon_n' \ldots \epsilon_1'(x - X)^n M_n . M_{n-1} \ldots M_1$$

i.e. $\quad\quad \epsilon_{n+1}' < \epsilon_1' . M_1 . M_2 \ldots M_n(x - X)^n$

i.e. $\quad\quad \epsilon_{n+1}' < \epsilon_1'(MR)^n$

where M is the greatest of the numbers M_1, M_2, etc., and $R = x - X$ the range of integration. If therefore $MR < 1$, that is, if in the range of integration $R < \dfrac{1}{M}$, the maximum error of the nth approximation may be made less than any assignable quantity by choosing n large enough, no matter how large ϵ_1' may be, that is, no matter how unsuitable the first approximation may be. In effect M is the maximum value of $\left|\dfrac{\partial f}{\partial y}\right|$ that occurs in the range, and although this cannot be specified initially with any great accuracy, a rough approximation can usually be made. In practice the range of valid approximation is much greater than that determined above, which is, indeed, only a safe lower limit. In the actual computation the effective range is indicated at quite an early stage by the rapidity of convergence at successive values of x.

Recollecting that y has been defined by means of (2), we have still to prove that the final values of y actually satisfy the differential equation. Differentiating (1)

$$\frac{dy_{n+1}}{dx} = f(x, y_n)$$

$$\left|\frac{dy_{n+1}}{dx} - f(x, y_{n+1})\right| = \left|f(x, y_n) - f(x, y_{n+1})\right|$$

$$< \left|y_n - y_{n+1}\right| \cdot \left|\frac{\partial f}{\partial y}\right|_{n, n+1}$$

$$< \left|(y_{n+1} - y) - (y_n - y)\right| \cdot \left|\frac{\partial f}{\partial y}\right|_{n, n+1}$$

$$< \left|\epsilon_{n+1} - \epsilon_n\right| \cdot \left|\frac{\partial f}{\partial y}\right|_{n, n+1}$$

As the right-hand side of this inequality can be made to approach indefinitely close to zero, it follows that the differential equation is ultimately satisfied.

3.8. Extension of range of integration.

Since the range is approximately measured by $1 \Big/ \left(\frac{\partial f}{\partial y}\right)_{\text{max.}}$, it is possible to form some idea initially as to whether in a given case an extended range may be expected. The differential equation $\frac{dy}{dx} = f(x, y)$ has the system of iso-clinals $c = f(x, y)$ and the slope at any point (x, y) on the isoclinal is given by $-\frac{\partial f}{\partial x} \Big/ \frac{\partial f}{\partial y}$. It follows that if $\frac{\partial f}{\partial y}$ is large both the slope of the isoclinals and the range of valid integration are small, and if $\frac{\partial f}{\partial y}$ is small, the range and slope are large. Thus the favourable case occurs when the slopes of the isoclinals are steep in the neighbourhood of integration.

When an extended range of integration is required, it is sometimes desirable to make use of the fact in the following manner. The isoclinals are first roughly sketched, and if their inclination to the axes of x is small, a new set of (x, y) axes is chosen, the x axis being as far as possible perpendicular to the isoclinals in the neighbourhood of the range considered. The new y-axis will therefore be parallel to the general trend of the isoclinals in the range considered. The old values of x and y will now be expressed as linear functions of the new values, and a modified differential equation will be obtained.

Thus if

$$\frac{d\eta}{d\xi} = \phi(\xi, \eta)$$

is the original equation, the transformation,

$$x = \xi \cos w + \eta \sin w$$
$$y = -\xi \sin w + \eta \cos w$$

which is equivalent to

$$\xi = x \cos w - y \sin w$$
$$\eta = x \sin w + y \cos w$$

w, being the angle between the positive direction of the x-axis and the positive direction of the ξ-axis, transforms the equation above into

$$\tan(\alpha - w) = \frac{dy}{dx} = f(x, y)$$

where
$$\tan \alpha = \frac{d\eta}{d\xi} = \phi(\xi, \eta).$$

The new equation $\frac{dy}{dx} = f(x, y)$ may now be used to obtain the integral of the original equation. In changing the axes by the above transformation it is best to arrange that the average slope of the isoclinals to be as steep as possible over the whole range, rather than that they shall be steepest at one *end* of the range.

The process should then be rapidly convergent for the new equation. The extreme case occurs when $f(x, y)$ is a function of y only so that the isoclinals are parallel to the axis of x. Their slopes being small, the range of integration will be small, and it becomes necessary to turn the axes so that the new axis of x is perpendicular to the isoclinals, that is to say, the new axis of x should be in the direction of the old axis of y. These requirements will be met if the rôle of the axes of x and y be interchanged, and instead of using the equation in the form $\dfrac{dy}{dx} = f(x, y)$, it is taken as $\dfrac{dx}{dy} = 1/f(x, y)$.

This suggests in fact that

a. If the isoclinals of $\dfrac{dy}{dx} = f(x, y)$ be of steep slope in the neighbourhood of the range of integration considered, the equation should be used in its existing form and the sequence for approximations is $\underline{\dfrac{dy_{n+1}}{dx} = f(x, y_n)}$.

b. If the isoclinals be of small slope the equation should be used in the form $\dfrac{dx}{dy} = 1/f(x, y)$ and the sequence for approximations is $\underline{\dfrac{dx_{n+1}}{dy} = 1/f(x_n, y)}$.

4. Systems of simultaneous equations.

The graphical method developed in the foregoing section for the solution of an equation involving one dependent variable only may be extended immediately to the case of a system of any number of equations involving the same number of dependent variables.

If $x, y, z \ldots$ are the dependent variables each implicitly functions of an independent variable t, and if the differential coefficients involved appear to the first order only, viz. $\dfrac{dx}{dt}, \dfrac{dy}{dt}, \dfrac{dz}{dt} \ldots$, then we may suppose the system solved algebraically for these differential coefficients so that we have finally :

$$\frac{dx}{dt} = X(x, y, z, \ldots t).$$

$$\frac{dy}{dt} = Y(x, y, z, \ldots t).$$

$$\frac{dz}{dt} = Z(x, y, z, \ldots t).$$

$$. \quad . \quad . \quad . \quad . \quad . \quad . \quad .$$

This is the form in which we can assume the equations to be given.

The method, closely analogous to that of a single equation, will be illustrated for the case of two dependent variables y and z.

4.1. Graphical integration of a system of two simultaneous equations of the first order.

Let the equations be

(1) $\dfrac{dz}{dt} = f(t, y, z).$

(2) $\dfrac{dy}{dt} = g(t, y, z),$ where $y = y_0,$ $z = z_0$ for $t = t_0.$

Operate simultaneously with two diagrams, as below, the y-axis being a continuation of the z-axis.

Fig. 1.

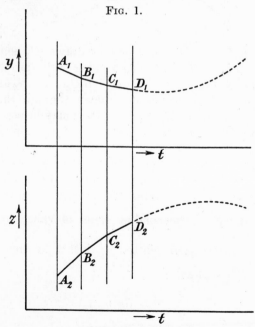

The initial values (t_0, y_0, z_0) determine two points $A_1,$ A_2 (A_1 vertically about A_2) in the two diagrams. On inserting these values into equations (1) and (2) the slopes at A_1 and A_2 in Figs. $1y$ and $1z$ are found, so that small tangents A_1B_1 and A_2B_2 may be drawn, their lengths being so adjusted that B_1 is vertically above B_2. The new co-ordinates of B_1 and B_2 can then be inserted into equations (1) and (2) and the slopes at B_1 and B_2 determined. New

FIG. 2.

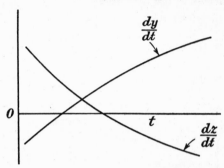

elements B_1C_1 and B_2C_2 can now be drawn, C_1 being again vertically above C_2. By continuing this process, two broken lines $A_1B_1C_1 \ldots N_1$ and $A_2B_2C_2 \ldots N_2$ are determined. If smooth curves are drawn through the points $A_1, B_1, C_1 \ldots$; $A_2, B_2, C_2 \ldots$ they may be regarded as first approximations to the solution of the simultaneous equations.

To derive a second approximation corresponding sets of values of (t, y, z) are read off the curves obtained as a first approximation (Figs. $1y$ and $1z$), inserted in equations (1) and (2), and the corresponding series of values of $\frac{dy}{dt}$ and $\frac{dz}{dt}$ are calculated and plotted against t in one diagram (Fig. 2). The sequences

$$\frac{dz_{n+1}}{dt} = f(t, y_n, z_n)$$

$$\frac{dy_{n+1}}{dt} = g(t, y_n, z_n)$$

are now employed to determine closer approximations to the solutions.

A direct integration of the curves for $\dfrac{dy}{dt}$ and $\dfrac{dz}{dt}$ by means of a planimeter or otherwise determines new values of y and z for corresponding values of t, and these constitute the second approximation.

Repeating the above process by inserting corresponding values of (t, y, z) from the second approximation in equations (1) and (2), and deriving a corrected form of Fig. 2, enables a third approximation to be obtained.

This process may be repeated until two successive approximations agree to the degree of accuracy desired.

The convergence of this graphical process is established below. In certain cases it may be better to choose y or z as the independent variable, instead of t, and this must be decided by the values of the partial derivatives required in the proof of convergence.

Thus, if f or g becomes too large, recourse may be had to the following equivalent systems :

$$\left.\begin{aligned} \frac{dy}{dx} &= f(x, y, z) \\ \frac{dz}{dx} &= g(x, y, z) \end{aligned}\right]$$

$$\left.\begin{aligned} \frac{dx}{dy} &= \frac{1}{f(x, y, z)} \\ \frac{dz}{dy} &= \frac{g(x, y, z)}{f(x, y, z)} \end{aligned}\right]$$

$$\left.\begin{aligned} \frac{dx}{dz} &= \frac{1}{g(x, y, z)} \\ \frac{dy}{dz} &= \frac{f(x, y, z)}{g(x, y, z)} \end{aligned}\right]$$

Finally, a new system of co-ordinates (x_1, y_1, z_1) may be introduced; this, however, will rarely be necessary for most cases can be satisfactorily integrated as above.

Example.—To illustrate the convergence of this graphical process the simultaneous equations

x.	y_1.	$\dfrac{dz_1}{dx}$	z_1.	$\dfrac{dy_2}{dx}$	y_2.	$\dfrac{dz_2}{dx}$	z_2.	$\dfrac{dy_3}{dx}$	y_3.	$\dfrac{dz_3}{dx}$	z_3.	$\dfrac{dy_4}{dx}$	y_4.	$J_0(x)$.
0	1	0	0	0	1	0	0	0	1	0	0	0	1·00	1·00
0·1	0·95	−0·095	−0·0048	−0·048	0·9976	−0·0998	−0·0049	−0·049	0·9975	−0·0998	−0·00499	−0·049	0·9975	0·9975
0·2	0·9	−0·18	−0·0185	−0·0925	0·9906	−0·1981	−0·0198	−0·099	0·9901	−0·1980	−0·0198	−0·099	0·9901	0·9900
0·3	0·85	−0·255	−0·0403	−0·134	0·9793	−0·2938	−0·0444	−0·148	0·9774	−0·2932	−0·0444	−0·148	0·9774	0·9776
0·4	0·8	−0·32	−0·0691	−0·1728	0·9640	−0·3856	−0·0784	−0·196	0·9602	−0·3841	−0·0784	−0·196	0·9602	0·9604
0·5	0·75	−0·375	−0·1039	−0·2078	0·9450	−0·4725	−0·1213	−0·243	0·9383	−0·4691	−0·1211	−0·243	0·9383	0·9385
0·6	0·7	−0·420	−0·1437	−0·2395	0·9226	−0·5601	−0·1829	−0·305	0·9109	−0·5465	−0·1719	−0·287	0·9118	0·9120
0·7	0·65	−0·455	−0·1875	−0·2679	0·8972	−0·6280	−0·2423	−0·346	0·8783	−0·6148	−0·2300	−0·329	0·8810	0·8812
0·8	0·6	−0·480	−0·2345	−0·2679	0·8704	−0·6963	−0·3085	−0·386	0·8317	−0·6654	−0·2940	−0·368	0·8461	0·8463
0·9	0·55	−0·495	−0·2831	−0·3165	0·8412	−0·7571	−0·3812	−0·423	0·7912	−0·7121	−0·3629	−0·403	0·8075	0·8075
1·0	0·5	−0·5	−0·3329	−0·3329	0·8087	−0·8087	−0·4594	−0·459	0·7471	−0·7471	−0·4359	−0·436	0·7655	0·7652

$$\left.\begin{aligned}\frac{dz}{dx} + xy = 0\\ x\frac{dy}{dx} - z = 0\end{aligned}\right\}$$

subject to $x = 0$, $y = 1$, $z = 0$ were integrated, and the results quoted on p. 46 were found in less than one hour by assuming as a first approximation

$$y_1 = 1 - 0\cdot 5x.$$

The more accurate solution of the equation is tabulated in the last column, and the percentage error in y_4 is everywhere less than $0\cdot 5$ per cent.

Use the sequences

$$z_{n+1} + \int_0^x xy_n dx = 0$$

$$y_{n+1} = \int_0^x \frac{z_n}{x}\,dx + 1$$

The solution is $\qquad y = J_0(x)$

4.2. Convergence of successive approximation applied to simultaneous equations.

The proof of the convergence of the method of successive approximation has already been given for the differential equation

$$\frac{dy}{dx} = f(x, y).$$

The following proof follows similar lines with but little deviation from the former proof.

Consider the equations

$$\frac{dy}{dx} = f(x, y, z) \quad . \quad . \quad . \quad . \quad . \quad \text{(i)}$$

and $\qquad \dfrac{dz}{dx} = g(x, y, z) \quad . \quad . \quad . \quad . \quad . \quad \text{(ii)}$

Let the initial condition be

$$x = x_0, \; y = y_0, \; z = z_0 \quad . \quad . \quad . \quad \text{(iii)}$$

Then
$$y_1 = y_0 + \int_{x_0}^{x} f(x, y_0, z_0) \cdot dx.$$

This is the first approximation to the value of y.
If y is the true value,

$$y = y_0 + \int_{x_0}^{x} f(x, y, z) \cdot dx.$$

Therefore

$$y - y_1 = \int_{x_0}^{x} [f(x, y, z) - f(x, y_0, z_0)] dx \qquad . \quad \text{(iv)}$$

Similarly

$$z - z_1 = \int_{x_0}^{x} [g(x, y, z) - g(x, y_0, z_0)] dx \quad . \quad . \quad \text{(v)}$$

Applying the theorem of mean value to the right-hand sides of equations (iv) and (v)

$$f(x, y, z) - f(x, y_0, z_0) = (y - y_0)\left(\frac{\partial f}{\partial y}\right)_m + (z - z_0)\left(\frac{\partial f}{\partial z}\right)_m$$

and

$$g(x, y, z) - g(x, y_0, z_0) = (y - y_0)\left(\frac{\partial g}{\partial y}\right)_m + (z - z_0)\left(\frac{\partial g}{\partial z}\right)_m$$

The values of the partial derivatives being calculated at some intermediate position in the range (x_0, y_0, z_0) to (x, y, z).

Therefore

$$y - y_1 = \int_{x_0}^{x} \left[(y - y_0)\left(\frac{\partial f}{\partial y}\right)_m + (z - z_0)\left(\frac{\partial f}{\partial z}\right)_m \right] dx. \quad . \quad \text{(vi)}$$

$$z - z_1 = \int_{x_0}^{x} \left[(y - y_0)\left(\frac{\partial g}{\partial y}\right)_m + (z - z_0)\left(\frac{\partial g}{\partial z}\right)_m \right] dx. \quad . \quad \text{(vii)}$$

Adding (vi) and (vii)

$$y - y_1 + z - z_1 = \int_{x_0}^{x} \Big[(y - y_0)\left\{\left(\frac{\partial f}{\partial y}\right)_m + \left(\frac{\partial g}{\partial y}\right)_m\right\}$$
$$+ (z - z_0)\left\{\left(\frac{\partial f}{\partial z}\right)_m + \left(\frac{\partial g}{\partial z}\right)\right\}_m \Big] dx. \quad . \quad \text{(viii)}$$

If M denotes the maximum value of whichever is the

greater of $\left\{\left|\dfrac{\partial f}{\partial y}\right| + \left|\dfrac{\partial g}{\partial y}\right|\right\}$ or $\left\{\left|\dfrac{\partial f}{\partial z}\right| + \left|\dfrac{\partial g}{\partial z}\right|\right\}$ in the range (x_0, y_0, z_0) to (x, y, z) then

$$y - y_1 + z - z_1 \leq \int_{x_0}^{x} M[(y - y_0) + (z - z_0)]dx.$$

Let λ_0 and μ_0 denote the maximum values of $|y - y_0|$ and $|z - z_0|$ respectively in the range (x_0, y_0, z_0) to (x, y, z), then with similar notations λ_1 and μ_1 for the corresponding maximum values of $|y - y_1|$, $|z - z_1|$ in the range (x_0, y_0, z_0) to (x, y, z).

$$\lambda_1 + \mu_1 \leq M(\lambda_0 + \mu_0)\left|\int_{x_0}^{x} . \, dx\right|$$

$$\leq M(\lambda_0 + \mu_0) . \, |x - x_0|.$$

Similarly

$$\lambda_2 + \mu_2 \leq M(\lambda_1 + \mu_1) . \, |x - x_0|$$

$$. \quad . \quad . \quad . \quad . \quad . \quad . \quad .$$

$$\lambda_n + \mu_n \leq M(\lambda_{n-1} + \mu_{n-1}) . \, |x - x_0|$$

the last equation holding for the nth approximation.

Hence, multiplying the left-hand sides and right-hand sides of these inequalities and dividing by the common factors

$$(\lambda_1 + \mu_1) \, . \, . \, . \, (\lambda_n + \mu_n) \leq \{M|x - x_0|\}^n . \, (\lambda_0 + \mu_0).$$

It is now clear that if $M|x - x_0| < 1$ the right-hand side can be made smaller than any positive quantity ϵ, however small ϵ may be. Therefore the nth approximations converge to the true values if

$$|x - x_0| < \frac{1}{M},$$

i.e. if $\qquad |x - x_0| < 1 \Big/ \left\{\left|\dfrac{\partial f}{\partial y}\right| + \left|\dfrac{\partial g}{\partial y}\right|\right\}$

or $\qquad\qquad < 1 \Big/ \left\{\left|\dfrac{\partial f}{\partial z}\right| + \left|\dfrac{\partial g}{\partial z}\right|\right\}$

where the partial derivatives are the greatest in the range. Thus by choosing the increment in x small enough, the process may be made convergent. It should be clear that if any of these partial derivatives should become infinite in the range, the process cannot be convergent.

By a transformation of axes it may be possible to make the partial derivatives take smaller values, and this will greatly speed up the convergence of the process. The student should therefore examine the values of these partial derivatives in the range before proceeding to the actual numerical calculation. In certain cases it might be much better to take y or z as the independent variable.

5. Extension to equations of higher order.

If the equation be of the second order

$$f\left(\frac{d^2y}{dx^2}, \frac{dy}{dx}, y, x\right) = 0$$

subject to boundary conditions of the type

$$x = x_0, \; y = y_0, \; \frac{dy}{dx} = p_0$$

then by direct solution for $\frac{d^2y}{dx^2}$ it may be thrown into the form

$$\frac{d^2y}{dx^2} = g\left(\frac{dy}{dx}, y, x\right)$$

the boundary conditions remaining unaltered.

Introduce a new variable $p = \frac{dy}{dx}$ so that $\frac{dp}{dx} = \frac{d^2y}{dx^2}$, then the original equation and its boundary conditions become

$$\frac{dp}{dx} = g(p, y, x)$$

$$\frac{dy}{dx} = p$$

where $p = p_0$, $y = y_0$ when $x = x_0$.

This is now a simple system of simultaneous differential equations and can be solved by the method of the preceding paragraphs.

5.1. Integration of second order equations.

Methods applicable to linear equations and to non-linear equations of the type

$$\frac{d^2y}{dx^2} = f\left(x, y, \frac{dy}{dx}\right)$$

subject to $x = x_0$, $y = y_0$, $y' = y_0'$.

The methods of integration described in this section are all applicable to linear equations, but special methods to be described later are available for this type of equation. The problem is solved by obtaining a first approximation to the solution and then refining this solution by sequence methods.

First approximation.

Method I.—The equation above may be written as the two simultaneous equations

$$\left.\begin{aligned} \frac{dz}{dx} &= f(x, y, z) \\ \frac{dy}{dx} &= z \end{aligned}\right\}$$

and

subject to $x = x_0$, $y = y_0$, $z = z_0$.

The integration of these equations has already been described under simultaneous equations.

Method II. The curvature method. Consider the equation written in the form

$$\frac{d^2y}{dx^2} = f(x, y, \tan \psi)$$

where

$$\frac{dy}{dx} = \tan \psi.$$

Now

$$\frac{d^2y}{dx^2} = \sec^2 \psi \cdot \frac{d\psi}{dx} = \sec^2 \psi \cdot \frac{d\psi}{ds} \cdot \frac{ds}{dx}$$

$$= \frac{1}{\cos^3 \psi} \cdot \frac{1}{\rho}$$

since the radius of curvature is given by $\rho = \frac{ds}{d\psi}$.

The equation may therefore be written in the form

$$\frac{1}{\rho} = \cos^3 \psi \cdot f(x, y, \tan \psi).$$

This equation specifies the radius of curvature and its sign at any point where x, y, and ψ are known. The method of procedure is to draw PO through the initial point perpendicular to PQ which is the direction of y_0' at P. If OP is made equal to ρ_0, a small arc with centre O and radius

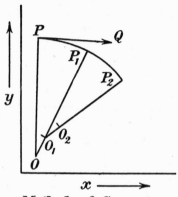

Method of Curvature

OP will be an approximation to the solution at P. If P_1 is the end of this small arc, then x, y, and ψ may be read off at the new point, and the new radius of curvature $P_1 O_1$ may be set off along $P_1 O$. The process may now be continued over the whole of the desired range and a first approximation to the solution is obtained.

It should be noted that the nature of the physical problem which is being investigated may suggest the first approximation, or a guess at the solution may be made. The sequence method now to be described very rapidly yields a solution which is accurate to within $\frac{1}{2}$ per cent. over a fairly wide range under average conditions with even a crude first approximation.

5.12. Improving the accuracy of the first approximation.

The values of x, y and $\frac{dy}{dx}$ are now available over the range of integration as a first approximation. By substitution in the differential equation the values of $\frac{d^2y}{dx^2}$ are obtained and plotted with x as abscissæ. This curve is integrated to give $\frac{dy}{dx}$, and, since $\left(\frac{dy}{dx}\right)_0$ is known, this curve may be drawn. The curve for $\frac{dy}{dx}$ upon integration and insertion of the value of y at $x = x_0$, yields the second approximation to the solution. In effect the sequence

$$\frac{d^2y_{n+1}}{dx^2} = f\left(x, y_n, \frac{dy_n}{dx}\right)$$

or
$$y_{n+1} = \int_{x_0}^{x} dx \int_{x_0}^{x} f\left(x, y_n, \frac{dy_n}{dx}\right) dx + y_0 + y_0' \cdot x$$

has been used, and by repeating the process a third approximation is found. When two successive approximations are the same within the specified degree of accuracy, the process may be stopped.

5.13. Linear differential equations of the second order

$$\frac{d^2y}{dx^2} + P\frac{dy}{dx} + Qy = R,$$

where P, Q and R are functions of x only.

It is shown on p. 183, where a much fuller discussion of this type of equation is given, that if any two solutions u and v are found to the above equation with the right-hand zero, then $Au + Bv$, where A and B are constants, is the general solution, and A and B may therefore be found to satisfy any given boundary conditions.

It follows, therefore, that if any particular solution of the original equation above is known, then the general solution may be written

$$y = Au + Bv + y_1,$$

where y_1 is any solution of the equation

$$\frac{d^2y}{dx^2} + P\frac{dy}{dx} + Qy = R$$

subject to any boundary conditions which it is convenient to impose. Using the two arbitrary constants A and B, this general solution may be made to satisfy any boundary conditions.

5.14. Linear equation of the second order of the type

$$\frac{d^2y}{dx^2} + Qy = R,$$

where R and Q are functions of x.

It is shown on p. 184 that if y_1 is a solution of the equation

$$\frac{d^2y}{dx^2} + Qy = 0$$

then

$$y = Ay_1 \int \frac{dx}{y_1{}^2} + By_1$$

is the general solution, and hence if y_2 is any particular solution of the original equation

$$\frac{d^2y}{dx^2} + Qy = R,$$

then the general solution is

$$y = Ay_1 \int \frac{dx}{y_1{}^2} + By_1 + y_2,$$

and the constants may be found to satisfy any arbitrary boundary conditions.

5.15. Graphical integration of the equations

$$(a)\ \frac{d^2y}{dx^2} = f(x,\, y)$$

$$(b)\ \frac{d^2y}{dx^2} = g\!\left(x,\, y,\, \frac{dy}{dx}\right)$$

when the boundary conditions relate to both ends of the range, viz. $x = x_0$, $y = y_0$; $x = x_1$, $y = y_1$.

By means of the transformations

$$X = \frac{x - x_0}{x_1 - x_0}; \quad Y = \frac{y - y_0}{y_1 - y_0}$$

it will readily be seen that the boundary conditions in the new differential equation become $x = 0$, $y = 0$ and $x = 1$, $y = 1$.

Also

$$\frac{dy}{dx} = \frac{(y_1 - y_0)}{(x_1 - x_0)} \cdot \frac{dY}{dX}$$

and

$$\frac{d^2y}{dx^2} = \frac{(y_1 - y_0)}{(x_1 - x_0)^2} \cdot \frac{d^2Y}{dX^2}.$$

Let us therefore return to the old variables with the more convenient boundary conditions.

It is proposed to use the sequences

$$y_{n+1} = \int_0^x dx \int_0^x f(x, y_n)dx + Ax + B$$

and

$$y_{n+1} = \int_0^x dx \int_0^x g\left(x, y_n, \frac{dy_n}{dx}\right) \cdot dx + Ax + B,$$

respectively. The geometrical process is quite straightforward, and consists of first obtaining an approximate solution of the equation between the two end-points of the range. This may be done for equation (a) by examining the value of $\frac{d^2y}{dx^2}$ over the range, and so determining the sign of the curvature. An approximation is now drawn to satisfy the boundary conditions, and having the sign of curvature specified as above. In many cases the nature of the physical problem which is being investigated suggests the first approximation. Another method of procedure is to take as the first approximation the integral of the constant coefficient equation

$$\frac{d^2y}{dx^2} = A + Bx + Cy$$

subject to the above boundary conditions where $A = f(x_0, y_0)$, $B = \left(\frac{\partial f}{\partial x}\right)_0$, $C = \left(\frac{\partial f}{\partial y}\right)_0$. However crude this first approximation may be, the sequence leads to a solution which is everywhere correct to within $\frac{1}{2}$ per cent. in a very few steps.

Having drawn the first approximation, this curve is used to give values of x and y $\left(\text{and } \dfrac{dy}{dx} \text{ for equation } (b)\right)$ which yield $\dfrac{d^2y}{dx^2}$ when they are substituted in the differential equation. The $\dfrac{d^2y}{dx^2}$ curve is now drawn, and when it is integrated by planimeter (or otherwise), a curve for $\dfrac{dy}{dx}$ may be plotted whose gradient $\dfrac{d^2y}{dx^2}$ is the ordinate of the previous

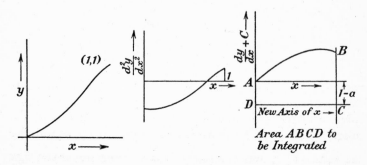

curve. It follows that the curve for $\dfrac{dy}{dx}$ may have an arbitrary constant added to all its ordinates without altering the gradient of the curve at any point. If this curve is integrated over the whole range, and α units is the result, $(1 - \alpha)$ is clearly the amount by which all its ordinates should be increased in order that the boundary conditions may be satisfied. The curve is therefore raised by $1 - \alpha$ by drawing a new axis of x, $(1 - \alpha)$ units below the old one, and by integrating this new curve y may be determined to satisfy the end conditions. The process may now be repeated until two approximations agree to within the prescribed degree of accuracy.

5.16. Convergence of sequence for second order equations.

Consider
$$\frac{d^2y}{dx^2} = f(x, y)$$

subject to the conditions

$$x = a, \; y = b, \; \frac{dy}{dx} = c.$$

Take the sequence determined by

$$y_{n+1} = \int_a^x dx \int_a^x f(x, y_n)dx + c(x - a) + b.$$

This satisfies the conditions that when

$$x = a, \; y_{n+1} = b \quad \text{and} \quad \frac{dy_{n+1}}{dx} = c.$$

Associate with it a function y defined by

$$y = \int_a^x dx \int_a^x f(x, y)dx + c(x - a) + b.$$

Then

$$y_{n+1} - y = \int_a^x dx \int_a^x [f(x, y_n) - f(x, y)] \; dx$$

$$= \int_a^x dx \int_a^x (y_n - y)\left(\frac{\partial f}{\partial y}\right)_\lambda \; dx$$

where $\left(\dfrac{\partial f}{\partial y}\right)_\lambda$ is a value of $f_y(x, y)$ at a value of y intermediate between y_n and y, both of which are functions of x.

Now

$$|y_{n+1} - y| < \int_a^x dx \int_a^x |y_n - y| \cdot \left|\left(\frac{\partial f}{\partial y}\right)_\lambda\right| dx.$$

Writing $\epsilon_n = y_n - y$ and M_n as the largest value of $\left(\dfrac{\partial f}{\partial y}\right)_\lambda$ that occurs anywhere in the range during the nth stage of the sequence

$$|\epsilon_{n+1}| < \int_a^x dx \int_a^x |\epsilon_n| \cdot M_n dx$$

$$< \epsilon_n' M_n \int_a^x dx \int_a^x dx$$

where ϵ_n' is the largest value of $|\epsilon_n|$ a positive function of x, that occurs in the range.

Thus $$|\epsilon_{n+1}| < \tfrac{1}{2}\epsilon_n' M_n(x-a)^2,$$

but a particular value of $|\epsilon_{n+1}|$ is its largest value, viz., ϵ_{n+1}' and therefore

$$\epsilon_{n+1}' < \tfrac{1}{2}R^2 \epsilon_n' M_n,$$

where R = range of integration.

Similarly $$\epsilon_n' < \tfrac{1}{2}R^2 \epsilon_{n-1}' \cdot M_{n-1}$$

$$\cdot \quad \cdot \quad \cdot \quad \cdot \quad \cdot \quad \cdot \quad \cdot$$

$$\epsilon_2' < \tfrac{1}{2}R^2 \epsilon_1' M_1.$$

Thus $$\epsilon_{n+1}' < \left(\frac{R^2}{2}\right)^n \epsilon_1' M_1 M_2 \ldots M_n.$$

If M is the greatest of $M_1, M_2 \ldots M_n$, then

$$\epsilon_{n+1}' < \left(\frac{MR^2}{2}\right)^n \cdot \epsilon_1'$$

and the sequence converges provided the range of integration R is such that

$$\frac{MR^2}{2} < 1 \quad \text{or} \quad R < \sqrt{\left(\frac{2}{M}\right)}.$$

Effectively M is the greatest value of $\left|\dfrac{\partial f}{\partial y}\right|$ that occurs in the range, and this investigation demonstrates the convergence of the process over a finite range. In practice the actual range of convergence will become evident quite early in the computation, so that very little extra labour is involved when M cannot initially be calculated.

5.17. Modified treatment when the boundary conditions do not all relate to one point.

Consider

$$\frac{d^2y}{dx^2} = f(x, y) \quad . \quad . \quad . \quad . \quad . \quad (1)$$

and let a solution satisfy the terminal conditions

$$x = a, \; y = A; \; x = b, \; y = B . \quad . \quad . \quad (1.1)$$

where we may suppose without restriction $b > a \geq 0$.

Write the equation in the form

$$y = \int_a^x dx \int_a^x f(x, y)dx + \lambda x + \mu.$$

To make this satisfy the terminal conditions we write it

$$y - A = \int_a^x dx \int_a^x f(x, y)dx + \lambda(x - a) . \quad . \quad (2)$$

where λ is determined from

$$B - A = \int_a^b dx \int_a^x f(x, y)dx + \lambda(b - a) . \quad . \quad (2.1)$$

Consider the sequence defined by

$$y_{n+1} - A = \int_a^x dx \int_a^x f(x, y_n) . dx + \lambda_n(x - a) . \quad . \quad (3)$$

where

$$B - A = \int_a^b dx \int_a^x f(x, y_n)dx + \lambda_n(b - a) . \quad . \quad (3.1)$$

Then, subtracting (3) and (3.1) from (2) and (2.1), respectively,

$$y_{n+1} - y = \int_a^x dx \int_a^x [f(x, y_n) - f(x, y)]dx + (\lambda_n - \lambda)(x - a) . \quad . \quad (3.2)$$

and

$$0 = \int_a^b dx \int_a^x [f(x, y_n) - f(x, y)]dx + (\lambda_n - \lambda)(b - a) \quad (3.3)$$

Hence from (3.2)

$$|y_{n+1} - y| < | \int_a^x dx \int_a^x [f(x, y_n) - f(x, y)]dx | + |\lambda_n - \lambda| . |x - a| . \quad . \quad (3.4)$$

But, since x is a point intermediate between a and b,

$$|x - a| < |b - a|.$$

Also from (3.3)

$$|\lambda_n - \lambda| . (b - a) = | \int_a^b dx \int_a^x [f(x, y_n) - f(x, y)] . dx |$$

$$= | \int_a^b dx \int_a^x (y_n - y) . \left(\frac{\partial f}{\partial y} \right)_n dx |,$$

where $\left(\dfrac{\partial f}{\partial y}\right)_n$ is the value of the partial derivative of $f(x, y)$ with respect to y at a position x, and at a value of y intermediate between y_n and y. This derivative is not merely a function of x, but of n also. Let the largest value it attains over the range $a \leq x \leq b$ be M_n, a function of n, but no longer of x. Also let $|y_n - y| = |\epsilon_n|$, also a function both of x and n. Let the greatest value this attains in the range $a \leq x \leq b$ be ϵ_n', then

$$|\lambda_n - \lambda| \, . \, (b - a) < \int_a^b dx \int_a^x \epsilon_n' M_n dx$$

i.e.
$$< \epsilon_n' M_n (b - a)^2 / 2 \quad . \quad . \quad . \quad . \quad (3.5)$$

Hence from (3.4)

$$|\epsilon_{n+1}| < M_n \epsilon_n' (x - a)^2 / 2 + \epsilon_n' M_n (b - a) / 2 \, . \, |x - a| \quad (3.6)$$

Hence, since ϵ_{n+1}' is the greatest value attained by $|\epsilon_{n+1}|$ at some position x, the inequality will still be true when $|\epsilon_{n+1}|$ is replaced by ϵ_{n+1}' on the left and $|x - a|$ is replaced by the larger number $b - a$ on the right. Thus (3.6) becomes

$$\epsilon_{n+1}' < M_n \epsilon_n' (b - a)^2.$$

Similarly

$$\epsilon_n' < M_{n-1} \epsilon_{n-1}' (b - a)^2$$
$$. \quad . \quad . \quad . \quad . \quad . \quad .$$
$$\epsilon_2' < M_1 \epsilon_1' (b - a)^2,$$

and accordingly

$$\epsilon_{n+1}' < M_1 M_2 \, . \, . \, . \, M_n \epsilon_1' (b - a)^{2n}$$
$$< M^n R^{2n} \, . \, \epsilon_1',$$

where M is the greatest among the positive numbers $M_1, M_2, \ldots M_n$ and $R = b - a =$ range of integration. It follows that the sequence (3) will be convergent, no matter how inaccurate the first approximation may be provided the range of integration R is restricted, so that

$$MR^2 < 1, \quad i.e. \quad R < \frac{1}{\sqrt{M}}$$

In effect M is the maximum value of $\dfrac{\partial f}{\partial y}$ that occurs in the range $a < x < b$, and since, in general, this is finite, the sequence will lead to a definite limit over a finite range. It remains to show that the limiting form of y_n actually satisfies the differential equation. From (3) by differentiating twice

$$\frac{d^2 y_{n+1}}{dx^2} = f(x,\, y_n)$$

and therefore

$$\left| \frac{d^2 y_{n+1}}{dx^2} - f(x,\, \dot{y}_{n+1}) \right| = \left| f(x,\, y_n) - f(x,\, y_{n+1}) \right|$$

$$= \left| y_{n+1} - y_n \right| \cdot \left| \frac{\partial f}{\partial y} \right|_m,$$

where $\left| \dfrac{\partial f}{\partial y} \right|_m$ is the value of $\dfrac{\partial f}{\partial y}$ at any position x and for a particular value of y intermediate between y_n and y_{n+1}.

Since $\left(\dfrac{\partial f}{\partial y} \right)_m$ is finite and

$$\left| y_{n+1} - y_n \right| = \left| \epsilon_{n+1} - \epsilon_n \right| < \epsilon_{n+1}{}' + \epsilon_n{}',$$

the expression

$$\frac{d^2 y_{n+1}}{dx^2} - f(x,\, y_{n+1})$$

may be made to approach as near to zero as may be desired by sufficiently increasing n.

It should be remarked that the permissible range of integration is in this case apparently smaller than that derived for the case where the terminal conditions all relate to one end. Although in both cases the practical range within which this process leads to a definite limiting solution is much greater than that derived from the investigation, it is, in fact, found that the range of accurate approximation is more contracted here than in the former case. A serious practical difficulty arises, therefore, when the two values of x at which y is specified are further apart than is permissible by this process. This will be dealt with later.

Example.—By a graphical method find to three places of decimals the solution of the equation

$$(3x + 2y - 1)\frac{d^2y}{dx^2} = 4x^2,$$

satisfying the conditions $x = 0$, $y = 0\cdot 5$, $x = 0\cdot 5$, $y = 0$.

CHAPTER III

NUMERICAL SOLUTION OVER A LIMITED RANGE

Introduction.

THE problem of the numerical integration of a differential equation is, in general, to find a function (say, y) to satisfy the equation for a given range of values of a variable x. The solution may take one of two forms, either

(a) that of an expression for y in terms of functions of x, from which values of y are obtained by direct substitution, or

(b) that of a series of values of y corresponding to tabulated values of x.

63

The methods of Picard, Taylor, and Frobenius yield power series in the independent variable, and belong to class (*a*), whereas the methods of Euler, of Runge, and Kutta, among many others, belong to class (*b*). Since those included under (*a*) embrace also cases where the expansion is expressed in terms of functions other than polynomials, it might be supposed that the methods of section (*a*) are preferable in all cases to those of section (*b*), for, once the series has been found, it appears that the process can be completed by direct substitution of the value of *x* corresponding to the value of *y* required. This is not always the case, however, for this method suffers in practice from several serious disadvantages, which may be briefly noted here.

(i) It may not be possible to obtain a convenient convergent series which represents the function *y* over the desired range of values of *x*. A possible procedure in this case is to divide the range into parts and find separate series to represent the function over these parts.

(ii) The determining of the coefficients of higher powers of *x* may become rapidly more complicated as the number of terms increases.

(iii) Calculating values of *y* by substitution in a power series for *x* may entail considerable labour, which has to be repeated for each value.

(iv) In those cases where the numerical values of the solution is required, and the labour in the calculation via the series becomes excessive, it is better to apply a numerical process direct to the differential equation.

In view of the above considerations, and particularly for the cases where the range of integration is wide, other methods of integration have been devised. These vary considerably in suitability. The methods of Euler, Runge, and Kutta are all methods of determining the increment of *y* corresponding to a given increment *x* in *x*, and are expressed by formulæ from which by direct substitution y is obtained. These formulæ are very suitable for calculating isolated function values. In general, even with the most accurate of these methods., viz., Kutta's method, the interval must nevertheless be kept small, and progress becomes slow, both because of the smallness of the interval and because the formulæ used involve cumbersome calculations. Such methods are therefore not satisfactory for tabulating function values at intervals over a wide range of integration. In such a case this has been achieved by having special processes for continuing the integration once it has been begun by one of the foregoing methods. To this process we apply the term " Integration Forward." Formulæ used for integration forward chiefly involve finite differences. It is hoped that the descriptions of the methods will suffice to enable them to be followed and applied even where a previous knowledge of finite differences is very slight. Alternative methods will frequently be described, but the precise choice of method in any particular case is not always easy. To assist towards this end there is included a short comparison of the methods as regards their suitability under specified conditions.

The importance of adequate checking of calculations must be borne continually in mind throughout this work, and systematic checks on the calculation have been incorporated as a part of the process of integration. A single undetected error may lead to hours of fruitless labour that might be avoided by a few extra minutes devoted to applying the check. Experience in numerical calculations enables errors to be detected with greater facility, but a mechanically applied check is a safeguard against such an error escaping detection.

6. Solution in series.

The methods of Picard and of Taylor to be described in this section are in general the most direct and convenient methods for starting the solution of an equation over a wide range. In addition, where the range is limited, they may yield solutions which are valid over the whole of the desired range. It has already been pointed out that the range may be divided into parts and a new series developed to apply to each part separately. In such a case the derivation would require to be very simple and the series rapidly convergent for this method to be preferable to those described later. In many cases the methods of Picard and Taylor may be considered as alternative processes, but in the case where y is finite, and one of the derivatives and those succeeding it are infinite at the initial point, such as is the case if the first power of x is a positive fraction, then expansion as a Taylor series fails, but Picard's method may still be applicable (see Example 2). It may be remarked that the method of Frobenius gives a solution under similar conditions for second-order equations, and is included in this section of the work. When a series is found by one of the above methods, and it is required to determine the range over which the series is valid to a specified degree of accuracy, the first neglected term in the series may be taken as approximately equal to the greatest allowable error. In this way the greatest value that the variable in the series may take is readily obtained. This process is shown in the worked examples.

6.1. Solution of a differential equation of the first order by Picard's method of successive approximations.

Let the differential equation be written in the form

$$\frac{dy}{dx} = f(x, y),$$

where it is given that $y = y_0$ when $x = x_0$.

A solution is sought in the form of a series of powers of x to represent y over a given range of values of x. The numerical values of y are found from this expression by direct substitution of the values of x.

The obvious method of procedure is to change the origin to the initial point (x_0, y_0) of the range by writing $x + x_0$ for x and $y + y_0$ for y, and then to proceed upon the assumption that for very small values of the new x the new value of y may be represented approximately in terms of x by the equation

$$y_1 = a \cdot x^n.$$

Upon substituting in the differential equation, the constants a and n can be determined and the expression for y_1 taken as the first approximation. This expression y_1 is now substituted for y in $f(x, y)$ in the differential equation, and a further integration supplies a new and more accurate expression for y—say, y_2. Repeating the process provides closer approximations at each step, and the process is terminated when two successive approximations provide values for y which do not differ to the degree of accuracy initially specified as desirable. The details of the process are best followed in particular examples.

Example.—Consider the differential equation

$$\frac{dy}{dx} = x^2 - y^2 \quad . \quad . \quad . \quad . \quad \text{(i)}$$

subject to $x = 0$, $y = 0$.

Suppose a solution to be required in the neighbourhood of $x = 0$. For a suitable first approximation at $x = 0$ let $y_1 = a \cdot x^n$, then, substituting in the equation (i)

$$anx^{n-1} = x^2 - a^2 \cdot x^{2n} \quad . \quad . \quad . \quad \text{(ii)}$$

this equation may be satisfied approximately when x is small by equating two of the terms provided in that case the other is negligible. Thus writing

$$n - 1 = 2$$

and $$an = 1$$

equation (ii) is satisfied; for when $n = 3$ the term a^2x^{2n} is $\frac{1}{9}x^6$, which may be neglected in comparison with x^3 when x is small.

Therefore

$$y_1 = \tfrac{1}{3}x^3 \quad . \quad . \quad . \quad . \quad . \quad \text{(iii)}$$

is the first approximation. By trying the remaining possibilities, it is seen to be the only valid first approximation of this type for small values of x.

The same approximation is also found by inserting the initial value of y and leaving the independent variable in the expression.

If the value of y is now replaced by $\frac{1}{3}x^3$ in (i)

$$\frac{dy_2}{dx} = x^2 - \frac{1}{9}x^6$$

therefore

$$y_2 = \int_0^x (x^2 - \frac{1}{9}x^6) \cdot dx$$

$$y_2 = \frac{1}{3} \cdot x^3 - \frac{x^7}{7 \cdot 9} \quad \cdots \quad \text{(iv)}$$

Replacing y in (i) by the right-hand side of (iv)

$$y_3 = \int_0^x \frac{dy_3}{dx} dx$$

$$= \int_0^x \left(x^2 - \frac{1}{9}x^6 + \frac{2x^{10}}{3 \cdot 7 \cdot 9} - \frac{x^{14}}{7^2 \cdot 9^2} \right) \cdot dx$$

$$= \frac{1}{3}x^3 - \frac{x^7}{7 \cdot 9} + \frac{2x^{11}}{3 \cdot 7 \cdot 9 \cdot 11} \quad \cdots \quad \text{(v)}$$

neglecting the term in x^{15} for the third approximation.

6.11. Convergence of the process.

The series obtained is rapidly convergent for small values of x. The convergence of the process in this particular example may be shown as follows.

Let y_n represent the nth approximation, then

$$\frac{dy_{n+1}}{dx} = x^2 - y_n^2$$

hence

$$y_{n+1} = \int_0^x (x^2 - y_n^2) \cdot dx$$

$$= \frac{1}{3}x^3 - \int_0^x y_n^2 \cdot dx.$$

Now, the correct value of y may be defined by

$$y = \int_0^x (x^2 - y^2) \cdot dx = \frac{1}{3}x^3 - \int_0^x y^2 \cdot dx.$$

By subtraction, therefore,

$$y_{n+1} - y = \int_0^x y^2 \, . \, dx - \int_0^x y_n{}^2 \, . \, dx$$

$$= \int_0^x (y^2 - y_n{}^2) \, . \, dx$$

$$= - \int_0^x (y_n - y)(y_n + y) \, . \, dx.$$

Denote $(y_n - y)$ by ϵ_n, the latter being therefore a function of x.

Then $\qquad \epsilon_{n+1} = - \int_0^x \epsilon_n(y_n + y) \, . \, dx$

thus $\qquad |\epsilon_{n+1}| = |\int_0^x \epsilon_n(y_n + y)dx|$

therefore $\qquad |\epsilon_{n+1}| < \int_0^x |\epsilon_n| \, . \, |y_n + y| \, . \, dx.$

All the functions under the integral sign on the right are functions of x. $|\epsilon_n|$ may vanish at points in the range, but remains positive, and will at some point have its largest value—say, ϵ_n'. Similarly, $|(y_n + y)|$ will have a greatest value—say, $2M_n$—somewhere in the range. Now, ϵ_n' and M_n are independent of x, therefore

$$|\epsilon_{n+1}| < 2\epsilon_n' \, . \, M_n \, . \, x$$

the integration being carried through for dx only.

With the above notation, it follows that, as a particular case

$$\epsilon_{n+1}' < 2\epsilon_n'M_n \, . \, x$$
$$\epsilon_n' < 2\epsilon_{n-1}'M_{n-1} \, . \, x$$
$$. \quad . \quad . \quad . \quad .$$
$$\epsilon_2' < 2\epsilon_1'M_1 \, . \, x.$$

Since all the numbers are positive, the left-hand sides and the right-hand sides of the inequalities may be multiplied

$$\epsilon_{n+1}' \, . \, \epsilon_n' \ldots \epsilon_2' < (2x)^n \, . \, \epsilon_n' \, . \, \epsilon_{n-1}' \ldots \epsilon_1' \, . \, M_n \, . \, M_{n-1} \ldots M_1.$$
Therefore $\epsilon_{n+1}' < (2x)^n \, . \, \epsilon_1'M_n \, . \, M_{n-1} \, . \, . \, . \, M_1$, and
if M is the greatest of the quantities M_n

$$\epsilon_{n+1}' < (2Mx)^n \, . \, \epsilon_1'.$$

Thus, however large ϵ_1' may be, provided that $2xM < 1$, then ϵ_{n+1}' may be decreased indefinitely. The process is therefore convergent provided the range of x is less than $\frac{1}{2M}$. In effect, M may be taken as the largest value of y in the range. This range of x is not necessarily a measure of the whole practical range of convergence, as is obvious from the manner in which the inequalities have been constructed.

It remains to prove that the values of y so obtained actually do satisfy the differential equation. The mere fact that $y_n - y$ may be made indefinitely small does not in itself imply this. The curve for y_n might cross and recross the curve for y a larger and larger number of times as n increases, and the slope of y_n at any point may consequently differ considerably from that of y, while $|y_n - y|$ diminishes indefinitely.

Now
$$\frac{dy_{n+1}}{dx} = x^2 - y_n^2,$$

therefore
$$\frac{dy_{n+1}}{dx} - x^2 + y_{n+1}^2 = y_{n+1}^2 + y_n^2$$
$$= (y_{n+1} - y_n)(y_{n+1} + y_n)$$
$$= (\epsilon_{n+1} - \epsilon_n)(y_{n+1} + y_n).$$

But since $|\epsilon_{n+1}|$ and $|\epsilon_n|$ diminish indefinitely as n increases

thus
$$\left| \frac{dy_{n+1}}{dx} - x^2 + y_{n+1}^2 \right| = |\epsilon_{n+1} - \epsilon_n| \cdot |y_{n+1} + y_n|$$
$$< \{|\epsilon_{n+1}| + |\epsilon_n|\} \cdot |y_{n+1} + y_n|$$

and therefore the right-hand side can be made indefinitely small; hence the differential equation will be more accurately satisfied by y_n as n is increased. The process is therefore convergent, and leads to a more and more accurate solution of the differential equation.

The example which has already been considered was taken as solved when a series for y was obtained in terms of x which gave the value of y to a sufficient degree of accuracy in the range of x required.

Thus $$\frac{dy}{dx} = x^2 - y^2$$

was found to give a solution

$$y = \frac{x^3}{3} - \frac{x^7}{7 \cdot 9} + \frac{2x^{11}}{3 \cdot 7 \cdot 9 \cdot 11}$$

for values of x in the neighbourhood of the value $x = 0$. This series can now be used to calculate the value of y corresponding to any given value of x in the range; thus when

$$y = 0 \cdot 8$$

$$y = \frac{(0 \cdot 8)^3}{3} - \frac{(0 \cdot 8)^7}{7 \cdot 9} + \frac{2(0 \cdot 8)^{11}}{3 \cdot 7 \cdot 9 \cdot 11}$$

$$= 0 \cdot 16742 \text{ correct to five decimal places.}$$

Note.—The convergence of the successive approximations to the true value is examined for the general case on p. 38.

In the example just considered it should be noted that when sufficient approximations were made to give the necessary degree of accuracy at $x = 0 \cdot 8$, the process was terminated, but for higher values of x the series may not be sufficiently accurate. In such a case it may be better not to carry the approximations further by this process, but to begin again from that value of x as the new origin.

Example.—Consider the differential equation

$$\frac{dy}{dx} = 3x^{-\frac{1}{2}} + y - 1$$

given that when $x = 0$, $y = 1$.

The origin need not of necessity be changed for

$$y = y_0 + \int_0^x \left(\frac{dy}{dx}\right) . dx.$$

To obtain the first approximation y is put equal to 1 in the right-hand side of the differential equation

$$y_1 = 1 + \int_0^x 3x^{-\frac{1}{2}} . dx = 1 + 6x^{\frac{1}{2}}$$

$$y_2 = 1 + \int_0^x (3x^{-\frac{1}{2}} + 6x^{\frac{1}{2}})dx = 1 + 6x^{\frac{1}{2}} + 4x^{\frac{3}{2}}$$

Similarly

$$y_3 = 1 + \int_0^x (3x^{-\frac{1}{2}} + 6x^{\frac{1}{2}} + 4x^{\frac{3}{2}})dx = 1 + 6x^{\frac{1}{2}} + 4x^{\frac{3}{2}} + \tfrac{8}{5}x^{\frac{5}{2}}$$

$$y_4 = 1 + \int_0^x (3x^{-\frac{1}{2}} + 6x^{\frac{1}{2}} + 4x^{\frac{3}{2}} - \tfrac{8}{5}x^{\frac{5}{2}})dx$$
$$= 1 + 6x^{\frac{1}{2}} + 4x^{\frac{3}{2}} + \tfrac{8}{5}x^{\frac{5}{2}} + \tfrac{16}{35}x^{\frac{7}{2}}$$

and

$$y_5 = 1 + \int_0^x (3x^{-\frac{1}{2}} + 6x^{\frac{1}{2}} + 4x^{\frac{3}{2}} + \tfrac{8}{5}x^{\frac{5}{2}} + \tfrac{16}{35}x^{\frac{7}{2}})dx$$
$$= 1 + 6x^{\frac{1}{2}} + 4x^{\frac{3}{2}} + \tfrac{8}{5}x^{\frac{5}{2}} + \tfrac{16}{35}x^{\frac{7}{2}} + \tfrac{32}{315}x^{\frac{9}{2}}.$$

The method in this case gives y as a power series in x.

Taking $\qquad\qquad x = 0.2$
$$y = 4.07306.$$

The first error term is $\tfrac{64}{3465} . x^{\frac{11}{2}}$, and its value when $x = 0.2$ is 0.0000026.

Hence in the range $0 \leq x \leq 0.2$ the formula for y_5 may be taken as correct to five decimal places.

For higher values of x the error in using the expression increases. The approximations may be continued, or the process repeated with new initial values;

Thus $\qquad y_1 = 4.07306 + \int_{0.2}^x (3x^{-\frac{1}{2}} + 3.07306)dx.$

Similarly, y_2 and y_3 may be obtained.

The method outlined in the last two examples is suitable only when the integrations which have to be performed are capable of evaluation in terms of elementary functions. In certain cases the difficulties in the repeated integration increase so rapidly in the successive approximations that the method becomes impracticable. Methods will be given later which are designed to overcome this difficulty.

6.12. The application of Picard's method to simultaneous differential equations and to equations of the second and higher orders.

Consider first the case of two first-order simultaneous differential equations,

$$\left.\begin{aligned} \frac{dy}{dx} &= f(x, y, z) \\ \frac{dz}{dx} &= g(x, y, z) \end{aligned}\right\} \quad \text{given that} \quad \left.\begin{aligned} x &= x_0 \\ y &= y_0 \\ z &= z_0 \end{aligned}\right\}$$

For the first approximations

$$y_1 = y_0 + \int_{x_0}^{x} f(x, y_0, z_0) \, . \, dx$$

$$z_1 = z_0 + \int_{x_0}^{x} g(x, y_0, z_0) \, . \, dx.$$

These values should now be used to obtain closer approximations by substitution in the original equations and integrating a second time,

thus
$$y_2 = y_0 + \int_{x_0}^{x} f(x, y_1, z_1) \, . \, dx$$

$$z_2 = z_0 + \int_{x_0}^{x} g(x, y_1, z_1) \, . \, dx.$$

This process may be continued until expressions for y and z are obtained which yield the prescribed accuracy in the given range of values of x. The method may readily be extended to systems of more than two equations.

In the application of the method to differential equations of higher order than the first, it should be noted that a differential equation of order n may be reduced to an equivalent system of n simultaneous differential equations, each of the first order, and provided, therefore, that initial values of the variables and of all the first $(n - 1)$ derivatives in the original equation are given, the above method is at once applicable (see p. 144). A second-order differential equation has been chosen in the example now given below to illustrate the practical working of the process described above.

Example.—Consider the second-order differential equation

$$\frac{d^2y}{dx^2} + 3x \, . \, \frac{dy}{dx} - 6y = 0.$$

If $y = 1$, $\frac{dy}{dx} = 1$, at $x = 0$ are the initial conditions, then this equation may be integrated by the same method of successive approximations.

Let

$$\frac{dy}{dx} = z$$

then

$$\frac{dz}{dx} = 6y - 3xz$$

$$\left.\begin{array}{c} \\ \\ \end{array}\right\} \qquad . \quad . \quad . \quad \text{(i)}$$

These two simultaneous equations are equivalent to the original equation

$$y = 1 + \int_0^x z \, . \, dx$$

$$z = 1 + \int_0^x (6y - 3xz) \, . \, dx.$$

First approximation $y_1 = 1 + x$ using $z = 1$
and $z_1 = 1 + 6x.$

Second approximation obtained by inserting the first approximations for y and z in equation (i)

$$y_2 = 1 + x + 3x^2$$
$$z_2 = 1 + \int_0^x (6 + 6x - 3x - 18x^2) \, . \, dx$$
$$= 1 + 6x + \tfrac{3}{2}x^2(- 6x^3).$$

Third approximation

$$y_3 = 1 + x + 3x^2 + \tfrac{1}{2}x^3(- \tfrac{3}{2}x^4)$$
$$z_3 = 1 + 6x + \tfrac{3}{2}x^2(- \tfrac{9}{8}x^4 + \tfrac{18}{5}x^5).$$

Fourth approximation

$$y_4 = 1 + x + 3x^2 + \tfrac{1}{2}x^3 - (\tfrac{9}{40}x^5 + \tfrac{3}{5}x^6)$$
$$z_4 = 1 + 6x + \tfrac{3}{2}x^2(- \tfrac{9}{8}x^4 - \tfrac{9}{5}x^5).$$

Fifth approximation

$$y_5 = 1 + x + 3x^2 + \tfrac{1}{2}x^3 - \tfrac{3}{40}x^5 + \ldots$$

The fourth and fifth approximations for y agree up to the term in x^5.

If, therefore, a solution is required correct, say, to four decimal places, a range of x may be chosen that ensures that $\tfrac{3}{40}x^5$ may be less than 0·00005. Thus x must be less than 0·23.

The expansion

$$y = 1 + x + 3x^2 + \tfrac{1}{2}x^3$$

will give a value of y accurate to four decimal places provided x lies in the range $0 \le x \le 0\cdot23$. It was clearly unnecessary, therefore, for this purpose to retain terms in the expressions for y and z of degrees higher than x^5.

Example.—To find series by Picard's method to represent x and y in terms of t, given that

$$\frac{dx}{dt} = (x + y)\,.\,t \quad . \quad . \quad . \quad . \quad \text{(i)}$$

$$\frac{dy}{dt} = (x - t)\,.\,y \quad . \quad . \quad . \quad . \quad \text{(ii)}$$

subject to

$$\left.\begin{array}{l} x = 0 \\ y = 1 \\ t = 0 \end{array}\right\}$$

From (ii)

$$y_1 = 1 + \int_0^t (-t)\,.\,dt$$

$$= 1 - \frac{t^2}{2}$$

$$x_1 = \int_0^t \left(1 - \frac{t^2}{2}\right)\,.\,t\,.\,dt$$

$$= \frac{t^2}{2} - \frac{t^4}{8}$$

$$y_2 = 1 + \int_0^t \left(-t + \frac{t^2}{2} - \frac{t^4}{8}\right)\left(1 - \frac{t^2}{2}\right)\,.\,dt$$

$$= 1 - \frac{t^2}{2} + \frac{t^3}{6} + \frac{t^4}{8} - \frac{3t^5}{40}$$

$$x_2 = \int_0^t \left(1 + \frac{t^3}{6} - \frac{3t^5}{40}\right)\,.\,t\,.\,dt$$

$$= \frac{t^2}{2} + \frac{t^5}{30} - \frac{3t^7}{280}$$

$$y_3 = 1 + \int_0^t \left(-t + \frac{1}{2}t^2 + \frac{1}{30}t^5 - \frac{3}{280}\,.\,t^7\right)$$

$$\left(1 - \frac{t^2}{2} + \frac{t^3}{6} + \frac{t^4}{8} - \frac{3t^5}{80}\right)\,.\,dt$$

$$= 1 + \int_0^t \left(-t + \frac{1}{2}t^2 + \frac{1}{2}t^3 - \frac{5}{12}t^4 - \frac{1}{120}t^5 + \frac{1}{10}t^6 \right) . dt$$

$$= 1 - \frac{t^2}{2} + \frac{t^3}{6} + \frac{t^4}{8} - \frac{t^5}{12} - \frac{t^6}{720}$$

$$x_3 = \int_0^t \left(1 + \frac{t^3}{6} + \frac{t^4}{8} - \frac{t^5}{20} \right) t . dt$$

$$= \frac{t^2}{2} + \frac{t^5}{30} + \frac{t^6}{48} - \frac{t^7}{140}$$

$$y_4 = 1 + \int_0^t \left(-t + \frac{t^2}{2} + \frac{t^5}{30} + \frac{t^6}{48} \right)$$
$$\left(1 - \frac{t^2}{2} + \frac{t^3}{6} + \frac{t^4}{8} - \frac{t^5}{12} + \frac{t^6}{720} \right) dt$$

$$= 1 - \frac{t^2}{2} + \frac{t^3}{6} + \frac{t^4}{8} - \frac{t^5}{12} - \frac{t^6}{720} + \frac{t^7}{42}$$

$$x_5 = \int_0^t \left(1 + \frac{t^3}{6} + \frac{t^4}{8} - \frac{t^5}{20} \right) . t . dt$$

$$= \frac{t^2}{2} + \frac{t^5}{30} + \frac{t^6}{48} - \frac{t^7}{140}$$

$$y_5 = 1 - \int_0^t \left(-t + \frac{t^2}{2} + \frac{t^5}{30} + \frac{t^6}{48} - .. \right)$$
$$\left(1 - \frac{t^2}{2} + \frac{t^3}{6} + \frac{t^4}{8} - \frac{t^5}{12} - \frac{t^7}{140} \right) dt$$

$$= 1 - \frac{t^2}{2} + \frac{t^3}{6} + \frac{t^4}{8} - \frac{t^5}{12} - \frac{t^6}{720} + \frac{t^7}{42} .$$

Hence x and y are expressed in terms of t as series up to the seventh powers of t. It should be noted that the final stages are made considerably less tedious when the terms which have established themselves by repetition are omitted from subsequent integrations, although, of course, they are rewritten at each new step.

6.13. The Picard method when an approximate solution is available in tabular form.

(a) *Boundary conditions at one end of the range only.* Suppose that an approximate solution of a differential equation can be determined over the whole of the required range as a table of function values. Then the method of checking and correcting function values which has just been described may be carried out over the complete range, and the function values thus found may again be checked and corrected until the final accuracy is satisfactory for the practical purposes in view. This amounts to applying successively the sequence

$$\frac{dy_{n+1}}{dx} = f(x, y_n),$$

the integrations being performed as described in the last paragraph.

For simultaneous equations, second-order equations, and equations of higher order, this process may be applied in succession, as in the cases which have been described, where a solution was found in functions of x, with the difference that the integrations of functions of x are replaced by numerical integrations.

Example.—Let us suppose that an approximate solution of the differential equation

$$\frac{d^2y}{dx^2} = e^x(4e^x - 1) + \sqrt{y}$$

is known over the range $0 < x < 0\cdot5$ subject to the boundary conditions $x = 0$, $y = 1$, $\dfrac{dy}{dx} = 2$.

$(y)_1$ is the first approximate solution which is supposed given. It should be noted that if the differential equation is of the form

$$\frac{d^2y}{dx^2} = f\left(x, y, \frac{dy}{dx}\right),$$

then the values of $\left(\dfrac{dy}{dx}\right)_1$ are also required approximately before the solution may be improved. For this purpose, supposing that values of y alone are given, then $\dfrac{(y_2)_1 - (y_0)_1}{2h}$ should yield a sufficiently accurate value of $(y_1)_1'$. Similar expressions may be used at other points, but the derivatives at the two end-points should be estimated from the intermediate values.

In order to show the convergence of the process, the numerical values are fully tabulated below.

x.	e^x.	$4e^{2x} - e^x$.	$y_1 = (1+x)^2$.	$\sqrt{y_1}$.	y_2''.	y_2'.
0	1	3	1	1	4	2
0·1	1·1051709	3·7804403	1·21	1·1	4·880	2·4440
0·2	1·2214028	4·7458960	1·44	1·2	5·946	2·9853
0·3	1·3498588	5·9386132	1·69	1·3	7·239	3·6445
0·4	1·4918247	7·4103349	1·96	1·4	8·810	4·4470
0·5	1·6487213	9·2244059	2·25	1·5	10·724	5·4327

x.	y_2.	$\sqrt{y_2}$.	y_3''.	y_3'.	y_3.	Error.
0	1	1	4	2	1	0
0·1	1·2222	1·1055	4·8858	2·44280	1·221402	0·000001
0·2	1·4937	1·2222	5·9681	2·98370	1·491826	−0·000001
0·3	1·8251	1·3510	7·2896	3·64438	1·822129	−0·000011
0·4	2·2297	1·4932	8·9035	4·45134	2·225571	−0·000031
0·5	2·7233	1·6502	10·8746	5·43695	2·718344	−0·000062

The error in the final column has been calculated from the actual solution, which is $y = e^{2x}$.

(b) *Boundary conditions at both ends of the range.* The process applied to equations of this type is fully described in Chap. V, p. 162, where examples will be found illustrating them.

Examples.

1. Establish the convergence of the sequence

$$y_{n+1} = \int_0^x \frac{x^2}{y_n^2 + 1}\, dx$$

to the solution of the differential equation

$$\frac{dy}{dx}(y^2 + 1) = x^2,$$

where $x = 0$, $y = 0$.

From the sequence find y at $x = 0.25$, $x = 0.5$ and $x = 1$, correct to three decimal places.

Show by integrating the differential equation directly that

$$y^3 + 3y = x^3,$$

and hence check the values of y obtained at $x = 0.25$, 0.5, 1.

Ans. x : 0.25, 0.5, 1.0.
y : 0.005, 0.042, 0.321.

2. If

$$\frac{dy}{dx} + y^2 = \frac{2y}{2x + 1},$$

where $y = 2.667$ when $x = 0.5$, find y to two places of decimals when $x = 1$, using the sequence

$$y_{n+1} - 2.667 = \int_{0.5}^{x} \left(\frac{2y_n}{2x + 1} - y_n^2 \right) dx$$

Ans. 1.50.

3. Obtain power series up to fourth powers in t for x and y which satisfy the simultaneous equations

$$y\frac{dx}{dt} = 2x - y$$

$$\frac{dy}{dt} = y^2 - x + t$$

by Picard's method where $t = 0$, $x = 0$, $y = 1$.

6.2. Solution of a differential equation by expansion as a Taylor's series.

Consider the equation

$$\frac{dy}{dx} = f(x, y)$$

subject to $x = a$, $y = b$.

By substitution in this equation y_0' is calculated at $x = a$, $y = b$.

Differentiating the equation

$$\frac{d^2y}{dx^2} = g\left(x, y, \frac{dy}{dx}\right)$$

and by substitution in this equation y_0'' is evaluated at $x = a$, $y = b$.

Similarly the successive differential coefficients are evaluated at the initial point, and the value of y in the neighbourhood of the initial point is then given by the equation

$$y - b = (x - a)\left(\frac{dy}{dx}\right)_0 + \frac{1}{2!}(x - a)^2\left(\frac{d^2y}{dx^2}\right)_0$$
$$+ \frac{1}{3!}(x - a)^3\left(\frac{d^3y}{dx^3}\right)_0 + \cdots$$

The range over which this series is valid depends upon the accuracy required in the values of y, and having first specified this accuracy, it is easy to determine by direct substitution the term at which the series may be ended.

For an equation of order n expressed in the form

$$\frac{d^ny}{dx^n} = f\left(x, y, \frac{dy}{dx}, \frac{d^2y}{dx^2} \cdots, \frac{d^{n-1}y}{dx^{n-1}}\right)$$

subject to $x = a$, $y = b$, $\frac{dy}{dx} = c_1 \cdots, \frac{d^{n-1}y}{dx^{n-1}} = c_{n-1}$, the same procedure may be adopted, for by substitution in the above equation $\frac{d^ny}{dx^n}$ is found, and by successive differentiation $\frac{d^{n+1}y}{dx^{n+1}}$, etc., may be determined, and the series for y written as before. An example of this process will be found in the description of the Adams–Bashforth method on p. 119.

Example.—To find a power series in x for y which satisfies the equation

$$\frac{d^2y}{dx^2} + 3x\frac{dy}{dx} - 6y = 0$$

subject to $x = 0$, $\frac{dy}{dx} = 0\cdot1$, $y = 1$

$$y'' = -3xy' + 6y$$
$$y_0'' = 6$$
$$y''' = -3xy'' - 3y' + 6y' = -3xy'' + 3y'$$
$$y_0''' = 0\cdot3$$
$$y^{iv} = -3xy''' - 3y'' + 3y'' = -3xy'''$$
$$y_0^{iv} = 0$$
$$y^{v} = -3xy^{iv} - 3y'''$$
$$y_0^{v} = -0\cdot9$$
$$y^{vi} = -3xy^{v} - 6y^{iv}$$

$$y_0{}^{vi} = 0$$
$$y^{vii} = - 3xy^{vi} - 9y^v$$
$$y_0{}^{vii} = + 0 \cdot 81$$

. . . .

Hence $y = 1 + 0 \cdot 1x + 3x^2 + \dfrac{1}{20}x^3 - \dfrac{3}{400}x^5 + \dfrac{9}{5600}x^7 -$.

To find the range of x for which this series represents y correct to $0 \cdot 0001$ up to the term in x^5, write the last term equal to or less than $0 \cdot 00005$

$$\frac{9}{5600}x_1{}^7 \leq 0 \cdot 00005$$

$$x_1{}^7 \leq \frac{0 \cdot 280}{9}$$

$$x_1 \leq 0 \cdot 6.$$

6.21. Application to simultaneous equations.

The process may best be illustrated by application to two simultaneous equations of the first order

$$\frac{dy}{dx} = f_1(x, y, z)$$

and
$$\frac{dz}{dx} = g_1(x, y, z)$$

subject to $x = x_0$, $y = y_0$, $z = z_0$.

The two equations determine $y_0{}'$ and $z_0{}'$.

By differentiation

$$y'' = f_2(x, y, z, y', z')$$
$$z'' = g_2(x, y, z, y', z').$$

These equations determine $y_0{}''$ and $z_0{}''$, since all the quantities on the right-hand sides of the equations are known at the initial point. Proceeding in this manner, $y_0{}'''$, $z_0{}'''$, etc., are determined, then y and z are given by the equations

$$y = y_0 + (x - x_0)y_0{}' + \frac{1}{2!}(x - x_0)^2 y_0{}'' + \frac{1}{3!}(x - x_0)^3 y_0{}''' + \ldots$$

$$z = z_0 + (x - x_0)z_0{}' + \frac{1}{2!}(x - x_0)^2 z_0{}'' + \frac{1}{3!}(x - x_0)^3 z_0{}''' + \ldots$$

In addition to the example below, a second worked example will be found on p. 83.

Example.—Obtain power series in t for x and y which satisfy

$$\frac{dx}{dt} = 2 \cdot \frac{t}{y} - 1; \quad \frac{dy}{dt} = y^2 - x + t,$$

subject to $x = 0$, $y = -1$, $t = 0$

$$x_0' = -1$$

$$x'' = \frac{2}{y} - \frac{2t}{y^2} \cdot y'$$

$$x_0'' = -2$$

$$x''' = -\frac{2}{y^2} \cdot y' - \frac{2}{y^2} \cdot y' - 2t\left(\frac{y''}{y^2} - \frac{2y'^2}{y^3}\right)$$

$$= -\frac{4y'}{y^2} - 2t \cdot \left(\frac{y''}{y^2} - \frac{2y'^2}{y^3}\right)$$

$$x_0''' = -4$$

$$x^{iv} = -\frac{4y''}{y^2} + \frac{8y'^2}{y^3} - 2\left(\frac{y''}{y^2} - \frac{2y'^2}{y^3}\right)$$

$$- 2t\left(\frac{y'''}{y^3} - \frac{6y'y''}{y^3} + \frac{6y'^2}{y^4}\right)$$

$$x_0^{iv} = -12$$

$$y_0' = 1$$

$$y'' = 2yy' - x' + 1$$

$$y_0'' = -2 + 1 + 1 = 0$$

$$y''' = 2yy'' + 2y'^2 - x''$$

$$y_0''' = 2 + 2 = 4$$

$$y^{iv} = 2yy''' + 2y'y'' + 4y'y'' - x'''$$

$$y_0^{iv} = -8 + 4 = -4$$

Up to fourth powers of x the expansions are therefore

$$x = -t - t^2 - \tfrac{2}{3}t^3 - \tfrac{1}{2}t^4 - \cdots$$
$$y = -1 + t + \tfrac{2}{3}t^3 - \tfrac{1}{6}t^4 + \cdots$$

Example.—To begin the solution of a pair of simultaneous equations by Taylor's expansions.

To solve the equations

$$\frac{dx}{dt} = (x + y)t, \quad \frac{dy}{dt} = (x - t)y \quad . \quad . \quad (1)$$

where $x = 0$ and $y = 1$ when $t = 0$, the values of x and y to be correct to four decimal places for the range $0 < t < 0\cdot4$.

By direct differentiation of (1) we obtain

$$x'' = x + y + (x' + y')t$$
$$x''' = 2(x' + y') + (x'' + y'')t$$
$$x^{\text{iv}} = 3(x'' + y'') + (x''' + y''')t$$

$$y' = (x - t)y$$
$$y'' = (x' - 1)y + (x - t)y'$$
$$y''' = x''y + 2(x' - 1)y' + (x - t)y''$$
$$y^{\text{iv}} = x'''y + 3x''y' + 3(x' - 1)y'' + (x - t)y'''.$$

Hence, on inserting the values of x and y at $t = 0$, we find

$$x_0' = 0, \; x_0'' = 1, \; x_0''' = 0, \; x_0^{\text{iv}} = 0, \; x_0^{\text{v}} = 4, \; x_0^{\text{vi}} = 15$$
$$y_0' = 0, y_0'' = -1, y_0''' = 1, y_0^{\text{iv}} = 3, y_0^{\text{v}} = -5, y_0^{\text{vi}} = -1.$$

Thus, using Maclaurin's Theorem,

$$x = \frac{t^2}{2} + \frac{t^5}{30} + \frac{t^6}{48} -$$
$$y = 1 - \frac{t^2}{2} + \frac{t^3}{6} + \frac{t^4}{8} - \frac{t^5}{12} - \frac{t^6}{720} +$$

It is clear from an examination of the last terms that x and y are determined by these formulæ correct to five decimal places for a range of t extending up to $t = 0\cdot2$. The problem is to extend the table for the full range required.

Examples.

1. Develop series up to the fifth power of the independent variable for starting the integration of the differential equations on p. 78, and compare the results with those obtained by applying Picard's method to the same problems. In each case state the range over which the accuracy is five significant figures.

2. Prove that the solution of $\frac{d^2y}{dx^2} + x \cdot y = 0$ subject to $x = 0$, $y = A$, $\frac{dy}{dx} = 0$ is given by

$$y_1 = A\left\{1 - \frac{1}{3!}x^3 + \frac{1.4}{6!}x^6 - \frac{1.4.7}{9!}x^9 + \ldots\right\}$$

and that the solution subject to $x = 0$, $y = 0$, $\dfrac{dy}{dx} = B$ is

$$y_2 = B.x\left(1 - \frac{2}{4!}x^3 + \frac{2.5}{7!}x^6 - \frac{2.5.8}{10!}.x^9 + \ldots\right).$$

Hence write down the solution subject to $x = 0$, $y = 1$, $\dfrac{dy}{dx} = 1$.

3. Expand y as a power series in x to satisfy the equation

$$x\frac{d^2y}{dx^2} + (x+1)\frac{dy}{dx} + 2y = 0$$

up to fifth powers of x and subject to $x = 0$, $y = 1$, $\dfrac{dy}{dx} = -2$.

Ans. $\quad y = 1 - 2x + \dfrac{3}{2!}x^2 - \dfrac{4}{3!}x^3 + \dfrac{5}{4!}x^4 - \dfrac{6}{5!}x^5 + \ldots$

SOLUTION OF DIFFERENTIAL EQUATIONS IN SERIES.

6.3. The method of Frobenius.

The method is applied to differential equations of the type

$$\frac{d^2y}{dx^2} + p(x)\frac{dy}{dx} + q(x).y = 0 \quad . \quad . \quad . \quad . \quad (1)$$

For a solution in the neighbourhood of $x = 0$, $p(x)$ must be expansible in a series of the form $p(x) = \dfrac{1}{x}(a_0 + a_1x + a_2x^2 + \ldots)$ and $q(x)$ in a series of the form $q(x) = \dfrac{1}{x^2}(b_0 + b_1x + b_2x^2 + \ldots)$. Any of the coefficients a_0, a_1, a_2, etc., b_0, b_1, b_2, etc., may be zero, and both the series in brackets must be convergent in the region considered. Thus at $x = 0$, $p(x)$ and $q(x)$ may, at most, have infinities of the first and second orders respectively. If $p(x)$ or $q(x)$ have infinities as above at $x = a$, and a solution is required in the neighbourhood of $x = a$, then the differential equation is transformed by changing the independent variable to t, where $t = x - a$ and the equation dealt with as below.

Let $\qquad y = x^a(c_0 + c_1x + c_2x^2 + \ldots) \quad . \quad . \quad . \quad (2)$

be a trial solution valid in the neighbourhood of $x = 0$.

Differentiating *

$$\frac{dy}{dx} = C_0\alpha x^{a-1} + C_1(\alpha+1)x^a + C_2(\alpha+2).x^{a+1} + \ldots \quad . \quad (2.1)$$

---

* Series (2) and (2.1) must be uniformly convergent in the region where the solution is required if this differentiation is to be valid.

$$\frac{d^2y}{dx^2} = C_0\alpha(\alpha - 1)x^{\alpha-2} + C_1(\alpha + 1) \cdot \alpha \cdot x^{\alpha-1}$$
$$+ C_2(\alpha + 2)(\alpha + 1) \cdot x^\alpha + \ldots \ldots \quad (2.2)$$

Substitute from (2), (2.1) and (2.2) in equation (1), then, in order that the series (2) may satisfy the equation identically, the coefficients of all the powers of x must vanish. These coefficients equated to zero yield : (a) the possible values of α, (b) the law connecting the coefficients C_0, C_1, etc.

The coefficient of the lowest power of x is clearly that of $x^{\alpha-2}$

viz. $\qquad C_0\alpha(\alpha - 1) + C_0\alpha \cdot a_0 + C_0 \cdot b_0$
$$= C_0\{\alpha^2 - (a_0 - 1)\alpha + b_0\}$$

Now, C_0 must not vanish, and therefore

$$\alpha^2 - (a_0 - 1)\alpha + b_0 = 0 \quad \ldots \ldots \quad (3)$$

Equation (3) is called the Indicial Equation, and its roots lead to possible solutions of the differential equation. The final forms of these solutions depend upon the nature of the roots of the indicial equation. Three main cases will be considered and some subsidiary cases.

Case I.—Roots of the Indicial Equation different, but not differing by an integer.

Consider the equation

$$2x^2\frac{d^2y}{dx^2} - x\frac{dy}{dx} + (1 - x^2) \cdot y = 0 . \quad \ldots \quad (i)$$

Let $y_1 = x^\alpha(C_0 + C_1x + C_2 \cdot x^2 + \ldots)$ be a trial solution.

If $D \equiv 2x^2\dfrac{d^2}{dx^2} - x\dfrac{d}{dx} + (1 - x^2)$

$Dy_1 = D(\sum_{n=0} C_nx^{n+\alpha})$

$\qquad = \sum_{n=0} C_n[2(n + \alpha)(n + \alpha - 1)x^{n+\alpha} - (n+\alpha)x^{n+\alpha} + x^{n+\alpha} - x^{n+\alpha-2}]$

$\qquad = \sum_{n=0} C_n[\{(n + \alpha)(2n + 2\alpha - 3) + 1\}x^{n+\alpha} - x^{n+\alpha+2}]$

$\qquad = C_0[(2\alpha^2 - 3\alpha + 1)x^\alpha - x^{\alpha+2}]$
$\qquad + C_1[\{(1 + \alpha)(2 + 2\alpha - 3) + 1\}x^{\alpha+1} - x^{\alpha+3}]$
$\qquad + C_2[\{(2 + \alpha)(4 + 2\alpha - 3) + 1\}x^{\alpha+2} - x^{\alpha+4}]$
$\qquad + \text{etc.} \ldots$
$\qquad + C_{n-2}[\{(n + \alpha - 2)(2n + 2\alpha - 7) + 1\}x^{n+\alpha-2} - x^{n+\alpha}]$
$\qquad + C_{n-1}[\{(n + \alpha - 1)(2n + 2\alpha - 5) + 1\}x^{n+\alpha-1} - x^{n+\alpha+1}]$
$\qquad + C_n[\{(n + \alpha)(2n + 2\alpha - 3) + 1\}x^{n+\alpha} - x^{n+\alpha+2}]$
$\qquad + \ldots$

In order that the coefficients of the various powers of x should vanish

$$C_n = C_{n-2}/(2n + 2\alpha - 1)(n + \alpha - 1) \quad . \quad . \quad (ii)$$

The series for y_1 is thus

$$y_1 = C_0 \cdot x^a \left[1 + \frac{x^2}{(2\alpha + 3)(\alpha + 1)} \right.$$
$$\left. + \frac{x^4}{(2\alpha + 3)(2\alpha + 7)(\alpha + 1)(\alpha + 3)} + \cdots \right] \quad . \quad . \text{ (iii)}$$

for in order that the coefficient of x^{a+1} should vanish $C_1 \cdot (2\alpha^2 + \alpha)$ $= 0$, and as this does not vanish by virtue of the indicial equation, it follows that $C_1 = 0$, and if this condition is considered in conjunction with equation (ii), it will be seen that the coefficients of all the odd powers of x in the trial solution must be zero. If y_1 as given by equation (iii) is substituted in the differential equation, the only term which does not vanish identically is that of lowest degree in x, viz., $C_0 x^a \cdot (2\alpha^2 - 3\alpha + 1)$.

The Indicial Equation is obtained by equating to zero the coefficient of this term of lowest degree in x.

Thus $\qquad\qquad (2\alpha^2 - 3\alpha + 1) \cdot C_0 = 0.$

As C_0 must not vanish,

therefore $\qquad\qquad 2\alpha^2 - 3\alpha + 1 = 0 \quad . \quad . \quad . \quad . \quad . \text{ (iv)}$
i.e. either $\qquad\qquad \alpha = 1$
or $\qquad\qquad\qquad \alpha = \frac{1}{2}.$

If these values of α are now substituted in turn in equation (iii), the following series are obtained :

$$y_1 = C_0 x \left\{ 1 + \frac{x^2}{2.5} + \frac{x^4}{2.5.4.9} + \frac{x^6}{2.5.4.9.6.13} + \cdots \right\}$$
and
$$y_2 = C_0 \cdot x^{\frac{1}{2}} \left\{ 1 + \frac{x^2}{2.3} + \frac{x^4}{2.3.4.7} + \frac{x^6}{2.3.4.7.6.11} + \cdots \right\}$$

These series are both solutions of the equation (i), and therefore the complete solution of (i) is

$$y = A \cdot x \cdot \left\{ 1 + \frac{x^2}{2.5} + \frac{x^4}{2.5.4.9} + \frac{x^6}{2.5.4.9.6.13} + \cdots \right\}$$
$$+ B \cdot x^{\frac{1}{2}} \left\{ 1 + \frac{x^2}{2.3} + \frac{x^4}{2.3.4.7} + \frac{x^6}{2.3.4.7.6.11} + \cdots \right\}$$

where A and B are arbitrary constants.

In general, if the roots of the Indicial Equation are different, not differing by an integer, two independent solutions of the differential equation are obtained by substituting in turn the roots of the indicial equation in the series for y.

Case II.—Roots of the Indicial Equation equal.
Consider Bessel's Equation of Order Zero.

$$x\frac{d^2y}{dx^2} + \frac{dy}{dx} + xy = 0 \quad . \quad . \quad . \quad . \quad . \text{ (i)}$$

As before, let $y_1 = \sum_{n=0} C_n x^{n+a}$ be a trial solution
$$= C_0 x^a + C_1 x^{a+1} + C_2 x^{a+2} + \cdots + C_n x^{a+n} +$$

Coefficient of term of lowest degree in x, viz. x^{a-1} is $C_0\alpha^2$.

Coefficient of x^a is $(\alpha + 1)^2 . C_1$.

Coefficient of x^{a+n} is $(\alpha + n)(\alpha + n + 1)C_{n+1} + (\alpha + n + 1)C_{n+1} + C_{n-1} = (\alpha + n + 1)^2 . C_{n+1} + C_{n-1}$

The coefficient of x^{a-1} will vanish if

$$\alpha^2 = 0 \quad . \quad . \quad . \quad . \quad . \quad . \quad . \quad \text{(ii)}$$

The coefficient of the isolated term in x^a will vanish only if $C_1 = 0$, and by virtue of the relationship between coefficients,

viz. $\qquad\qquad C_{n+1} = - C_{n-1}/(\alpha + n + 1)^2,$

the coefficients of all the odd powers of x vanish.

The series for y_1 is therefore

$$y_1 = C_0 x^a\left[1 - \frac{x^2}{(\alpha + 2)^2} + \frac{x^4}{(\alpha + 2)^2(\alpha + 4)^2} + \cdots\right] \quad . \quad . \quad \text{(iii)}$$

If α is put equal to zero in (iii), *only* one solution of the differential equation is obtained, and therefore the most general solution is not yet found.

If the series (iii) is substituted in equation (i), the term which remains is $C_0 . \alpha^2 . x^{a-1}$. This term vanishes when $\alpha = 0$, *and its partial differential coefficient* with regard to α vanishes when $\alpha = 0$, *i.e.* $2C_0 . \alpha x^{a-1} + C_0\alpha^2 x^{a-1} . \log_\epsilon x$ vanishes when $\alpha = 0$.

If $\qquad\qquad D \equiv x\dfrac{d^2}{dx^2} + \dfrac{d}{dx} + x$

$$\frac{\partial}{\partial\alpha}[D\{y_1\}] = 2C_0\alpha x^{a-1} + C_0\alpha^2 x^{a-1} . \log x.$$

By a well-known rule of differential operators, this may be written:

$$D\left\{\frac{\partial y_1}{\partial\alpha}\right\} = 2C_0\alpha x^{a-1} + C_0\alpha^2 . x^{a-1} . \log x$$

From this last equation $\dfrac{\partial y_1}{\partial\alpha}$ is clearly a solution of the differential equation if α is put equal to zero after the differentiation has been carried out. This provides the second solution and this taken with the first gives the most general solution.

Now $y_1 = C_0 x^a\left[1 + \sum\limits_{n=1}^{n=\infty} \dfrac{x^{2n} . (-1)^n}{(\alpha + 2)^2(\alpha + 4)^2 \ldots (\alpha + 2n)^2}\right]$

Therefore

$$\frac{\partial y_1}{\partial\alpha} = y_1 \log x + c_0 x^a \frac{\partial}{\partial\alpha}\left[\sum_1^\infty \frac{x^{2n} . (-1)^n}{(\alpha + 2)^2(\alpha + 4)^2 \ldots (\alpha + 2n)^2}\right]$$

Let $\qquad u = 1/(\alpha + 2)^2(\alpha + 4)^2 \ldots (\alpha + 2n)^2$

$\qquad\qquad \log u = -2\{\log(\alpha + 2) + \log(\alpha + 4) + \ldots + \log(\alpha + 2n)\}$

Hence $\quad \dfrac{1}{u} . \dfrac{\partial u}{\partial\alpha} = -2\left\{\dfrac{1}{(\alpha + 2)} + \dfrac{1}{(\alpha + 4)} + \ldots + \dfrac{1}{(\alpha + 2n)}\right\}$

$$\frac{\partial u}{\partial \alpha} = - 2u\left\{\frac{1}{(\alpha + 2)} + \frac{1}{(\alpha + 4)} + \cdots + \frac{1}{(\alpha + 2n)}\right\}$$

and when $\alpha = 0$,

$$\frac{\partial u}{\partial \alpha} = \frac{-1}{2^2 . 4^2 \cdots (2n)^2}\left\{1 + \frac{1}{2} + \frac{1}{3} + \cdots + \frac{1}{n}\right\}$$

Therefore

$$\left[\frac{\partial y_1}{\partial \alpha}\right]_{a=0} = C_0 x^0 \log x . \left\{1 - \frac{x^2}{2^2} + \frac{x^4}{2^2 4^2} - \frac{x^6}{2^2 4^2 6^2} + \cdots \right\}$$
$$+ C_0 . x^0 \left\{\frac{x^2}{2^2}(1) - \frac{x^4}{2^2 4^2}\left(1 + \frac{1}{2}\right) + \frac{x^6}{2^2 4^2 6^2}\left(1 + \frac{1}{2} + \frac{1}{3}\right) \cdots \right\}. \quad \text{(iv)}$$

$$[y_1]_{a=0} = C_0 x^0 \left\{1 - \frac{x^2}{2^2} + \frac{x^4}{2^2 4^2} - \frac{x^6}{2^2 4^2 6^2} + \cdots \right\} \quad . \quad \text{(v)}$$

If the right-hand sides (iv) and (v) be u and v respectively, then the most general solution of equation (i) is

$$y = A . u + B . v.$$

In general, if the Indicial Equation has a repeated root, then there are two independent solutions obtained by putting α equal to this root in the series for y_1 and in the expression obtained by differentiating this series partially with regard to α.

i.e.
$$[y_1]_{a=\varrho} \text{ and } \left[\frac{\partial y_1}{\partial \alpha}\right]_{a=\varrho},$$

where ϱ is the repeated root of the Indicial Equation, are two independent solutions of the differential equation.

Case III.—Roots different and differing by an integer.

(*a*) When the series obtained by inserting the value of one of the roots has coefficients which assume infinite values.

Consider Bessel's Equation of Order Unity

$$x^2 \frac{d^2 y}{dx^2} + x \frac{dy}{dx} + (x^2 - 1) . y = 0 \quad . \quad . \quad . \quad \text{(i)}$$

Try
$$y_1 = x^a . [C_0 + C_1 x + C_2 x^2 + \cdots].$$

Coefficient of term of lowest degree in x, viz. x^a is $C_0(\alpha^2 - 1)$.

Coefficient of x^{a+1} is $(\alpha + 1) . \alpha . C_1 + (\alpha + 1) . C_1 - C_1$
$$\equiv (\alpha^2 + 2\alpha) . C_1.$$

Coefficient of x^{a+n} is $(\alpha + n)(\alpha + n - 1)C_n + (\alpha + n)C_n - C_n + C_{n-2}$
$$\equiv C_n\{(\alpha + n)^2 - 1\} + C_{n-2}.$$

Therefore
$$C_n = - \frac{C_{n-2}}{(\alpha + n - 1)(\alpha + n + 1)} \quad . \quad . \quad . \quad \text{(ii)}$$

Since the coefficient of the isolated term in x^{a+1} does not vanish by virtue of the indicial equation, C_1 must be zero, and by virtue of (ii) all the odd coefficients in the series for y_1 are zero. The series for y_1 is therefore

$$y_1 = C_0 x^a \left[1 - \frac{x^2}{(\alpha + 1)(\alpha + 3)} + \frac{x^4}{(\alpha + 1)(\alpha + 3)^2(\alpha + 5)} \right.$$
$$\left. - \frac{x^6}{(\alpha + 1)(\alpha + 3)^2(\alpha + 5^2)(\alpha + 7)} + \cdots \right] \quad . \quad \text{(iii)}$$

The Indicial Equation is $\alpha^2 - 1 = 0$.
Thus $\qquad\qquad\qquad\qquad\qquad \alpha = \pm 1$.

If α is put equal to 1 in equation (iii), a solution of the equation (i) is obtained, but if $\alpha = -1$, all the coefficients of the various powers of x in the bracket (x^2 and successive terms) become infinite. The difficulty may be met, however, by changing the constant C_0 to k, where $k(\alpha + 1) = C_0$.

Substituting in the series for y_1 yields the equation

$$y_1 = k x^a \left[(\alpha + 1) - \frac{x^2}{(\alpha + 3)} + \frac{x^4}{(\alpha + 3)^2(\alpha + 5)} \right.$$
$$\left. - \frac{x^6}{(\alpha + 3)^2(\alpha + 5)^2(\alpha + 7)} + \cdots \right] \quad . \quad \text{(iv)}$$

If (iv) is substituted in the differential equation, the only remaining term is

$$k(\alpha + 1)(\alpha^2 - 1) \cdot x^a \equiv k(\alpha + 1)^2(\alpha - 1) \cdot x^a.$$

Thus, if $\qquad\qquad D \equiv x^2 \cdot \frac{d^2}{dx^2} + x \frac{d}{dx} + (x^2 - 1)$
$$D y_1 = k(\alpha + 1)^2 \cdot (\alpha - 1) \cdot x^a.$$

Therefore as before $\alpha = -1$ substituted in series (iv) and $\left[\dfrac{\partial y_1}{\partial \alpha} \right]_{a = -1}$ obtained by differentiating equation (iv) and putting $\alpha = -1$ after differentiating give two independent solutions of the original differential equation.

Putting $\alpha = -1$ in (iv) gives

$$y_1 = k \cdot x^{-1} \left[-\frac{1}{2} x^2 + \frac{x^4}{2^2 4} - \frac{x^6}{2^2 4^2 6} + \cdots \right] \quad . \quad . \quad \text{(v)}$$

$$\left[\frac{\partial y_1}{\partial \alpha} \right]_{a = -1} = \log x \cdot [y_1]_{a = -1}$$
$$+ k x^{-1} \left[1 + \frac{x^2}{2^2} - \frac{x^4}{2^2 4} \left(\frac{2}{2} + \frac{1}{4} \right) + \frac{x^6}{2^2 4^2 6} \left(\frac{2}{2} + \frac{2}{4} + \frac{1}{6} \right) \right.$$
$$\left. - \frac{x^8}{2^2 4^2 6^2 8} \left(\frac{2}{2} + \frac{2}{4} + \frac{2}{6} + \frac{1}{8} \right) + \cdots \right] \quad . \quad . \quad . \quad \text{(vi)}$$

It is found that when $\alpha = 1$ is substituted in equation (iii), the series obtained is a numerical multiple of the series given by (v). This result might have been anticipated, as clearly three independent solutions of the second order differential equation would not have been possible. The general solution if series (v) and (vi) are denoted by u and v is

$$y = A \cdot u + B \cdot v.$$

In general, if the roots of the Indicial Equation differ by an integer, then the constant C_0 must be changed to $k \cdot (\alpha - \rho)$, where ρ is the smaller of the two roots of the indicial equation. If y_1 is the series now obtained for the solution, then two independent solutions of the original differential equation are obtained by substituting $\alpha = \rho$ in y_1 and in $\dfrac{\partial y_1}{\partial \alpha}$ after differentiation.

Case IIIa.—Roots of Indicial Equation differing by an integer and when a coefficient of the series for y_1 becomes indeterminate.

Consider the equation

$$(1 - x^2)\frac{d^2y}{dx^2} + 2x\frac{dy}{dx} - 3y = 0 \quad . \quad . \quad . \quad (i)$$

Let

$$y_1 = C_0 x^a + C_1 x^{a+1} + C_2 x^{a+2} + \cdots$$

be a trial solution; substituting the series into the equation (i),

Coefficient of x^{a-2} is $\alpha(\alpha - 1)C_0$.

Coefficient of x^{a-1} is $(\alpha + 1) \cdot \alpha C_1$.

Coefficient of x^{a+n} is $(\alpha + n + 2)(\alpha + n + 1)C_{n+2}$
$$- (\alpha + n)(\alpha + n - 1)C_n$$
$$+ (\alpha + n) \cdot 2C_n - 3C_n$$

i.e. $(\alpha + n + 2)(\alpha + n + 1)C_{n+2} - \{(\alpha + n)(\alpha + n - 3) + 3\} \cdot C_n.$

In order that the differential equation may be satisfied

$$C_{n+2} = \frac{(\alpha + n)(\alpha + n - 3) + 3}{(\alpha + n + 1)(\alpha + n + 2)} C_n \quad . \quad . \quad (ii)$$

Now, the coefficient of the isolated term $-(\alpha + 1) \cdot \alpha C_1 x^{a-1}$ may vanish by virtue of the Indicial Equation, viz. $\alpha(\alpha - 1) = 0$.

Hence C_1 is indeterminate. Using the relation (ii), there are two series obtained when $\alpha = 0$, one from the terms of even degree, and one from terms of odd degree.

$$y_1 = C_0 x^0 \left[1 + \frac{\alpha(\alpha - 3) + 3}{(\alpha + 1)(\alpha + 2)} \cdot x^2 \right.$$
$$\left. + \frac{\{\alpha(\alpha - 3) + 3\}}{(\alpha + 1)(\alpha + 2)} \cdot \frac{\{(\alpha + 2)(\alpha - 1) + 3\}}{(\alpha + 3)(\alpha + 4)} \cdot x^4 + \cdots \right] \quad (iii)$$

and

$$y_1 = C_1 \cdot x^0 \left[x + \frac{(\alpha + 1)(\alpha - 2) + 3}{(\alpha + 2)(\alpha + 3)} \cdot x^3 \right.$$
$$\left. + \frac{\{(\alpha + 1)(\alpha - 2) + 3\}}{(\alpha + 2)(\alpha + 3)} \cdot \frac{\{(\alpha + 3) \cdot (\alpha) + 3\}}{(\alpha + 4)(\alpha + 5)} \cdot x^5 + \cdots \right] \quad (iv)$$

If we make $\alpha = 1$, C_1 is no longer indeterminate, and must vanish with all the remaining odd coefficients, and on substituting in the equation for y_1 the series below is obtained :

$$y_1 = C_0 x \left[1 + \frac{(\alpha)(\alpha - 3) + 3}{(\alpha + 1)(\alpha + 2)} \cdot x^2 \right.$$
$$\left. + \frac{\alpha(\alpha - 3) + 3}{(\alpha + 1)(\alpha + 2)} \cdot \frac{(\alpha + 2)(\alpha - 1) + 3}{(\alpha + 3)(\alpha + 4)} \cdot x^4 + \cdots \right]$$

When $\alpha = 1$, this last series is identical with series (iv), when $\alpha = 0$; hence (iii) and (iv) are two independent solutions of the original equation. In this case the solutions are

$$y_1 = C_0[1 + \tfrac{3}{2}x^2 + \tfrac{3}{2} \cdot \tfrac{1}{12} \cdot x^4 + \tfrac{3}{2} \cdot \tfrac{1}{12} \cdot \tfrac{7}{30}x^6 + \ldots]$$
$$y_2 = C_1[x + \tfrac{1}{3}x^3 + \tfrac{1}{3} \cdot \tfrac{3}{20}x^5 + \ldots]$$

The complete solution is

$$y = Ay_1 + By_2.$$

Thus, in general, if the roots of the Indicial Equation differ by an integer, and if one of the coefficients in the series for y_1 becomes indeterminate when one of the roots is substituted, then the complete solution is given by the series for y_1, which then contains two arbitrary constants.

Examples.

1. Integrate the differential equation

$$x\frac{d^2y}{dx^2} + (x + a) \cdot \frac{dy}{dx} + (a + 1) \cdot y = 0.$$

(i) When $a = \tfrac{1}{2}$.
(ii) When $a = 0$.
(iii) When $a = 1$.

2. Integrate the equation

$$x\frac{d^2y}{dx^2} + (1 + x^2)\frac{dy}{dx} + xy = 0.$$

3. Integrate the equation

$$x^2y'' + xy' + (x^2 - n^2)y = 0.$$

(i) When n is not an integer.
(ii) When n is an integer.

7. The methods of Euler, Runge and Kutta.

The following methods of determining the increment in a function y corresponding to a given increment in the independent variable x are to be preferred when isolated increments are required, or where the increments in x lack uniformity, since the processes are evaluations of formulæ by substitutions. The methods are applicable when it is required to tabulate y at equal intervals in x, but suffer from the serious disadvantage (except the modified method of Euler) that no checking of the calculations (except a repetition of the calculation) is systematically applied. In addition, the more accurate formulæ of Kutta, which it is essential to apply if considerable accuracy is required, are rather unwieldy and laborious to apply continuously over a fairly wide range of integration. The methods find their chief application in this work in starting the solution of a differential equation which is required over a wide range. Even so, before proceeding to forward integration the values obtained are checked and corrected. The modified method of Euler, if carefully used with small increments, can be made to provide rapidly a solution of an equation which may be sufficiently accurate for practical purposes, and especial attention is drawn to it as the one method in this section in which the calculations include a systematic checking process by successive approximation.

7.1. The method of Euler.

If y is expressed as a function of x by the equation $\dfrac{dy}{dx} = f(x, y)$, the increment in y corresponding to an increment Δx in x is given approximately by the equation $\Delta y = f(x, y)\Delta x$, the value of $f(x, y)$ being that at the beginning of the interval Δx. Thus if (x_0, y_0) are corresponding initial values of the argument x and the function y, the first increment Δy_1 is given $\Delta y_1 = f(x_0, y_0)\Delta x_1$, where Δx_1 is the first increment in x. A second increment Δy_2 in y is

$$\Delta y_2 = f(x + \Delta x_1, y_0 + \Delta y_1) \cdot \Delta x_2,$$

where Δx_2 is the second increment in x. These expressions give

$$y_1 = y_0 + \Delta y_1$$
$$y_2 = y_1 + \Delta y_2 = y_0 + \Delta y_1 + \Delta y_2.$$

Proceeding in this manner, the value of y corresponding to any value of x, say x_n, can be obtained by dividing the range $x_n - x_0$ into n suitable intervals. The process is very slow, and to ensure a reasonable accuracy very small increments must be taken in the argument. The method is consequently suitable only for functions which change slowly with the argument. The increments in x may be increased or decreased at will.

7.2. Modified method of Euler.

In taking the value of $\frac{dy}{dx}$ at the beginning of an interval in place of the true average value over the interval, a considerable error is made, which in general becomes intensified as the process is continued. In practice, therefore, the foregoing method is modified in the following manner. The values x_1, y_1 found above provide an approximate value of $\frac{dy}{dx}$ at the end of the first interval, say, $\left(\frac{dy}{dx}\right)_1$; the average of $\left(\frac{dy}{dx}\right)_0$ and $\left(\frac{dy}{dx}\right)_1$ is then multiplied by the increment Δx_1, thus giving a more accurate value of y_1 than before—say, y_{11}. This value y_{11} may be used to give a third approximation y_{111} if necessary before proceeding to the next interval. This final value of y_1 is then used for the second interval, and the process is repeated.

Using the notation of the next paragraph, the error of this process is

$$\tfrac{1}{12}(\Delta x)^3\{f_{11} + 2f_{12} \cdot f + f_{22}f^2 + f_2(f_1 + f_2f)\}.$$

The following examples will explain the two methods and comparisons with later methods are given at the end of this chapter.

Example.—Determine the values of y when $x = 0.02$, 0.04, 0.06, 0.08, 0.1, given that $y = 1$ when $x = 0$ and $\frac{dy}{dx} = x^2 + y$.

Clearly at $x = 0$, $y = 1$, $\left(\frac{dy}{dx}\right)_0 = 1$.

Then　　$\Delta y_1 = \left(\frac{dy}{dx}\right)_0 \cdot \Delta x_1$

　　　　　　$= 0.02$

i.e.　　　$y_1 = 1.02$ at $x = 0.02$

　　　　$\left(\frac{dy}{dx}\right)_1 = 1.02 + 0.0004$ from the original equation

　　　　　　$= 1.0204$

giving $\quad \Delta y_2 = 1.0204 \times 0.02$
$$= 0.0204$$

Thus $\quad y_2 = 1.0404$ at $x = 0.04$

$$\left(\frac{dy}{dx}\right)_2 = 1.0404 + 0.0016$$
$$= 1.0420$$

and $\quad \Delta y_3 = 1.0420 \times 0.02$
$$= 0.0208$$
$$y_3 = 1.0612 \text{ at } x = 0.06$$

$$\left(\frac{dy}{dx}\right)_3 = 1.0612 + 0.0036$$
$$= 1.0648$$

$$\Delta y_4 = 0.0213 \text{ retaining four figures only}$$
$$y_4 = 1.0825 \text{ at } x = 0.08$$

$$\left(\frac{dy}{dx}\right)_4 = 1.0825 + 0.0064$$
$$= 1.0889$$
$$\Delta y_5 = 1.0889 \times 0.02$$
$$= 0.0218$$

Finally $\quad \underline{y_5 = 1.1043 \text{ at } x = 0.10}$

[Error $- 0.0012$.]

Example.—Consider this same case

$$\frac{dy}{dx} = y + x^2$$

with the same initial point and taking steps of 0.1 in x

$$= 1 + 0$$
$$\Delta y_1 = \left(\frac{dy}{dx}\right)_0 . \Delta x_1$$
$$= 1 \times 0.1$$
$$= 0.1, \qquad \text{therefore} \qquad y_1 = 1.1$$
$$\left(\frac{dy}{dx}\right)_1 = 1.1 + 0.01 = 1.11.$$

Average value of $\frac{dy}{dx}$ over the first interval from $x = 0$ to $x = 0.1$

$$= \frac{1.11 + 1}{2} = 1.055$$

$$y_{\text{II}} = 1 \cdot 055 \times 0 \cdot 1 = 0 \cdot 1055, \qquad y_{\text{II}} = 1 \cdot 1055$$
$$\left(\frac{dy}{dx}\right)_{11} = 1 \cdot 1055 + 0 \cdot 01 = 1 \cdot 1155.$$

Corrected average value of $\dfrac{dy}{dx}$

$$= \frac{1 \cdot 1155 + 1}{2} = 1 \cdot 0578$$

$$\Delta y_{\text{III}} = 0 \cdot 1058, \qquad \text{thus} \qquad y_{\text{III}} = 1 \cdot 1058$$
$$\left(\frac{dy}{dx}\right)_{111} = 1 \cdot 1058 + 0 \cdot 01 = 1 \cdot 1158.$$

Second corrected value of $\dfrac{dy}{dx}$

$$= \frac{1 \cdot 1158 + 1}{2} = 1 \cdot 0579$$

$$\Delta y_{\text{IV}} = 0 \cdot 1058, \qquad\qquad y_{\text{IV}} = 1 \cdot 1058.$$

The process of correcting the second value of y is thus completed, as no further accuracy is possible by the repetition of the process.

In a similar manner for the intervals up to $x = 0 \cdot 4$ the following results are obtained :

$x = 0 \cdot 1$	$y_1 = 1 \cdot 1058$	Error $= 0 \cdot 0003$
$x = 0 \cdot 2$	$y_2 = 1 \cdot 2248$	Error $= 0 \cdot 0006$
$x = 0 \cdot 3$	$y_3 = 1 \cdot 3606$	Error $= 0 \cdot 0010$
$x = 0 \cdot 4$	$y = 1 \cdot 5170$	Error $= 0 \cdot 0015.$

In each case the number of operations performed before the same value is repeated happens to be the same in the above example.

It will be seen from the first example that the method is slow, and that even with small intervals the increasing error to which the process is subject quickly shows itself. As no provision is made in the method for correcting or checking values, the method is not very reliable, except over a very limited range.

The second example illustrates the modified method, which is considerably more accurate than the first, and attains the possible accuracy much more rapidly. Once more, however, an increasing error enters, and with a chosen increment in the argument the accuracy is strictly limited to that obtained when two successive values of the function repeat by continuing the process of averaging $\frac{dy}{dx}$ over the given interval.

In neither case is a check on the accuracy of previously calculated values of the function provided, nor do they provide any scheme of correction once the values are calculated.

Later methods which follow are designed to meet these requirements. Nevertheless, the above methods are available initially for obtaining a solution over a very narrow range if necessary.

7.3. The method of Runge.

Euler's approximation for the increment in y corresponding to an increment x_0 in x is given by

$$\Delta y_0 = f(x_0, y_0) . \Delta x_0 . \quad . \quad . \quad . \quad . \quad (1)$$

in which x_0, y_0 are initial values of the function y and its argument x. An immediate improvement in accuracy is effected by writing

$$\Delta y = f[x + \tfrac{1}{2}\Delta x, y_0 + \tfrac{1}{2}f(x_0, y_0) . \Delta x] . \Delta x \quad . \quad (1.1)$$

This expression corresponds to the Tangent Polygon expression in the simpler case of integration of a function and agrees with it exactly, if $f(x, y)$ is a function of x only. Again corresponding to the chord polygon expression there is the approximation

$$\Delta y = \tfrac{1}{2}\{f(x_0, y_0) + f[x_0 + \Delta x, y_0 + f(x_0, y_0) . \Delta x]\} . \Delta x \quad (1.2)$$

By expanding the true and approximate values of the integral in power series in Δx (see below), it is at once obvious that Euler's expression is in error as to the term in Δx^2, and that the errors of (1.1) and (1.2) are of order Δx^3.

The true value as far as $(\Delta x)^3$ is

$$\Delta y = f . \Delta x + \tfrac{1}{2}(f_1 + f_2 f)\Delta x^2 + \tfrac{1}{6}\{f_{11} + 2f_{12}f + f_{22}f^2 + f_2(f_1 + f_2 f)\} . \Delta x^3 + \cdots$$

and the following are the approximate values from (1.0), (1.1), and (1.2)

$$\Delta y = f . \Delta x . \quad . \quad . \quad . \quad . \quad . \quad . \quad . \quad (1.01)$$

$$\Delta y = f . \Delta x + \tfrac{1}{2}(f_1 + f_2 f)\Delta x^2 + \tfrac{1}{6}(f_{11} + 2f_{12}f + f_{22}f^2) . \Delta x^3 + \quad . \quad . \quad (1.11)N_1$$

$$\Delta y = f . \Delta x + \tfrac{1}{2}(f_1 + f_2 f)\Delta x^2 + \tfrac{1}{4}(f_{11} + 2f_{12}f + f_{22}f^2) . \Delta x^3 + \quad . \quad . \quad (1.21)N_2$$

$x.$	$y.$	$f(x, y) \cdot \Delta x.$	$x.$	$y.$	$f(x, y) \cdot \Delta x.$
x_0	y_0	$f(x_0, y_0) \cdot \Delta x = \Delta'$	$x_0 + \Delta x$	$y_0 + \Delta'$	$f(x_0 + \Delta x, y_0 + \Delta') \cdot \Delta x = \Delta''$
$x_0 + \tfrac{1}{2}\Delta x$	$y_0 + \tfrac{1}{2}\Delta y$	$f(x_0 + \tfrac{1}{2}\Delta x, y_0 + \tfrac{1}{2}\Delta') \cdot \Delta x = \Delta'''$	$x_0 + \Delta x$	$y_0 + \Delta''$	$f(x_0 + \Delta x, y_0 + \Delta'') \cdot \Delta x = \Delta'''$
		$\tfrac{1}{2}(\Delta' + \Delta''')$			Δ'
		$3\overline{\smash{)}\,\tfrac{1}{2}(\Delta' + \Delta''') - \Delta'''}$			$2\overline{\smash{)}\,\Delta' + \Delta''}$
		$\tfrac{1}{3}\{\tfrac{1}{2}(\Delta' + \Delta''') - \Delta'''\}$			$\tfrac{1}{2}(\Delta' + \Delta'')$
		Δ''''			
		$\Delta y = \Delta'''' + \tfrac{1}{3} \text{ difference}$			
$x_0 + \Delta x$	$y_0 + \Delta y$				

where

$$f_1 = \left(\frac{\partial f}{\partial x}\right)_0 ; \; f_2 = \left(\frac{\partial f}{\partial y}\right)_0 ; \; f_{11} = \left(\frac{\partial^2 f}{\partial x^2}\right)_0 ; \; f_{12} = \left(\frac{\partial^2 f}{\partial x \partial y}\right)_0 ; \; f_{22} = \left(\frac{\partial^2 f}{\partial y^2}\right)_0$$

etc.

If the expressions (N_1) and (N_2) are combined as in Simpson's rule, that is, to (N_1) add one third the difference $(N_2) - (N_1)$, then the new value

$$f \cdot \Delta x + \tfrac{1}{2}(f_1 + f_2 f) \cdot \Delta x^2 + \tfrac{1}{6}(f_{11} + 2f_{12}f + f_{22}f^2) \cdot \Delta x^3 + \ldots \quad (1.3)$$

is obtained. This corresponds to

$$N_1 + \tfrac{1}{3}(N_2 - N_1) \; \text{or} \; \tfrac{2}{3}N_1 + \tfrac{1}{3}N_2.$$

The latter expression is correct as far as the term in Δx^2 and, if f is independent of y, as far as the term in Δx^3. In place of expression (1.3) another approximation is taken which reduces to the chord polygon expression when f is independent of y, viz.

$$\tfrac{1}{2}(\Delta' y + \Delta''' y) \quad \ldots \quad \ldots \quad (1.31)$$

where
$$\begin{aligned}
\Delta' y &= f(x_0, y_0) \cdot \Delta x \\
\Delta'' y &= f(x_0 + \Delta x, y_0 + \Delta' y) \cdot \Delta x \\
\Delta''' y &= f(x_0 + \Delta x, y_0 + \Delta'' y) \cdot \Delta x.
\end{aligned}$$

When (1.31) is expanded as a power series in Δx, the result is

$$f \cdot \Delta x + \tfrac{1}{2}(f_1 + f_2 f) \cdot \Delta x^2 + \tfrac{1}{4}\{f_{11} + 2f_{12}f + f_{22}f^2 + 2f_2(f_1 + f_2 f)\} \cdot \Delta x^3 + \ldots \quad {}^{\bullet}N_3$$

The difference between (N_3) and (N_1) is now

$$\{\tfrac{1}{8}(f_{11} + 2f_{12}f + f_{22}f^2) + \tfrac{1}{2}f_2(f_1 + f_2 f)\} \cdot \Delta x^3 + \ldots$$

and if one third of this difference is added to (N_1) the value

$$f \cdot \Delta x + \tfrac{1}{2}(f_1 + f_2 f) \cdot \Delta x^2 + \tfrac{1}{6}\{f_{11} + 2f_{12}f + f_{22}f^2 + f_2(f_1 + f_2 f)\} \cdot \Delta x^3 + \ldots$$

is obtained, which agrees with the true value of Δy as far as the term of third degree in Δx. The table on p. 97 shows the systematic application of these results to an actual case.

Solution of $\dfrac{dy}{dx} = f(x, y)$ **given the initial point** (x_0, y_0).

Example.—Find the value of y when $x = 1$, given that $y = 1$ when $x = 0$ and that $\dfrac{dy}{dx} = \dfrac{y - x}{y + x}$.

The table on p. 99 should be self-explanatory:

7.31. An extension of Runge's method.

The following extension of Runge's method of integrating the differential equation $\dfrac{dy}{dx} = f(x, y)$ is due to Piaggio.

Let $\left.\begin{aligned} x &= a \\ y &= b \end{aligned}\right\}$ be the initial point.

$x.$	$x.$	
$x = 0$ $\Delta x = 0\cdot2$	$\Delta x = 0\cdot2$	$f(x, y) \cdot \Delta x = f(0, 1) \times 0\cdot2 = \Delta' = 0\cdot2$ $f(x + \Delta x, y + \Delta') \cdot \Delta x = f(0\cdot2, 1\cdot2) \cdot \Delta x$ $\qquad = 0\cdot2 \times 1/1\cdot4$ $\qquad = 0\cdot1429 = \Delta''$ $f(x + \Delta x, y + \Delta'') \cdot \Delta x = f(0\cdot2, 1\cdot429) \times 0\cdot2$ $\qquad = 0\cdot1404 = \Delta''$ $\tfrac{1}{2}(\Delta' + \Delta'') = 0\cdot1702$
		$f(x + \tfrac{1}{2}\Delta', y + \tfrac{1}{2}\Delta') \cdot \tfrac{1}{2}\Delta x = \tfrac{1}{2} \times 0\cdot2 = 0\cdot1$ $f(x + \tfrac{1}{2}\Delta x, y + \tfrac{1}{2}\Delta') \cdot \Delta x = f(0\cdot1, 1\cdot1) \times 0\cdot2$ $\qquad = 1\cdot687$ $\qquad = 0\cdot1702$ Difference $= 0\cdot0035$ $\qquad\qquad = 0\cdot0012$ $\tfrac{1}{2}(\Delta' + \Delta'') = \tfrac{1}{2} \times$ $y_1 = 1 + 0\cdot1687 + 0\cdot0012$ $\quad = 1\cdot1679$
$0\cdot2$ $\Delta x = 0\cdot3$	$0\cdot2$ $\Delta x = 0\cdot3$	$f(0\cdot2, 1\cdot1679) \times 0\cdot2 = 0\cdot2123 = \Delta'$ $y_1 + \Delta' = 1\cdot3802$ $f(0\cdot5, 1\cdot3802) \times 0\cdot3 = 0\cdot1404 = \Delta''$ $y_1 + \Delta'' = 1\cdot3083$ $f(0\cdot5, 1\cdot3083) = 0\cdot1341 = \Delta'''$ $\tfrac{1}{2}(\Delta' + \Delta'') = 0\cdot1732$
		$\tfrac{1}{2}\Delta' = f(0\cdot2, 1\cdot1679) \times \tfrac{1}{2} \times 0\cdot2 = 0\cdot1061$ $y_1 + \tfrac{1}{2}\Delta' = 1\cdot2740$ $f(x + \tfrac{1}{2}\Delta x, y + \tfrac{1}{2}\Delta') \cdot \Delta x$ $f(0\cdot35, 1\cdot2740) \times 0\cdot3 = 0\cdot1707$ $\tfrac{1}{2}(\Delta' + \Delta'') = 0\cdot1732$ Difference $= 0\cdot0025$ $\qquad\qquad , = 0\cdot0008$ $y_1 + \Delta'''' + \tfrac{1}{2} \times \text{difference}$ $\quad = 1\cdot1679 + 0\cdot1707 + 0\cdot0008$ $y_2 = 1\cdot3394$
$0\cdot5$ $\Delta x = 0\cdot5$	$0\cdot5$ $\Delta x = 0\cdot5$	$\Delta' = 0\cdot2280$ $y_1 + \Delta' = 1\cdot5674$ $f(1, 1\cdot5670) \times 0\cdot5 = 0\cdot1104 = \Delta''$ $f(1, 1\cdot4498) \times 0\cdot5 = 0\cdot0918 = \Delta'''$ $\tfrac{1}{2}(\Delta' + \Delta''') = 0\cdot1599$
		$\tfrac{1}{2}\Delta' = f(0\cdot5, 1\cdot3394) \times 0\cdot25 = 0\cdot1140$ $y_2 + \tfrac{1}{2}\Delta' = 1\cdot4534$ $f(0\cdot75, 1\cdot4534) \times 0\cdot5 = 0\cdot1596$ $\tfrac{1}{2}(\Delta' + \Delta''') = 0\cdot1599$ Difference $= 0\cdot0003$ $\qquad\qquad = 0\cdot0001$ $y_3 = y_2 + \Delta'''' + \tfrac{1}{2} \times \text{difference}$ $\quad = 1\cdot3394 + 0\cdot1596 + 0\cdot0001$ $\quad = 1\cdot4991$ Error $0\cdot0008.$

$f(x, y)$ is supposed to be restricted to the range a to $a + h$ for x and $b - h$ to $b + h$ for y, the numerical increment in y being less than that of x. (See conditions below.) The inequalities which follow are subject to the conditions :—

1. $f(x, y)$, together with its first and second partial derivatives, are finite and continuous in the range.
2. $f(x, y) \leq 1$. If this condition is not satisfied as has already been pointed out, it is usually better to work with $\dfrac{dx}{dy}$, where y becomes the independent variable.
3. Neither $\dfrac{d^3y}{dx^3}$ nor $\dfrac{\partial f}{\partial y}$ changes sign.

Let m and M be two numbers such that

$$- 1 \leq m < f(x, y) < M \leq 1.$$

If the values of y are $b + j$ and $b + k$, respectively, when x is $a + \frac{1}{2}h$ and $a + h$, then

$$- \tfrac{1}{2}h \leq \tfrac{1}{2}mh < j < \tfrac{1}{2}Mh \leq \tfrac{1}{2}h$$

and $$- h \leq mh < k < Mh \leq h.$$

Thus, if $\dfrac{\partial f}{\partial y}$ is $+ ve$ (f increasing with y)

$$f(a + \tfrac{1}{2}h, b + \tfrac{1}{2}mh) < f(a + \tfrac{1}{2}h, b + j) < f(a + \tfrac{1}{2}h, b + \tfrac{1}{2}Mh)$$

and $$f(a + h, b + mh) < f(a + h, b + k) < f(a + h, b + Mh)$$

while if $\dfrac{\partial f}{\partial y}$ is $- ve$, the inequality signs in the last two inequalities are reversed.

Now since $\dfrac{d^3y}{dx^3}$ is $+ ve$ and $\dfrac{\partial f}{\partial y}$ is $+ ve$

$$p < k < Q$$

where $$p = hf(a + \tfrac{1}{2}h, b + \tfrac{1}{2}mh)$$

and $Q = \frac{1}{4}h[f(a, b) + 2f(a + \tfrac{1}{2}h, b + \tfrac{1}{2}Mh) + f(a + h, b + Mh)]$

while if $\dfrac{d^3y}{dx^3}$ is $+ ve$ and $\dfrac{\partial f}{\partial y}$ is $- ve$

$$P < k < q$$

where $P = hf(a + \tfrac{1}{2}h, b + \tfrac{1}{2}Mh)$

and $q = \frac{1}{4}h[f(a, b) + 2f(a + \tfrac{1}{2}h, b + \tfrac{1}{2}mh) + f(a + h, b + mh)]$

Similarly, if $\dfrac{d^3y}{dx^3}$ and $\dfrac{\partial f}{\partial y}$ are both $- ve$

$$p < k < Q$$

and if $\dfrac{d^3y}{dx^3}$ is $- ve$ and $\dfrac{\partial f}{\partial y}$ is $+ ve$

$$P > k > q.$$

Thus in every case above k, the increment in y, lies between the greatest and least of the four members p, P, q, and Q.

As an approximate formula

$$k \doteqdot \tfrac{2}{3}[Q \text{ or } q] + \tfrac{1}{3}[p \text{ or } P].$$

Example.

If

$$\frac{dy}{dx} = \frac{y-x}{y+x}$$

where $x = 0$, $y = 1$ for the range

$$0 \geq x \ \ 0 \cdot 5 \leq,$$

and if $M = 1$ and $m = 0$, then

$$Q > q > P > p.$$

Show further that the value of y at $x = 0 \cdot 5$ calculated from Piaggio's formula

$$k \doteqdot \tfrac{2}{3}Q + \tfrac{1}{3}p$$

is more accurate than that derived from Runge's formula.

7.4. Kutta's modification of Runge's method.

The method of integrating the equation $\dfrac{dy}{dx} = f(x, y)$ due to Runge was later developed by Heun and Kutta, but as Heun's work is contained in that of Kutta, only the latter's work will be discussed here. The methods used by Kutta in obtaining his approximations will be illustrated by showing how his third-order approximations were obtained. For higher-order approximations the results only will be quoted, and examples given using these approximations. Worked examples will be found on p. 107.

7.41. Kutta's third-order approximations.

Using the same notation as in the case of Runge's approximation, Kutta generalised the process by taking

$$\Delta'y \ = f(x, y) \cdot \Delta x$$
$$\Delta''y \ = f(x + m \cdot \Delta x, y + m \cdot \Delta'y) \cdot \Delta x \cdot$$
$$\Delta'''y \ = f(x + \lambda \cdot \Delta x, y + \rho \cdot \Delta''y + (\lambda - \rho) \cdot \Delta'y) \cdot \Delta x.$$

With these values for $\Delta'y$, $\Delta''y$, and $\Delta'''y$, the increment Δy is given by

$$y = a \cdot \Delta'y + b \cdot \Delta''y + c \cdot \Delta'''y$$

m, λ, ρ, a, b, and c are constants which are to be determined. For convenience in the following analysis, let k_1, k_2, k_3 replace $\Delta'y$, $\Delta''y$, $\Delta'''y$, and let h replace Δx_t
Then

$$k_1 = h \cdot f$$
$$k_2 = h[f + mh(f_1 + f_2 f) + \tfrac{1}{2}m^2h^2(f_{11} + 2f_{12}f + f_{22}f^2) + \cdots]$$
$$k_3 = h[f + \lambda \cdot h(f_1 + f_2 f) + \tfrac{1}{2}h^2\{2m \cdot f_2 \cdot \rho(f_1 + f_2 f) \\ + \lambda^2(f_{11} + 2f_{12} \cdot f + f_{22}f^2)\} + \cdots]$$

Therefore

$$ak_1 + b \cdot k_2 + ck_3 = hf(a + b + c) + h^2(bm + c\lambda)(f_1 + f_2 f)$$
$$+ \tfrac{1}{2}(bm^2 + c\lambda^2) \cdot h^3(f_{11} + 2f_{12} \cdot f + f_{22} \cdot f^2)$$
$$+ c\rho m h^3 \cdot f_2(f_1 + f_2 f) + \cdots$$

The actual expansion at the point (x, y) can now be compared with this expression.

Now

$$\Delta y = k = h \cdot f + \tfrac{1}{2}h^2(f_1 + f_2 f)$$
$$+ \tfrac{1}{6}h^3[f_{11} + 2f_{12} \cdot f + f_{22}f^2 + f_2(f_1 + f_2 f)] + \cdots$$

That these expressions may be identical as far as the third-order term, the following equations must be satisfied

$$\left.\begin{array}{r} a + b + c = 1 \\ bm + c\lambda = \tfrac{1}{2} \\ bm^2 + c\lambda^2 = \tfrac{1}{3} \\ c\rho m = \tfrac{1}{6} \end{array}\right\} \quad \cdots \cdots \quad (1.40)$$

A system of solutions may be represented by

$$\left.\begin{array}{l} \rho = \lambda(\lambda - m)/m(2 - 3m), \\ a = [6m\lambda - 3(m + \lambda) + 2]/6m \cdot \lambda \\ b = (2 - 3\lambda)/6m(m - \lambda) \\ c = (2 - 3m)/6\lambda(\lambda - m) \end{array}\right\} \quad (1.41)$$

Thus four of the constants are expressed in terms of the remaining two, and so a doubly infinite set of values may be deduced.

The system $\lambda = \rho$ corresponds to Heun's work on this subject, viz.,

$$\lambda = 3m(1 - m); \quad a = (2 - 12m + 27m^2 - 18m^3)/18m^2(1 - m)$$
$$b = (3m - 1 - 6m^2)/6m^2; \quad c = \{18m^2(1 - m)\}^{-1}.$$

Particular values of the above systems of solutions are :

$$m = \tfrac{2}{3}, \lambda = 0, b = \tfrac{3}{4}, c = 1/(4\rho), a = \tfrac{1}{4} - 1/(4\rho) \quad . \quad . \quad (1.42)$$
$$m = \tfrac{2}{3}, \lambda = \tfrac{2}{3}, a = \tfrac{1}{4}, c = 1/(4\rho), b = \tfrac{3}{4} - 1/(4\rho) \quad . \quad . \quad (1.43)$$
$$\lambda = \tfrac{2}{3}, a = \tfrac{1}{4}, b = 0, c = \tfrac{3}{4}, \rho = 2/(9m) \quad . \quad . \quad . \quad . \quad (1.44)$$
$$\lambda = (3m - 2)/3(2m - 1); \quad a = 0 \quad . \quad . \quad . \quad . \quad . \quad (1.45)$$

In cases (1.44) and (1.45) two function values only need be retained in the final formula.

c cannot be zero, and a and b cannot be small together. The final formula must contain at least two function values. Each of the sets above gives a simple infinity of solutions.

Returning to the original notation, the following special cases may be quoted :

$$m = \tfrac{2}{3}, \lambda = \tfrac{2}{3}, \rho = \tfrac{2}{3}$$
$$a = \tfrac{1}{4}, b = c = \tfrac{3}{8}$$

$$\Delta y \quad = \tfrac{1}{8}(2\Delta' + 3\Delta'' + 3\Delta''') \quad . \quad . \quad . \quad . \quad (1.5)$$

where
$$\left.\begin{array}{l} \Delta' = f(x, y) \cdot \Delta x \\ \Delta'' = f(x + \tfrac{2}{3}\Delta x, y + \tfrac{2}{3}\Delta') \cdot \Delta x \\ \Delta''' = f(x + \tfrac{2}{3}\Delta x, y + \tfrac{2}{3}\Delta'') \cdot \Delta x \end{array}\right\} \quad . \quad . \quad . \quad (1.51)$$

$m = \frac{1}{3}$, $\lambda = \rho = \frac{2}{3}$; using (1.44) or (1.41)

$$\Delta y = \frac{1}{4}(\Delta' + 3\Delta'') \quad \ldots \ldots \ldots \quad (1.60)$$

where
$$\left.\begin{aligned}
\Delta' &= f(x, y) \cdot \Delta x \\
\Delta'' &= f(x + \tfrac{1}{3}\Delta x, y + \tfrac{1}{3}\Delta') \cdot \Delta x \\
\Delta''' &= f(x + \tfrac{2}{3}\Delta x, y + \tfrac{2}{3}\Delta'') \cdot \Delta x
\end{aligned}\right\} \quad \ldots \ldots \quad (1.61)$$

$m = \frac{2}{3} = \lambda$; $\rho = \frac{1}{3}$

$$\Delta y = \frac{1}{4}(\Delta' + 3\Delta''') \quad \ldots \ldots \ldots \quad (1.70)$$

where
$$\left.\begin{aligned}
\Delta' &= f(x, y) \cdot \Delta x \\
\Delta'' &= f(x + \tfrac{2}{3}\Delta x, y + \tfrac{2}{3}\Delta') \cdot \Delta x \\
\Delta''' &= f(x + \tfrac{2}{3}\Delta x, y + \tfrac{1}{3}(\Delta' + \Delta'')) \cdot \Delta x
\end{aligned}\right\} \quad \ldots \quad (1.71)$$

$m = \frac{1}{2}$, $\lambda = 1$

$$\Delta y = \frac{1}{6}(\Delta' + 4\Delta'' + \Delta''') \quad \ldots \ldots \quad (1.80)$$

where
$$\left.\begin{aligned}
\Delta' &= f(x, y) \cdot \Delta x \\
\Delta'' &= f \cdot (x + \tfrac{1}{2}\Delta x, y + \tfrac{1}{2}\Delta') \cdot \Delta x \\
\Delta''' &= f \cdot (x + \Delta x, y + 2\Delta'' - \Delta') \cdot \Delta x
\end{aligned}\right\} \quad \ldots \quad (1.81)$$

The last formula will be recognised as analogous to Simpson's Rule.

7.42. Kutta's fourth-order approximations.

Kutta extended the foregoing process to the case when the error allowable was that of order $(\Delta x)^5$.
Taking

$$\begin{aligned}
\Delta' &= f(x, y) \cdot \Delta x \\
\Delta'' &= f(x + m\Delta x, y + m\Delta') \cdot \Delta x \\
\Delta''' &= f(x + \lambda \cdot \Delta x, y + \rho \cdot \Delta'' + (\lambda - \rho) \cdot \Delta') \cdot \Delta x \, .
\end{aligned}$$

and

$$\Delta^{iv} = f(x + \mu\Delta x, y + \sigma \cdot \Delta''' + \tau \cdot \Delta'' + (\mu - \sigma - \tau) \cdot \Delta') \cdot \Delta x$$

the required approximation then becomes

$$\Delta y = a\Delta' + b\Delta'' + c\Delta''' + d \cdot \Delta^{iv}$$

The equations determining the constants are then

$$\begin{aligned}
a + b + c + d &= 1; & c\rho m + d(\sigma\lambda + \tau m) &= \tfrac{1}{6} \\
bm + c\lambda + d\mu &= \tfrac{1}{2}; & bm^3 + c\lambda^3 + d\mu^3 &= \tfrac{1}{4} \\
bm^2 + c\lambda^2 + d\mu^2 &= \tfrac{1}{3}; & c\rho m\lambda + d(\sigma\lambda + \tau m)\mu &= \tfrac{1}{8} \\
& & c\rho m^2 + d(\sigma\lambda^2 + \tau m^2) &= \tfrac{1}{12} \\
& & d\rho\sigma m &= \tfrac{1}{24}.
\end{aligned}$$

There are eight equations for ten unknowns, thus, taking m and λ as arbitrary, the remainder of the constants are expressible in terms of them. Two cases only are given here:

a. *Kutta's Simpson's rule.*

The simplest formula with this degree of accuracy is given by $m = \lambda = \frac{1}{2}$, $\mu = 1$, $a = d = \frac{1}{6}$, $b = c = \frac{2}{6}$, $\sigma = 1$.

$$y = \frac{1}{6}(\Delta' + 2\Delta'' + 2\Delta''' + \Delta^{iv})$$

where
$$\Delta'' = f(x_0 + \tfrac{1}{2}\Delta x, \; y_0 + \tfrac{1}{2}\Delta'x) \cdot \Delta x$$
$$\Delta''' = f(x_0 + \tfrac{1}{2}\Delta x, \; y_0 + \tfrac{1}{2}\Delta'') \cdot \Delta x$$
$$\Delta^{iv} = f(x_0 + \Delta x, \; y_0 + \Delta''') \cdot \Delta x.$$

If
$$p = \tfrac{1}{2}(\Delta'' + \Delta''') : q = \tfrac{1}{2}(\Delta' + \Delta^{iv})$$
then
$$\Delta y = p + \tfrac{1}{3}(q - p).$$

The student should note that when $f(x, y)$ is independent of y this reduces to Simpson's rule.

b. *Kutta's three-eighths rule.*

When
$$m = \tfrac{1}{3}, \; \lambda = \tfrac{2}{3}$$
$$\Delta y = \tfrac{1}{8}(\Delta' + 3\Delta'' + 3\Delta''' + \Delta^{iv})$$
where
$$\Delta' = f(x_0, y_0) \cdot \Delta x$$
$$\Delta'' = f(x + \tfrac{1}{3}\Delta x, \; y + \tfrac{1}{3}\Delta') \cdot \Delta x$$
$$\Delta''' = f(x + \tfrac{2}{3}\Delta x, \; y + \tfrac{1}{3}(3\Delta'' - \Delta')) \cdot \Delta x)$$
$$\Delta^{iv} = f(x + \Delta x, \; y + \Delta''' - \Delta'' + \Delta') \cdot \Delta x.$$

Further information on the work of Kutta will be found in *Zeitschrift für Mathematik und Physik*, Band 46 (1901), pp. 435–53.

8. Comparison of accuracy of methods.

To compare the results obtained by using some of the previous formulæ the same example already given as an illustration of Runge's method is here solved.

1. By Taylor's expansion to the term of fourth order in Δx.
2. Euler's method (modified).
3. Runge's method. See example on Runge's method, p. 99.
4. Heun's method. Formula (1.60), (1.61) correct to the third order in Δx and necessitating the calculation of three function values.
5. Kutta's $\tfrac{3}{8}$ formula. Correct to the fourth order and requiring four function values to be calculated.

The tables below are self explanatory.

	Interval $x = 0$ to $0 \cdot 2$ $[\Delta y]_0^{0 \cdot 2}$.	Error.	Interval $x = 0 \cdot 2$ to $0 \cdot 5$ $[\Delta y]_0^{0 \cdot 5}$.	Error	Interval $x = 0 \cdot 5$ to 1 $[\Delta y]_0^1$.	Error.
Taylor's expansion .	0·1667	– 0·0011	0·3369	– 0·0023	0·4937	– 0·0046
Euler (modified) . .	0·1708	+ 0·0030	0·3458	+ 0·0066	0·5113	+ 0·0130
Runge . .	0·1679	+ 0·0001	0·3394	+ 0·0002	0·4991	+ 0·0008
Heun . .	0·1680	+ 0·0002	0·3396	+ 0·0004	0·4990	+ 0·0007
Kutta . .	0·167845	+ 0·000003	0·339216	+ 0·000007	0·498294	+ 0·000016
True value . .	0·167842		0·339209		0·498278	

The same approximate formulæ used over the complete interval $x = 1$ give the following results, except for Taylor's method, where the series is not convergent by $x = 1$.

	Δy.	Error.
Euler (modified) . . .	0·6180	+0·1197
Runge	0·5238	+0·0255
Heun	0·5161	+0·0178
Kutta	0·49914	+0·00086
True value	0·49828	—

Kutta's fourth-order approximation, as was to be expected, thus offers much greater accuracy than any of the third-order approximations. Here also Heun's third-order approximation is superior to that of Runge.

9. Collected formulæ for approximate integration.

$$\Delta' = f(xy) \cdot \Delta x \text{ in all cases.}$$

1. Runge's Original Formula :

$$\Delta'' = f(x + \Delta x, y + \Delta') \cdot \Delta x$$
$$\Delta''' = f(x + \Delta x, y + \Delta'') \cdot \Delta x$$
$$\Delta'''' = f(x + \tfrac{1}{2}\Delta x, y + \tfrac{1}{2}\Delta') \cdot \Delta x.$$

Then $\quad \underline{\Delta y = \Delta'''' + \tfrac{1}{3}\{\tfrac{1}{2}(\Delta' + \Delta'') - \Delta''''\}}$ Error of order $(\Delta x)^4$.

2. Heun :

$$\Delta'' = f(x + \tfrac{1}{3}\Delta x, y + \tfrac{1}{3}\Delta') \cdot \Delta x$$
$$\Delta''' = f(x + \tfrac{2}{3}\Delta x, y + \tfrac{2}{3}\Delta'') \cdot \Delta x$$
$$\underline{\Delta y = \tfrac{1}{4}(\Delta' + 3\Delta''')}. \quad \text{Error of order } (\Delta x)^4.$$

3. Kutta's third-order rule :

$$\Delta'' = f(x + \tfrac{1}{2}\Delta x, y + \tfrac{1}{2}\Delta') \cdot \Delta x$$
$$\Delta''' = f(x + \Delta x, y + 2\Delta'' - \Delta') \cdot \Delta x$$
$$\underline{\Delta y = \tfrac{1}{6}(\Delta' + 4\Delta'' + \Delta''')}. \quad \text{Error of order } (\Delta x)^4.$$

4. Kutta's three-eighths rule. $\quad$ } see p. 103, (a) and (b).
5. Kutta's Simpson's rule. $\quad$

Example.—Apply the methods of

(i) Euler.
(ii) Modified method of Euler.
(iii) Runge.
(iv) Kutta's Simpson's rule

to obtain a tabulated solution of the equation

$$\frac{dy}{dx} = 0 \cdot 1 y^2 + x$$

subject to $x = 0$, $y = 0$ for the range $0 < x < 0.5$ at intervals of 0.1 in x. Compare the solutions correct to five places of decimals with that obtained by using Taylor's expansion up to fifth powers of x.

9.1. Application to simultaneous equations.

In order to illustrate the application of the formulæ which have been developed, to simultaneous equations, Kutta's Simpson's rule has been chosen, and it will be applied to a system of two simultaneous first-order differential equations. Extension to other systems may readily be carried out by proceeding along similar lines.

Let the equations be

$$\left. \begin{aligned} \frac{dy}{dx} &= f(x,\, y,\, z) \\ \frac{dz}{dx} &= g(x,\, y,\, z) \end{aligned} \right\}$$

subject to $x = x_0$, $y = y_0$, $z = z_0$.

The procedure is readily understood upon inspecting the scheme set out below, for the actual calculations involve simple substitutions only.

Writing

$$\begin{aligned}
\Delta' &= f(x_0,\, y_0,\, z_0)\,.\,\Delta x \\
\Delta'' &= f(x_0 + \tfrac{1}{2}\Delta x,\, y_0 + \tfrac{1}{2}\Delta',\, z_0 + \tfrac{1}{2}\delta')\,.\,\Delta x \\
\Delta''' &= f(x_0 + \tfrac{1}{2}\Delta x,\, y_0 + \tfrac{1}{2}\Delta'',\, z_0 + \tfrac{1}{2}\delta'')\,.\,\Delta x \\
\Delta^{\text{iv}} &= f(x_0 + \Delta x,\, y_0 + \Delta''',\, z_0 + \delta''')\,.\,\Delta x
\end{aligned}$$

and

$$\begin{aligned}
\delta' &= g(x_0,\, y_0,\, z_0)\,.\,\Delta x \\
\delta'' &= g(x_0 + \tfrac{1}{2}\Delta x,\, y_0 + \tfrac{1}{2}\Delta',\, z_0 + \tfrac{1}{2}\delta')\,.\,\Delta x \\
\delta''' &= g(x_0 + \tfrac{1}{2}\Delta x,\, y_0 + \tfrac{1}{2}\Delta'',\, z_0 + \tfrac{1}{2}\delta'')\,.\,\Delta x \\
\delta^{\text{iv}} &= g(x_0 + \Delta x,\, y_0 + \Delta''',\, z_0 + \delta''')\,.\,\Delta x.
\end{aligned}$$

From these

$$\begin{aligned}
\Delta y &= \tfrac{1}{6}(\Delta' + 2\Delta'' + 2\Delta''' + \Delta^{\text{iv}}) \\
\Delta z &= \tfrac{1}{6}(\delta' + 2\delta'' + 2\delta''' + \delta^{\text{iv}}).
\end{aligned}$$

The successive increments may be obtained in a similar manner, or the solution continued by the method of finite differences when sufficient values of y and z are obtained to start the process.

Example.—*Kutta's Simpson's rule applied to two simultaneous differential equations of the first order.*

Consider the differential equation

$$\frac{d^2y}{dx^2} + 3x\frac{dy}{dx} - 6y = 0$$

subject to $x = 0$, $y = 1$, $\frac{dy}{dx} = 0\cdot1$.

This equation may be written as the equivalent system of first-order equations

$$\left.\begin{aligned}\frac{dz}{dx} &= 6y - 3xz\\[4pt]\frac{dy}{dx} &= z\end{aligned}\right\}$$

subject to $x = 0$, $y = 1$, $z = 0\cdot1$.

Following the scheme set out on the previous page

$$\frac{dy}{dx} = z \qquad\qquad \frac{dz}{dx} = 6y - 3xz.$$

Initial conditions $x = 0$, $y = 1$, $z = 0\cdot1$. Let the range be divided into equal intervals of $0\cdot1$ in x so that $\Delta x = 0\cdot1$.

Using Kutta's Simpson's rule

$$\begin{aligned}
\Delta' &= 0\cdot1 \times 0\cdot1 & &= 0\cdot01\\
\Delta'' &= (0\cdot1 + 0\cdot3) \times 0\cdot1 & &= 0\cdot04\\
\Delta''' &= (0\cdot1 + 0\cdot2985) \times 0\cdot1 & &= 0\cdot03985\\
\Delta^{iv} &= (0\cdot70602) \times 0\cdot1 & &= 0\cdot07060\\[6pt]
\delta' &= (6 \times 1 - 0) \times 0\cdot1 & &= 0\cdot6\\
\delta'' &= [6(1\cdot005) - 3 \times 0\cdot05 \times 0\cdot4] \times 0\cdot1 & &= 0\cdot597\\
\delta''' &= [6(1\cdot020) - 3 \times 0\cdot05 \times 0\cdot3985] \times 0\cdot1 & &= 0\cdot60602\\
\delta^{iv} &= [6(1\cdot03985) - 3 \times 0\cdot1 \times 0\cdot70602] \times 0\cdot1 & &= 0\cdot60273
\end{aligned}$$

$$\begin{aligned}
\Delta y_1 &= \tfrac{1}{6}(\Delta' + 2\Delta'' + 2\Delta''' + \Delta^{iv})\\
&= \tfrac{1}{6}(0\cdot01 + 0\cdot08 + 0\cdot07970 + 0\cdot07060)\\
&= 0\cdot04005
\end{aligned}$$

$$\begin{aligned}
y_1 &= y_0 + \Delta y_1\\
y_1 &= 1\cdot04005
\end{aligned}$$

$$\Delta z_1 = \tfrac{1}{6}(\delta' + 2\delta'' + 2\delta''' + \delta^{iv})$$
$$= 0.60146$$
$$z_1 = z_0 + \Delta z_1$$
$$z_1 = 0.70146$$

In precisely the same way the succeeding values may be obtained for y and z.

10. A method of correcting the approximate initial values of y and $\dfrac{dy}{dx}$.

The following is a simple but rapid process of checking and correcting the initial values of y and $\dfrac{dy}{dx}$ found by one of the preceding methods.

Let the initial values of y and $\dfrac{dy}{dx}$ be denoted by y_0, y_1, y_2, y_3, y_4, q_0, q_1, q_2, q_3, and q_4.

Now

$$y_1 - y_0 = h\int_{r=0}^{r=1} q(a + rh) \, . \, dr \qquad [q_r = q(a + rh)]$$

$$= h\int_{r=0}^{r=1} \left[q_0 + r\Delta q_0 + \frac{1}{2!} r(r-1)\Delta^2 q_0 \right.$$
$$\left. + \frac{1}{3!} r(r-1)(r-2)\Delta^3 q_0 + \cdots \right]$$

$$\doteqdot h\left[q_0 + \frac{1}{2}\Delta q_0 - \frac{1}{12}\Delta^2 q_0 + \frac{1}{24}\Delta^3 q_0 - \frac{1}{40}\Delta^4 q_0 \right]$$

$$\text{Error } \frac{h}{720}\Delta^4 q_0.$$

Correction Process.

1. Using the formula last found for $y_1 - y_0$, correct y_1 to $(y_1)_1$ and substitute $(y_1)_1$ in the differential equation, thus obtaining a corrected value of q_1, say, $(q_1)_1$.

2. Simpson's rule is now applied to correct y_2.

Thus $\quad (y_2)_1 = y_0 + \dfrac{1}{3}h[q_2 + 4(q_1)_1 + q_0]$.

$$= y_0 + h\left[2(q_1)_1 + \frac{1}{3}(\Delta^2 q_0)_1 \right]. \quad \text{Error } \frac{h}{90}\Delta^4 q_0.$$

From this value of $(y_2)_1$ the corrected value $(q_2)_1$ is obtained. Clearly, if $\frac{1}{3}h[(q_2)_1 - q_2]$ affects the accuracy required in y, this quantity should be added to $(y_2)_1$ as a correction, and $(q_2)_2$ should also be calculated before proceeding.

3. The process described in (2) is repeated for the remaining values y_3 and y_4, so that a complete set of corrected values of y and q are available. These values should themselves be corrected as above, if upon applying Simpson's rule to checking, say, $(y_3)_1 - (y_1)_1$, the correction necessitated in $(y_3)_1$ affects the required accuracy in y. This will only be necessary when the initial values are of a comparatively low degree of accuracy, such as may result from using Euler's process. An example is now given showing the application of the above method.

Example.—On p. 94 the differential equation

$$\frac{dy}{dx} = y + x^2 \text{ subject to } \begin{matrix} x = 0 \\ y = 1 \end{matrix}$$

is integrated by the modified process of Euler, using intervals of 0·1 in x. The results are given below, and the difference table of the q's is formed.

x.	y.	$q = \dfrac{dy}{dx}$.	Δ.	Δ^2.	Δ^3.	Δ^4.
0	1	1				
			1158			
0·1	1·1058	1·1158		332		
			1490		36	
0·2	1·2248	1·2648		368		2
			1858		38	
0·3	1·3606	1·4506		406		
			2264			
0·4	1·5170	1·6770				

Using

$(y_1)_1 - y_0 = h[q_0 + \frac{1}{2}\Delta q_0 - \frac{1}{12}\Delta^2 q_0 + \frac{1}{24}\Delta^3 q_0 - \frac{1}{40}\Delta^4 q_0]$

$(y_1)_1 - y_0 = 0\cdot10553$

$\underline{(y_1)_1 \qquad = 1\cdot10553}$ and therefore $\underline{(q_1)_1 = 1\cdot11553.}$

Again,

$$(y_2)_1 = y_0 + \tfrac{1}{3}h[q_2 + 4(q_1)_1 + q_0] = y_0 + h[2(q_1)_1 + \tfrac{1}{3}\Delta^2 q_0]$$
$$(y_2)_1 = 1\cdot22423 \text{ and } (q_2)_1 = 1\cdot26423.$$

But

$$(y_2)_2 = (y_2)_1 + \tfrac{1}{3}h[(q_2)_1 - q_2]$$
$$= -0\cdot00002$$

therefore

$$\underline{(y_2)_2 = 1\cdot22421} \text{ and } \underline{(q_2)_2 = 1\cdot26421}.$$

These corrected values of the y's and q's are used in determining y_3 and y_4, and it is found that the values of y and q finally obtained using one correction only are all correct to the fourth decimal place. Greater accuracy may be obtained by the process up to the point at which $\dfrac{h}{90}\Delta^4 q$ can no longer be neglected.

CHAPTER IV

FORWARD INTEGRATION OF FIRST-ORDER EQUATIONS

11. Forward integration of first-order equations.

When the methods described in Chapter I become too laborious over a wide range of integration, for reasons already discussed, it becomes necessary to devise methods which will enable an integration which is begun by one of the methods of Chapter III to be continued with a reasonable amount of labour. These methods should maintain a specified degree of accuracy, and provide systematic checking and correcting processes. When a number of values of a continuous function having continuous derivatives over a certain range have been determined, then, upon the assumption that a polynomial function of x (the independent variable) can be found to represent this function over the given range, this polynomial may be used to extrapolate a value a little beyond the given range. When this approximate function value has been extrapolated, then it may be used to enable more accurate estimates of the function value to be made by using the differential equation in the sequence form

$$\left(\frac{dy}{dx}\right)_{n+1} = f(x, y_n)$$

in which y_n is the approximate extrapolated value.

Such is the basis of the methods used in the present chapter. The convergence of the above sequence is discussed in the general case on p. 38.

The methods to be described in this section include those already described in the last section as an essential part of the complete process of integration. The processes have been systematised so that the integrations may be carried out as simply as possible, and the numerical examples have been fully described. Comparison of the methods is carried out at the end of the chapter, when it is felt it will have more value.

Attention is drawn to the following important considerations which critically affect the successful application of these methods.

11.1. Accuracy of tabulated values.

If the integration is required over a wide range correct to a number of significant figures, then two more figures should be retained in the table. When the range is not too great, one more significant figure than the number required may be retained. Since in the integrations the values of $\dfrac{dy}{dx}$ and $\dfrac{d^2y}{dx^2}$ used in determining y are multiplied by small coefficients, the accuracy of the entries in these tables need not in general be equal to those in the y table. Actual experience of the influence of the last figures retained on the integration will soon indicate which final figures are redundant.

11.2. The magnitude of the increment in x.

General experience has shown that it is better to keep the increment in x small, and thus simplify the formulæ of integration, than to use more elaborate formulæ with larger increments. The accuracy of difference formulæ for the increment in y corresponding to a given increment in x increases rapidly as the increment in x is diminished, and when processes of successive approximation are used this usually means that the utmost accuracy is obtained from the formulæ in a small number of steps. The rapid convergence of the successive approximations is very effective in reducing the amount of labour, and is therefore of considerable importance.

11.3. Checking processes.

No method of integrating a differential equation is complete unless at each stage of the integration the calculations involve a process of checking which allows the integration to be carried on with absolute confidence in the correctness of the previous calculations.

Where no check is provided in the systematic integration, a check should be devised. Herein lies a great advantage possessed by difference methods.

The regular way in which differences of higher orders change during an integration is of extreme value in checking the accuracy of calculations. An irregularity in higher differences indicates the presence of an error almost unfailingly, and the stage at which the error entered the calculations. To see the way in which an error introduced into the column of y's affects the difference table, examine the table below :—

a_0	Δ	Δ^2	Δ^3	Δ^4	Δ^5
					ϵ
a_1				$+\ \epsilon$	
			ϵ		$-\ 5\epsilon$
a_2		ϵ		$-\ 4\epsilon$	
	$+\ \epsilon$		$-\ 3\epsilon$		$+\ 10\epsilon$
$(a_3 + \epsilon)$		$-\ 2\epsilon$		$+\ 6\epsilon$	
	$-\ \epsilon$		3ϵ		$-\ 10\epsilon$
a_4		$+\ \epsilon$		$-\ 4\epsilon$	
			$-\ \epsilon$		$+\ 5\epsilon$
a_5				$+\ \epsilon$	

Only the error term itself is entered in the table, from which it is seen that the error in the table oscillates more violently as it passes into the higher difference terms and is greatest along the central difference terms through the entry which is in error. In many cases it is worth while calculating higher differences when not required for the actual integration, solely as a check. Processes of successive approximation are also of great value in checking previous calculations, for the corrections, especially the small corrections, usually change very slowly, and a slight irregularity is at once detected. The convergence of the successive approximations should be arranged to be as rapid as possible by altering the increment in x, and in this way calculations which would otherwise be necessary as a check become part of the actual process of integration.

11.4. Estimation of the total error over the range of integration.

The estimation of the total error over a range of integration is naturally of the greatest importance, and in some of the examples this has been done to indicate the accuracy to be expected of such an estimate. The method adopted is to take the first error term and sum this up over the range of integration. This estimate should be doubled at least, as a safety-first precaution, and as the integration proceeds its value can be re-estimated with greater accuracy and the increment in x decreased if there is any possibility of the required accuracy not being maintained in the final values of y.

11.5. Changing the increment in x.

When the increment in y decreases during an integration the accuracy may be maintained with a larger increment in x, and if the increment in y increases, it may be necessary to decrease the increment in x to maintain the same degree of accuracy. For purposes of decreasing or increasing the increment in x it has been found necessary to use the interpolation formula

$$q_{\frac{1}{2}} = \tfrac{1}{2}(q_0 + q_1) - \tfrac{1}{16}(\Delta^2 q_0 + \Delta^2 q_1) + \tfrac{3}{256}(\Delta^4 q_{-1} + \Delta^4 q_{-2}).$$

The process of adding interpolated values between pairs of known values must be carried out with accuracy at least equal to that of the entries used for the purpose. When the interval is to be reduced, halving the interval is usually enough, although halving again may be carried out if necessary. For increasing the interval, no interpolation is needed for doubling the interval, and inserting an interpolated value after every two entries enables $2\frac{1}{2}$ times the interval to be used.

11.6. Starting the integration.

The methods of starting the integration which have already been described are available. The number of values calculated in this way varies between three and five, according to the method of forward integration adopted. In general, it is better to start the integration with a reserve of accuracy, and this may mean using an increment in x for the first few values, smaller than it is necessary to use in the subsequent forward integration.

The methods of increasing the size of the increment described in the last paragraph find an important application at this stage of the integration. If one of the methods of integration is used which requires only three function values to allow the forward integration to be begun, these initial values must be found to the final specified accuracy. Where five initial values are required, these can be corrected to the desired accuracy by processes to be described, and therefore their initial values need not attain the final accuracy desired.

12.0. METHOD I. Integration of differential equations of the first-order by the method of Bashforth and Adams.

Let the differential equation to be integrated be written in the form

$$\frac{dy}{dx} = f(x, y) \quad . \quad . \quad . \quad . \quad (1)$$

subject to the condition that when $x = x_0$ $y = y_0$. Let

(x, y) in the first instance be a point in the neighbourhood of (x_0, y_0), then it is known that a solution of the above equation may be expressed in the form

$$y - y_0 = (x - x_0)\left(\frac{dy}{dx}\right)_0 + \frac{1}{2!}(x - x_0)^2\left(\frac{d^2y}{dx^2}\right)_0$$
$$+ \frac{1}{3!}(x - x_0)^3\left(\frac{d^3y}{dx^3}\right)_0 + \ldots \quad \ldots \quad (1.1)$$

where the differential coefficients are calculated at (x_0, y_0). In the immediate neighbourhood of (x_0, y_0) the expansion (1.1) will in general be convergent, but as $x - x_0$ increases the rapidity of convergence decreases, and more and more terms in this expansion will be required to maintain a given accuracy in the solution.   Let us suppose that the accuracy of the required solution is definitely specified in advance, e.g., a solution may be required to 7 decimal places.   Further, suppose an expansion (1.1) has been found, carried just far enough for the labour in the computation to be bearable. From an examination of the magnitude of the final term used in this expansion it is possible to specify the range of x beyond x_0 for which this expansion provides a solution within the degree of accuracy required.   Suppose this range be subdivided, so that $x_{max} = x_0 + 4h$, where h is the step to be taken in x, thus dividing the range into four equal steps.

By calculation at the points $x_0 + h$, $x_0 + 2h$, $x_0 + 3h$, $x_0 + 4h$ in equation (1.1) the values y_1, y_2, y_3, and y_4 are determined, and thus we may say that the equation has been integrated over this small region.   The Adams–Bashforth method proposes to estimate the next value of y by extrapolation.   This is done in the following manner.

The values of $h\frac{dy}{dx}(= q)$ at the points x_0, x_1, etc., are available, and can be calculated by substituting (x_0, y_0), (x_1, y_1), etc., in equation (1), thus giving q_0, q_1, q_2, q_3, and q_4.   With the usual notation of finite differences we have

$$E - \Delta = 1$$
$$E^r = [E/(E - \Delta)]^r = [(E - \Delta)/E]^{-r}$$
$$= [1 - \Delta E^{-1}]^{-r}$$

Now $\quad E^r q_n = q_{n+r}$

thus $\quad q_{n+r} = [1 - \Delta E^{-1}]^{-r} \cdot q_n$

Again

$$[1 - \Delta E^{-1}]^{-r} = 1 + r\Delta E^{-1} + \frac{1}{2!} r(r+1)\Delta^2 \cdot E^{-2} + \cdots$$

therefore

$$q_{n+r} = q_n + r\Delta q_{n-1} + \frac{1}{2!} r(r+1)\Delta^2 \cdot q_{n-2} + \cdots$$

where r is any number.

Now $y_{n+1} - y_n = y(x_0 + (n+1)h) - y(x_0 + nh)$

$$= \int_{x_0 + nh}^{x_0 + (n+1)h} \frac{dy}{dx} \cdot dx$$

$$= h^{-1}\int_{x_0 + nh}^{x_0 + (n+1)h} q(x) \cdot dx.$$

If we change the variable in this integral from x to r, such that

$$x = x_0 + (n + r) \cdot h$$
$$dx = h \cdot dr.$$

Then $y_{n+1} - y_n = h^{-1}\int_0^1 q_{n+r} \cdot h dr, \quad \left[q_{n+r} = h\left(\frac{dy}{dx}\right)_{x_0 + (n+r)h} \right]$

$$= \int_0^1 q_{n+r} \cdot dr$$

$$= \int_0^1 dr\left[q_n + r\Delta q_{n-1} + \frac{r(r+1)}{2!} \Delta^2 q_{n-2} + \cdots \right]$$

The numbers q_n, Δq_{n-1}, etc., are independent of r, and consequently

$$y_{n+1} - y_n = q_n + \tfrac{1}{2}\Delta q_{n-1} + \tfrac{5}{12}\Delta^2 q_{n-2} + \tfrac{3}{8}\Delta^3 q_{n-3}$$
$$+ \tfrac{251}{720}\Delta^4 q_{n-4} + \cdots \cdots \quad (1.3)$$

This formula can be used to obtain y_{n+1} if y_n, q_n, Δq_{n-1}, etc., are determined. It will be shown presently how these latter quantities may be systematically calculated. Applying the result (1.3) to the case which is being considered

$$y_5 - y_4 = q_4 + \tfrac{1}{2}\Delta q_3 + \tfrac{5}{12}\Delta^2 q_2 + \tfrac{3}{8}\Delta^3 q_1 + \tfrac{251}{720}\Delta^4 q_0 + \ldots (1.4)$$

In the present circumstances the last term on the right-hand side is the last term available from the values already calculated. The error introduced by breaking off at this fourth difference is of the order $\tfrac{1}{5}\Delta^5 q_{-1}$, which can if necessary easily be estimated. y_5 is obtained by using equation (1.4), and by substituting in the differential equation, q_5 is found, and hence the next step to y can be made. Proceeding in this way, succeeding values of y_6 may be found. The accuracy will, of course, tend to diminish as the number of steps increases.

The following table indicates the method of tabulating the results and forming the required coefficients.

x_0	y_0	q_0				
			Δq_0			
x_1	y_1	q_1		$\Delta^2 q_0$		
			Δq_1		$\Delta^3 q_0$	
x_2	y_2	q_2		$\Delta^2 q_1$		$\Delta^4 q_0$
			Δq_2		$\Delta^3 q_1$	
x_3	y_3	q_3		$\Delta^2 q_2$		
			Δq_3			
x_4	y_4	q_4				
x_5	y_5	by extrapolation.				

Example.—Let

$$x \frac{dy}{dx} = x - y$$

be the differential equation. Given that when $x = 2$, $y = 2$, it is required to find a solution of the equation in the range of $2 \leq x \leq 2.5$, to four places of decimals.

Let the region be divided into ten equal parts :

$$x_0, \, x_0 + h, \, \ldots \, x_0 + 10h.$$

Then
$$x_0 = 2$$
$$h = 0.05.$$

The values of y corresponding to x equal to 2, 2·05, 2·1, 2·15, 2·2, . . . 2·5 are required.

Expanding y in the neighbourhood of $x = 2$

$$y = y_0 + (x - 2)y_0' + \frac{1}{2!}(x - 2)^2 \cdot y_0'' + \frac{1}{3!}(x - 2)^3 y_0''' +$$

where y_0, y_0', etc., are the values of y, $\frac{dy}{dx}$, etc., at $x = 2$.

$$y_0' = [(x - y)/x]_{(x=2, y=2)} = 0$$
$$y'' = (y/x^2) - (y'/x) = (2y - x)/x^2, \qquad \underline{y_0'' = \tfrac{1}{2}}$$
$$y''' = \{x^2(2y' - 1) - (2y - x) \cdot 2x\}/x^4$$
$$ = 3(x - 2y)/x^4, \qquad \underline{y_0''' = -\tfrac{3}{4}}$$
$$y^{\mathrm{iv}} = -12(x - 2y)/x^4, \qquad \underline{y_0^{\mathrm{iv}} = \tfrac{3}{2}}$$
$$y^{\mathrm{v}} = 60(x - 2y)/x^5, \qquad \underline{y_0^{\mathrm{v}} = -3\tfrac{3}{4}}$$
$$y^{\mathrm{vi}} = -360(x - 2y)/x^6 \qquad \underline{y_0^{\mathrm{vi}} = +11\tfrac{1}{4}}$$

Thus

$$y = y_0 + (x - 2) \cdot 0 + \tfrac{1}{4}(x - 2)^2 - \tfrac{1}{8}(x - 2)^3 + \tfrac{1}{16}(x - 2)^4 +$$
$$- \tfrac{1}{32}(x - 2)^5 + \ldots \ldots \quad (a)$$

From series (a) it is required to find y_0, y_1, y_2, y_3, and y_4 and therefore the greatest numerical value of the term

$$-\tfrac{1}{32}(x - 2)^5 \quad \text{is} \quad -\tfrac{1}{32}(0 \cdot 2)^5 = -0 \cdot 00001$$

and of $\quad +\tfrac{1}{64}(x - 2)^6 \quad$ is $\quad +\tfrac{1}{64}(0 \cdot 2)^6 = +0 \cdot 000001$.

Since the terms in the series are alternately positive and negative, it follows that the values of y from series (a) will be correct to the fifth decimal place.

The values of y calculated in this way are $y_1 = 2 \cdot 00061$, $y_2 = 2 \cdot 00248$, $y_3 = 2 \cdot 00523$, $y_4 = 2 \cdot 00909$.

From the differential equation

$$h \cdot y^{\mathrm{I}} = q = h\left(1 - \frac{y}{x}\right)$$
$$q_n = 0 \cdot 05\{1 - (y_n/x_n)\}$$

Using this equation

$y_0 = 2$	$q_0 = 0 \cdot 00000$			
		$\Delta q_0 = 0 \cdot 00120$		
$y_1 = 2 \cdot 00061$	$q_1 = 0 \cdot 00120$		$\Delta^2 q_0 = -0 \cdot 00008$	
		$\Delta q_1 = 0 \cdot 00112$		$\Delta^3 q_0 = +0 \cdot 00001$
$y_2 = 2 \cdot 00238$	$q_2 = 0 \cdot 00232$		$\Delta^2 q_1 = -0 \cdot 00007$	$\Delta^4 q_0 = -0 \cdot 00002$
		$\Delta q_2 = 0 \cdot 00105$		$\Delta^3 q_1 = -0 \cdot 00001$
$y_3 = 2 \cdot 00523$	$q_3 = 0 \cdot 00337$		$\Delta^2 q_2 = -0 \cdot 00008$	
		$\Delta q_3 = 0 \cdot 00097$		$\Delta^3 q_2 \quad +0 \cdot 00002$
$y_4 = 2 \cdot 00909$	$q_4 = 0 \cdot 00434$		$\Delta^2 q_3 = -0 \cdot 00006$	
		$\Delta q_4 = 0 \cdot 00091$		
	$q_5 = 0 \cdot 00525$			

From the above table it is clear that the second differences of q are nearly constant, and therefore the third and fourth differences should be taken as zero to the fifth decimal place.

Now

$$y_{n+1} - y_n = q_n + \tfrac{1}{2}\Delta q_{n-1} + \tfrac{5}{12}\Delta^2 q_{n-2} + \tfrac{3}{8}\Delta^3 q_{n-3}$$
$$+ \tfrac{251}{720}\Delta^4 q_{n-4} + \cdots$$
$$y_5 = y_4 + q_4 + \tfrac{1}{2}\Delta q_3 + \tfrac{5}{12}\Delta^2 q_2 + \tfrac{3}{8}\Delta^3 q_1$$
$$+ \tfrac{251}{720}\Delta^4 q_0 + \cdots$$
$$= 2\cdot00909 + 0\cdot00434 + \tfrac{1}{2}(0\cdot00097) + \tfrac{5}{12}(-0\cdot00008)$$
$$= 2\cdot00909$$
$$0\cdot00434$$
$$0\cdot000485$$

$$\overline{}$$
$$2\cdot013915$$
$$0\cdot000033$$

$$\overline{}$$
$$= 2\cdot01388$$

This now enables us to calculate

$$q_5 = 0\cdot05[1 - y_5/x_5]$$
$$= 0\cdot05[1 - 2\cdot01388/2\cdot25]$$
$$= 0\cdot00525$$
$$y_6 = y_5 + q_5 + \tfrac{1}{2}\Delta q_4 + \tfrac{5}{12}\Delta^2 q_3 + \cdots$$
$$= 2\cdot01388 + 0\cdot00525 + 0\cdot000455 + (-0\cdot000025)$$
$$0\cdot00525$$
$$0\cdot00043$$

$$\overline{}$$
$$= 2\cdot01956$$

Proceeding as above, the following table shows the final results.

y	Error			
		$q_4 = 0\cdot00434$		
			$\Delta q_4 = 0\cdot00091$	
$y_5 = 2\cdot01388$	$-0\cdot00001$	$q_5 = 0\cdot00525$		$\Delta^2 q_4 = -0\cdot00006$
			$\Delta q_5 = 0\cdot00085$	
$y_6 = 2\cdot01956$	$-0\cdot00001$	$q_6 = 0\cdot00610$		$\Delta^2 q_5 = -0\cdot00006$
			$\Delta q_6 = 0\cdot00079$	
$y_7 = 2\cdot02606$	$-0\cdot00001$	$q_7 = 0\cdot00689$		$\Delta^2 q_6 = -0\cdot00004$
			$\Delta q_7 = 0\cdot00075$	
$y_8 = 2\cdot03332$	$-0\cdot00001$	$q_8 = 0\cdot00764$		$\Delta^2 q_7 = -0\cdot00005$
			$\Delta q_8 = 0\cdot00070$	
$y_9 = 2\cdot04132$	$-0\cdot00001$	$q_9 = 0\cdot00834$		
$y_{10} = 2\cdot04999$	$-0\cdot00001$			

The constancy of the error indicates that the method maintains the accuracy of the value of y at which the Adams–Bashforth method was applied. Greater accuracy may be obtained by taking the first calculations for y_0, y_1, y_2, etc., to a higher degree of accuracy, and if the second differences are not constant to this accuracy, the terms with the higher differences should be taken into account.

The complete solution of the equation

$$x \frac{dy}{dx} = x - y$$

where $x = 2$ when $y = 2$ is

$$y = \frac{x}{2} + \frac{2}{x}.$$

When $x = 2\cdot5 \qquad y = 2\cdot05$
which compares with $\qquad y = 2\cdot04999$.

Checking the integration.

The above process is the complete Adams–Bashforth process. Checking the process is only possible by repetition of calculations or by depending upon the regularity of the fourth difference column. An added check, however, which is applied in methods about to be described is to use the formula

$$y_n - y_{n-1} = h[q_n - \tfrac{1}{2}\Delta q_{n-1} - \tfrac{1}{12}\Delta^2 q_{n-2} - \tfrac{1}{24}\Delta^3 q_{n-3} - \tfrac{1}{36}\Delta^4 q_{n-4}]$$

to check Δy_{n-1} before proceeding to the evaluation of y_{n+1}. The error term in this formula may be taken as

$$- \frac{h}{3}\Delta^5 q_{n-5} + \frac{h}{720}\Delta^4 q_{n-4}.$$

Examples.—Use the Adams–Bashforth method to obtain the solutions correct to four decimal places of the following equations for the ranges indicated :—

1. $\dfrac{dy}{dx} = \dfrac{x-y}{x+y}$, where $x = 0$, $y = 1$; $\qquad$ range $0 < x < 0\cdot25$.

2. $\dfrac{dy}{dx} = \dfrac{x^2 + y^2}{x + y}$, where $x = 0$, $y = 0$;   range $0 < x < 0\cdot5$.

3. $\dfrac{dy}{dx} = x^2 + y^2 - 1$, where $x = 0$, $y = 0$;   range $0 < x < 0\cdot2$

4. $\dfrac{dy}{dx} = \dfrac{x}{y} + \dfrac{y}{x}$, where $x = 1$, $y = 0\cdot5$;   range $1 < x < 1\cdot25$.

12.01. METHOD II. A method of successive approximation by finite differences using initial values found by the modified method of Euler.

It has been shown that any function and its derivatives continuous over a certain range may be approximately represented over that range by polynomial functions of its argument. The formula we propose to consider is that corresponding to Newton's backward formula. Thus, if q_x represent the derivative of the functional argument, then

$$q_x = q_0 + x\Delta q_{-1} + \frac{1}{2\,!}\, x(x + 1)\Delta^2 q_{-2}$$
$$+ \frac{1}{3\,!}\, x(x + 1)(x + 2)\Delta^3 q_{-3} + \ldots \quad (1)$$

in which

$$q_x = \left(\frac{dy}{d(xh)}\right)_{a + xh}$$

The increment in y over the range $x = 0$ to $x = 1$ is given by

$$\int_0^1 q_x d(xh).$$

Thus

$$\Delta y_1 = \int_0^1 q_x \cdot d(xh)$$
$$= h\Big[q_0 x + \frac{1}{2}\, x^2 \cdot \Delta q_{-1} + \frac{1}{2\,!}\Big(\frac{x^3}{3} + \frac{x^2}{2}\Big)\Delta^2 q_{-2}$$
$$+ \frac{1}{3\,!}\Big(\frac{x^4}{4} + x^3 + x^2\Big)\Delta^3 q_{-3}$$
$$+ \frac{1}{24}\Big(\frac{x^5}{5} + \frac{3}{2}\, x^4 + \frac{11}{3}\, x^3 + 3x^3\Big) \times \Delta^4 q_{-4} + \ldots \Big]_0^1$$
$$= h\big(q_0 + \tfrac{1}{2}\Delta q_{-1} + \tfrac{5}{12}\Delta^2 q_{-2} + \tfrac{3}{8}\Delta^3 q_{-3}$$
$$+ \tfrac{251}{720}\Delta^4 q_{-4} + \ldots \big) \quad . \quad . \quad (2)$$

Similarly

$$\Delta y_{-1} = h(q_0 - \tfrac{1}{2}\Delta q_{-1} - \tfrac{1}{12}\Delta^2 q_{-2} - \tfrac{1}{24}\Delta^3 q_{-3}$$
$$- \tfrac{19}{720}\Delta^4 q_{-4} - \ldots) \quad . \quad . \quad (2.1)$$

First error term is $\tfrac{1}{3}h\Delta^5 q_{-5}$.

$$\Delta y_{-2} = h(q_0 - \tfrac{3}{2}\Delta q_{-1} + \tfrac{5}{12}\Delta^2 q_{-2} + \tfrac{1}{24}\Delta^3 q_{-3}$$
$$+ \tfrac{11}{720}\Delta^4 q_{-4} + \ldots) \quad . \quad . \quad (2.2)$$

$$\Delta y_{-3} = h(q_0 - \tfrac{5}{2}\Delta q_{-1} + \tfrac{23}{12}\Delta^2 q_{-2} - \tfrac{3}{8}\Delta^3 q_{-3}$$
$$- \tfrac{19}{720}\Delta^4 q_{-4} - \ldots) \quad . \quad . \quad (2.3)$$

$$\Delta y_{-4} = h(q_0 - \tfrac{7}{2}\Delta q_{-1} + \tfrac{53}{12}\Delta^2 q_{-2} - \tfrac{55}{24}\Delta^3 q_{-3}$$
$$+ \tfrac{251}{720}\Delta^4 q_{-4} + \ldots) \quad . \quad . \quad (2.4)$$

In which

$$\Delta y_{-r} = \int_{-r}^{-(r-1)} q_x d(xh).$$

Similarly

$$\int_{-1}^{+1} q_x d(xh) = h[2q_0 + \tfrac{1}{3}(\Delta^2 q_{-2} + \Delta^3 q_{-3} + \Delta^4 q_{-4} + \ldots)] \quad (2.5)$$

$$\int_{-2}^{0} q_x . d(xh) = 2h[q_0 - \Delta q_{-1} + \tfrac{1}{6}\Delta^2 q_{-2} - \tfrac{1}{180}\Delta^4 q_{-4} \ldots] \quad (2.6)$$

The formulæ (1) to (2·6) are expressed in differences of the derivative of values of the function that proceed backwards, thus requiring only previously calculated derivatives for their determination.

Formulæ (2) and (2.5) are used for integrating ahead, while the remainder are valuable as check formulæ; especially is this so with formula (2.1), which checks the integration ahead effected by formula (2), and formula (2.6), which checks two consecutive intervals. The formulæ (2.2), (2.3), and (2.4) are in general used only for checking the initial values calculated before integration by finite differences is begun.

An example already examined will be continued by the above method.

Example.—In the example p. 94 the following results are obtained :—

x.	y.	q.	Δq.	$\Delta^2 q$.	$\Delta^3 q$.	$\Delta^4 q$.
0	1	1				
			0·1158			
0·1	1·1058	1·1158		332		
			0·1490		36	
0·2	1·2248	1·2648		368		2
			0·1858		38	
0·3	1·3606	1·4506		406		
			0·2264			
0·4	1·5170	1·6770				

Using formula (2.4)

$$\Delta y_{-4} = 0 \cdot 1[1 \cdot 6770 - \tfrac{7}{2} \times 0 \cdot 2264 + \tfrac{53}{12} \times 0 \cdot 0406$$
$$- \tfrac{55}{12} \times 0 \cdot 0038 + \tfrac{251}{720} \times 0 \cdot 0002]$$
$$= 0 \cdot 1055$$

Using formula (2.3)

$$\Delta y_{-3} = 0 \cdot 1[1 \cdot 6770 - \tfrac{5}{2} \times 0 \cdot 2264 + \tfrac{23}{12} \times 0 \cdot 0406$$
$$- \tfrac{3}{8} \times 0 \cdot 0038 - \tfrac{19}{720} \times 0 \cdot 0002]$$
$$= 0 \cdot 1187$$

Using formula (2.2)

$$\Delta y_{-2} = 0 \cdot 1[1 \cdot 6770 - \tfrac{3}{2} \times 0 \cdot 2264 + \tfrac{5}{12} \times 0 \cdot 0406$$
$$+ \tfrac{1}{24} \times 0 \cdot 0038 + \tfrac{11}{720} \times 0 \cdot 0002]$$
$$= 0 \cdot 1354$$

Using formula (2.1)

$$\Delta y_{-1} = 0 \cdot 1[1 \cdot 6770 - \tfrac{1}{2} \times 0 \cdot 2264 - \tfrac{1}{12} \times 0 \cdot 0406$$
$$- \tfrac{1}{24} \times 0 \cdot 0038 - \tfrac{19}{720} \times 0 \cdot 0002]$$
$$= 0 \cdot 1560.$$

The corrected values of y are therefore

y.	q.	Δq.	$\Delta^2 q$.	$\Delta^3 q$.	$\Delta^4 q$.
1	1				
1·1055	1·1155	1155			
1·2242	1·2642	1487	332		
1·3596	1·4492	1854	367	35	
1·5156	1·6756	2260	406	39	4

When these values are again checked by the previous process, all are found correct except the last value, which corresponds to an increment of 0·1559 instead of 0·1560. Making this change, the table is now ready to be augmented by integrating ahead using formula (2). The values are inserted in the table correct to four decimal places, but it is advisable to keep five decimal places, in order that there shall be no doubt about the fourth place.

Estimate of total error.

Taking the first error term as $\frac{h}{3}\Delta^5 q_{-5}$,* the total error estimated after the first integration ahead is clearly too small to affect the accuracy required.

x.	y.	q.	Δq.	$\Delta^2 q$.	$\Delta^3 q$.	$\Delta^4 q$.
0·4	1·5155	1·6755	2259	405	38	3
0·5	1·6962	1·9462	2707	448	43	5
0·6	1·9064	2·2664	3202	495	47	4
0·7	2·1513	2·6413	3749	547	52	5
0·8	2·4366	3·0766	4353	604	57	5
0·9	2·7688	3·5788	5022	669	65	8
1·0	3·1548	4·1548	5760	738	69	4

By formula (2)

$$\Delta y_4 = 0\cdot1[1\cdot6755 + \tfrac{1}{2} \times 0\cdot2259 + \tfrac{5}{12} \times 0\cdot0405$$
$$+ \tfrac{3}{8} \times 0\cdot0038 + \tfrac{251}{720} \times 0\cdot0003]$$
$$= 0\cdot18068.$$

The new value of y, viz. y_5, is now calculated by adding 0·18068 to y_4, and the new line of differences is constructed for q, having first determined q_5 from the differential equation.

Thus $q_5 = y_5 + x_5{}^2 = 1\cdot6962 + 0\cdot25 = \underline{1\cdot9462}.$

* There is also a term $+ \dfrac{h}{720}\Delta^4 q_{-4}$, but in general this is much smaller than the term quoted.

Using formula (2.1) to check y_5

$$\Delta y_4 = 0 \cdot 1[1 \cdot 9462 - 0 \cdot 013535 - 0 \cdot 000373 - 0 \cdot 000018$$
$$- 0 \cdot 000001]$$
$$= 0 \cdot 18069 \text{ as compared with } 0 \cdot 18068.$$

There is therefore no correction necessary to y. Proceeding in the above manner, the table is completed up to $x = 1$. To check the accuracy of the last increment

$$\Delta y_{10} = 0 \cdot 1 \left[4 \cdot 158 - \tfrac{1}{2} \times 0 \cdot 5760 - \tfrac{1}{12} \times 0 \cdot 0738 \right.$$
$$\left. - \tfrac{1}{24} \times 0 \cdot 0069 - \tfrac{1}{36} \times 0 \cdot 0004\right]$$
$$= 0 \cdot 36804 \text{ as compared with } 0 \cdot 36803.$$

This is confirmation that the process is maintaining the necessary accuracy. The value $3 \cdot 1548$ of y when $x = 1$ is correct to the fourth decimal place.

12.02. METHOD III. **Complete integration of the differential equation** $\dfrac{dy}{dx} = f(x, y)$ **given initial values of** x **and** y.

(a) *Beginning the solution of* $\dfrac{dy}{dx} = f(x, y)$ *using Kutta's Simpson's rule.* Let five initial values of y and $q\left(= \dfrac{dy}{dx}\right)$ be obtained by integrating four times using Kutta's Simpson's rule. This means calculating the following functions,

$$\Delta' = f(x, y) \cdot \Delta x$$
$$\Delta'' = f(x + \tfrac{1}{2}\Delta x, y + \tfrac{1}{2}\Delta') \cdot \Delta x$$
$$\Delta''' = f(x + \tfrac{1}{2}\Delta x, y + \tfrac{1}{2}\Delta'') \cdot \Delta x$$
$$\Delta^{\mathrm{iv}} = f(x + \Delta x, y + \Delta''') \cdot \Delta x,$$

and substituting in the equation

$$(\Delta y)_1 = \tfrac{1}{6}(\Delta' + 2\Delta'' + 2\Delta''' + \Delta^{\mathrm{iv}}).$$

In this manner five initial values of y are derived, for which the error is at most of the order h^5. There remains only the fifth value of $q\left(= \dfrac{dy}{dx}\right)$ to be calculated to complete the five corresponding values of q, the previous four being already known. Now a very easily applied formula (see p. 108) may be used to check Δy_1 for

$$(\Delta y_1) = h(f_0 + \tfrac{1}{2}\Delta f_0 - \tfrac{1}{12}\Delta^2 f_0 + \tfrac{1}{24}\Delta^3 f_0 - \tfrac{1}{40}\Delta^4 f_0).$$

This formula is $\dfrac{h}{720}\Delta^4 f_0$ in error, so that it may be considered as correct to terms including fourth differences. Having checked and corrected y_1 and q_1, the remainder of the values may be corrected by applying the formula

$$
\begin{aligned}
y_n &= y_{n-2} + \tfrac{1}{3}h(q_{n-2} + 4q_{n-1} + q_n) \\
&= y_{n-2} + h(2q_{n-1} + \tfrac{1}{3}\Delta^2 q_{n-2})
\end{aligned}
$$

to successive overlapping intervals of $2h$. This formula is in error

$$\frac{h}{90}[\Delta^4 q_{n-2} - \Delta^5 q_{n-2}]$$

and may be taken in practice as correct to fifth differences. The value of y_1 may be checked a second time, if the first correction was found to be sufficient to affect the accuracy required, and, if necessary, the above process repeated. Five initial corresponding values of y and q are now determined, and the process of forward integration may be continued as described in the following example.

It may be noted that $y_0, y_1 \ldots y_4$ in this example are all correct to six decimal places. Hence, although the checking of the initial values is essential, no corrections were found to be necessary in this case. In general, the accuracy obtainable with Kutta's formula is much greater than may be deduced from the statement that the error is of order h^5 at most.

(b) *Forward integration. A new method.* The following difference method of continuing the integration of the differential equation

$$\frac{dy}{dx} = f(x, y)$$

has been designed to secure a minimum of labour for the high degree of accuracy which it achieves. The check which it provides in the calculations requires the use of one previously calculated quantity, and one other which is itself necessary for a subsequent step in the integration. It will be assumed that the early stage of the integration has been begun by one of the methods already outlined, and that this is of such accuracy as to involve fourth differences. Let the five corresponding values of y and q thus supposed known be

$$y_0, y_1, y_2, y_3, y_4 : q_0, q_1, q_2, q_3, q_4.$$

Consider the formula

$$(y_5)_1 = y_3 + h \cdot [2q_4 + \tfrac{1}{3}\Delta^2 q_0 + \Delta^3 q_1] \quad . \quad . \quad (3)$$

If this expression is expanded in q_3 and its differences, it will be found to err in excess by

$$\frac{h}{90}\Delta^4 q_3 - \frac{31h}{90} \cdot \Delta^5 q_3 . \quad . \quad . \quad . \quad (3.1)$$

It follows, therefore, that this formula will probably yield results in general correct to fourth differences. Should it be suspected that the term in fifth differences may have a greater importance than the term in fourth differences, the effect can be at once estimated by evaluating

$$(y_5)_2 = y_3 + h[2q_4 + \tfrac{1}{3}\Delta^2 q_3] . \quad . \quad . \quad (3.2)$$

This formula errs in excess by

$$\frac{h}{90}[\Delta^4 q_3 - \Delta^5 q_3] \quad . \quad . \quad . \quad . \quad (3.3)$$

The difference $(y_5)_2 - (y_5)_1$ is therefore a good measure of the term in fifth differences in (3.1). In (3.1) the terms will in general counteract each other's effect, but if either becomes sufficiently large to influence appreciably the accuracy required, then the interval h must be reduced. In this reduction of the magnitude of h finite differences provide a very convenient and rapid method. Thus, to interpolate a value of q between two values of q_0 and q_1, say—

$$q_{\frac{1}{2}} = \tfrac{1}{2}(q_0 + q_1) - \tfrac{1}{16}(\Delta^2 q_0 + \Delta^2 q_{-1}) + \tfrac{3}{256}(\Delta^4 q_{-1} + \Delta^4 q_{-2}) + \ldots$$

If the precautions indicated in the above account are taken, the required accuracy will be achieved without the rather tedious process of successive approximation. In the following problem the method is quite severely tested, and the results demonstrate the high degree of accuracy which the formula provides.

Example.—Integral of $\dfrac{dy}{dx} = y + x^2$ from $x = 0$ to $x = 2$, at intervals of 0·1, with the initial condition $x = 0, y = 1$. The difference table is a horizontal table, and the starred terms

$y.$	$2q.$	$q.$	$\Delta.$	$\Delta^2.$	$\Delta^3.$
1		1			
1·105513		1·115513	115,513		
1·224209		1·264209	148,696	33,183*	
				11,061	
1·359577		1·449577	185,368	36,672	3,489
				12,224	
1·515475	3·350950	1·675475	225,898	40,530	3,858*
				13,510	
1·696164	3·892328	1·946164	270,689	44,791	4,261
				14,930	
1·906356	4·532712	2·266356	320,192	49,503	4,712
				16,501	
2·151257	5·282514	2·641257	374,901	54,709	5,206
				18,236	
2·436621	6·153242	3·076621	435,364	60,463	5,754
				20,154	
2·768807	7·157614	3·578807	502,187	66,823	6,360
				22,274	
3·154842	8·309684	4·154842	576,035	73,848	7,025
				24,616	
3·602493	9·624986	4·812493	657,651	81,616	7,768
				27,205	
4·120345	11·120690	5·560345	747,852	90,201	8,585
				30,067	
4·717882	12·815764	6·407882	847,537	99,685	9,484
				33,228	
5·405590	14·731180	7·365590	957,708	110,171	10,486
				36,724	
6·195055	16·890110	8·445055	1,079,465	121,757	11,586
				40,586	
7·099082	19·318164	9·659082	1,214,027	134,562	12,805
				44,854	
8·131824	22·043648	11·021824	1,362,742	148,715	14,153
				49,572	
9·308921	25·097842	12·548921	1,527,097	164,355	15,640
10·647658	28·515316	14·257658	1,708,737	181,640	17,285
12·167138		16·167138	1,909,480	200,743	19,103

show the two difference terms to be taken together, and each second difference term is divided by 3 in the table. Any integration may be very rapidly checked by formula (3.2), before continuing the integration, in which case the check provides the second difference term two integrations ahead.

The final value 12·167138 should be 12·167167, whence the error at this stage is found to be 0·000029 in deficiency. This shows that the fifth differences have actually more than counterbalanced the fourth difference term in the expression (3.1). It will be seen that towards the end of the calculation the error term reaches a value of 0·000003 in deficiency. Just how long this error may be allowed to continue without diminishing the interval depends upon the accuracy required in the subsequent integration.

The method is, of course, applicable to simultaneous differential equations (p. 159), the procedure followed being similar in outline to that described in integrating a differential equation of the second order by resolving it into the equivalent simultaneous pair of first-order equations.

Estimation of total error.

The total error in using the formula (3) may be estimated by using the expression

$$E = \tfrac{1}{90}h \sum_{x=0}^{x=n-1} [\Delta^4 q_x - 28\Delta^5 q_x]$$

which is obtained from formula (3.1) by replacing q_3 by q_0.

Hence $\quad E = \tfrac{1}{90}h[(\Delta^3 q_n - \Delta^3 q_{-1}) - 28(\Delta^4 q_n - \Delta^4 q_{-1})]$

n is the number of integrations performed.

$\Delta^3 q_{-1}$ and $\Delta^4 q_{-1}$ are terms which must be estimated from the differences which begin with $x = 0$. In the table on the previous page $n = 15$ gives

$$\underset{x=0}{\overset{x=14}{E}} = \frac{0·1}{90}[(15{,}640 - 3154) - 28(1645 - 349)] \times 10^{-6}$$

$$= \frac{0·1}{90} \times 23{,}802 \times 10^{-6}$$

$$= \underline{26·4 \times 10^{-6}}.$$

If this is compared with 29×10^{-6}, the agreement will be found to be satisfactory.

Systematic method of integrating and correcting the approximation to the solution of $\dfrac{dy}{dx} = f(x, y)$.

It has been shown that the method of integration just described is capable, even without corrections, of giving very satisfactory results. It will now be shown that the extra labour involved in applying the correction, by using formula (3.2), is very small.

With the previous notation

$$(y_5)_1 = y_3 + h[2q_4 + (\tfrac{1}{3}\Delta^2 q_0 + \Delta^3 q_1)].$$

Let the term $\tfrac{1}{3}\Delta^2 q_0 + \Delta^3 q_1$ be set aside.

When this value of $(y_5)_1$ has been used in the differential equation to obtain $(q_5)_1$ this value may be used in the check formula

$$(y_5)_2 = y_3 + h[2q_4 + \tfrac{1}{3}\Delta^2 q_3].$$

Now $(y_5)_2 - (y_5)_1$ is the correction, and is given by

$$(y_5)_2 - (y_5)_1 = [\tfrac{1}{3}\Delta^2 q_3 - (\tfrac{1}{3}\Delta^2 q_0 + \Delta^3 q_1)] \cdot h.$$

But this latter correction is extremely easy to evaluate and is rapidly inserted. Again, as has already been pointed out, $\tfrac{1}{3}\Delta^2 q_3$ is available for subsequent integrations by formula (3). If it should be suspected that the correction of $(q_5)_1$ obtained by substituting $(y_5)_2$ in the differential, equation might influence the value of $(y_5)_2$ again by a second use of formula (3.2), then calculate $\tfrac{1}{3}h[(q_5)_2 - (q_5)_1]$, and if this affects the accuracy required in y, the correction should be made. This, however, is seldom required.

Examples.

1. Tabulate y at intervals of 0·05 in x to satisfy the equation

$$(1 + y^2)\frac{dy}{dx} = 1 + 2xy,$$

where $y = 1$ when $x = 0$; range $0 \leq x \leq 0.4$ correct to five significant figures.

2. Tabulate the solution of the equation

$$\frac{dy}{dx} + P \cdot y = Q$$

subject to $x = 0$, $y = 0$ at intervals of 0·1 in x for the range $0 < x < 1$ correct to four significant figures. P and Q are tabulated below.

x	0	0·1	0·2	0·3	0·4	0·5	0·6	0·7	0·8	0·9	1·0
P	0	0·0872	0·1736	0·2588	0·3420	0·4226	0·5000	0·5736	0·6428	0·7071	0·7660
Q	1	0·9962	0·9848	0·9659	0·9379	0·9063	0·8660	0·8192	0·7660	0·7071	0·6428

3. Tabulate the solution of the equation

$$\frac{dy}{dx} = 0{\cdot}1 \cdot y^2 + x^2$$

subject to $x = 0$, $y = 1$ at intervals of 0·05 in x for the range $0 < x < 0·5$ correct to five significant figures.

4. Tabulate y at intervals of 0·1 in x from $x = 0$ to $x = 1$ to satisfy the differential equation

$$\frac{dy}{dx} = x^2(y + 1)$$

subject to $x = 0$, $y = 1$.

Note.—Start the solution by applying Taylor's expansion or Picard's method to obtain the initial values.

12.03. METHOD IV.—A method of integrating the differential equation

$$\frac{dy}{dx} = f(x, y)$$

subject to $x = a$, $y = b$ by successive approximation.

Consider the equation

$$y_{r+1} = y_{r-1} + h[2q_r + \tfrac{1}{3}\Delta^2 q_{r-1}].$$

This equation has been shown to possess an error in excess given by

$$\frac{h}{90} [\Delta^4 q_{r-1} - \Delta^5 q_{r-1}].$$

If in the above equation $\Delta^2 q_{r-1}$ is replaced by $\Delta^2 q_{r-2}$, then the new equation

$$y_{r+1} = y_{r-1} + h[2q_r + \tfrac{1}{3}\Delta^2 q_{r-2}]$$

has a first error term of $\dfrac{h}{3}\Delta^3 q_{r-2}$, a term which is in general much greater than the first error term of the first equation. The latter equation gives an approximate value of y when the two previous values of y and the corresponding values of q are known. Hence to start the forward integration y_0, y_1, y_2, q_0, q_1, and q_2 may be determined, say by Taylor's expansion. In that only three initial values of y are required, the method has an advantage over that previously described, and especially so is this the case when initial values are troublesome to obtain.

Having calculated $(y_{r+1})_1$ this value substituted in the differential equation gives $(q_{r+1})_1$. If the latter value is used to determine $\Delta^2 q_{r-1}$, the first corrected value of $(y_{r+1})_2$ is obtained. This should be carried out by evaluating $\dfrac{h}{3}[(\Delta^2 q_{r-1})_1 - \Delta^2 q_{r-2}]$, and adding the result to $(y_{r+1})_1$. The second correction to y_{r+1} follows at once by adding $\dfrac{h}{3}[(\Delta^2 q_{r-1})_2 - (\Delta^2 q_{r-1})_1]$ _i.e._ $\dfrac{h}{3}[(q_{r+1})_2 - (q_{r+1})_1]$ to $(y_{r+1})_2$. The process should be repeated until it is clear that repetition does not add further to the accuracy required in y_{r+1}. The process of successive approximation is then ended. In practice the corrections can be made with considerable facility, and serve the purpose of checking previous calculations—an extremely important operation.

Example.—To demonstrate the process of integration, the following table contains the complete calculations for the integration of the equation

$$\frac{dy}{dx} = y + x^2$$

subject to $x = 0$, $y = 1$ over the range $x = 0$ to $x = 1$ all values to be correct to four decimal places.

$x.$	$y.$	$2qh.$	$q.$	$\Delta q.$	$\Delta^2 q.$	$\frac{1}{2}(\Delta^2 q_{r-1} - \Delta^2 q_{r-2}).$	$\frac{1}{2}[(\Delta^2 q_{r-1})_1 - (\Delta^2 q_{r-1})_1].$
0·0	1		1				
0·1	1·105513		1·115513	0·115513	33,183		
	0·2528418				11,061		
	0·0011061						
	1·359461		1				
0·2	1·224209	0·2528418	1·264209	0·148696	36,556		
	1·359461		1·449461	0·185252	12,185	1124	
	112						
	1·359573		1·449573	0·185364	36,668		
	4				12,223		38
0·3	1·359577	0·2899154	1·449577	0·185368	36,672		
	1·515347	12224	1·675347	0·225770	12,224		
	124	1·224209			40,402		
	1·515471	1·5153468	1·675471	0·225894	13,467	1243	
	4				40,526		41
					13,509		
0·4	1·515475	0·3350950	1·675475	0·225898	40,530		
	1·696023	13510	1·946023	0·270548	13,510		
	137	1·359577			44,650		
	160	1·6960230	160	685	14,883	1373	
	5				44,787		
					14,929		46
0·5	1·696165	0·3892339	1·946165	0·270690	44,792		
	1·906202	14931	2·266202	0·320037	14,931		
	152	1·515475			49,347		
	354	1·9062020	354	189	16,449	1518	
	5				49,499		
					16,500		51
0·6	1·906359	0·4532718	2·266359	0·320194	49,504		
	2·151087	16501	2·641087	0·374728	16,501		
	168	1·696165			54,534		
	255	2·1510869	255	896	18,178	1677	
	5				54,702		
					18,234		56
0·7	2·151261	0·5282521	2·641261	0·374902	54,708		
	2·436435	18236	3·076435	0·435174	18,236		
	185	1·906359			60,272		
	620	2·436435	620	359	20,091	1855	
	6				60,457		
					20,152		61
0·8	2·436626	0·6153252	3·076626	0·435635	60,463		
	2·768602	20154	3·578602	0·501976	20,154		
	205	2·151261			66,611		
	807	2·7686016	807	2181	22,204	2050	
	7				66,816		
					22,272		68
0·9	2·768814	0·7157628	3·578814	0·502188	66,823		
	3·154616	22274	4·154616	0·575802	22,274		
	226	2·436626			73 614		
	842	3·154616	842	6028	24,538	2264	
	8				73,840		
1·0	3·154850				24,613		75

In order to explain the entries in the table, one complete step in the integration is set out on the opposite page.

1. $(y_3)_1 = y_1 + h[2q_2 + \frac{1}{3}\Delta^2 q_0]$
   $= 1 \cdot 05513 + 0 \cdot 2528418 + 0 \cdot 0011061$
   $= \underline{1 \cdot 359461}$

2. $(y_3)_2 = (y_3)_1 + \frac{h}{3}[(\Delta^2 q_1)_1 - \Delta^2 q_0]$
   $= 1 \cdot 359461 + (0 \cdot 0012185 - 0 \cdot 0011061)$
   $= 1 \cdot 359461 + 0 \cdot 0001124$
   $= 1 \cdot 359573$

3. $(y_3)_3 = (y_3)_2 + \frac{h}{3}[(\Delta^2 q_1)_2 - (\Delta^2 q_1)_1]$
   $= (y_3)_2 + \frac{h}{3}[(q_3)_2 - (q_3)_1]$
   $= 1 \cdot 359573 + \frac{0 \cdot 1}{3}(1 \cdot 449573 - 1 \cdot 449461)$
   $= 1 \cdot 359573 + 0 \cdot 0000037$
   $= \underline{1 \cdot 359577}$

The next line of differences may now be added since a glance at the process shows that the next correction to y_3 amounts to

$$0 \cdot 0000038 \times \frac{0 \cdot 1}{3}$$

a value which is too small to affect the accuracy required in the value of y_3, and it is therefore not necessary to carry through the process again. The value of y_{10} is $3 \cdot 154850$, and this errs in excess by the amount $0 \cdot 000005$. Could this error have been estimated, and to what degree of accuracy ?

From the entries in the second difference column it is easy to see that

$$\frac{h}{90}\Delta^3 q_0$$
$$= \frac{0 \cdot 1}{90} \times 369.$$

Hence, supposing this error to be repeated at each step in eight steps, the total error is $0 \cdot 0000024$, which affords a rough estimate of the error to be expected, and therefore, if this is well within the accuracy desired, the integration may be continued over the given range with confidence.

12.1. METHOD V.—Alternative method of forward integration not requiring a difference table.

The following is yet another form of integration of the differential equation alternative to that of the preceding pages. Its special feature lies in the fact that no finite differences are necessary to perform the actual operations involved, but it is capable of yielding the same degree of accuracy as that of previous methods. It is moreover simple and rapid in operation, and a check upon the accuracy of the calculations is provided.

Suppose, as before, that five initial corresponding values of y and $q\left(=\dfrac{dy}{dx}\right)$ have been calculated. If these be y_0, y_1, y_2, y_3, y_4 and q_0, q_1, q_2, q_3, q_4 then

$$\begin{aligned}
q_5 &= E^5 q_0 \\
&= (1 + \Delta)^5 q_0 \\
&= q_0 + 5\Delta q_0 + 10\Delta^2 q_0 + 10\Delta^3 q_0 + 5\Delta^4 q_0 + \Delta^5 q_0.
\end{aligned}$$

Leave out the term that in Δ^5 and

$$q_5 = 5q_4 - 10q_3 + 10q_2 - 5q_1 + q_0 \quad . \quad . \quad (4)$$

This value of q is easily computed, and is correct to fourth differences. If this be now substituted in the equation

$$y_5 = y_3 + \tfrac{1}{3}h[q_5 + 4q_4 + q_3] \quad . \quad . \quad . \quad (4.1)$$

the value of y_5 will be in error by $\dfrac{h}{90}\Delta^4 q_0$.

Thus it may justifiably be considered correct to terms in h^5 with an error of the order h^6. If this value of y be now substituted in the differential equation, q_5 may be checked, and, if necessary, corrected, and the integration may proceed using the corrected value.

The method may be summarised as follows :

I. Evaluate

$$(q_5)_1 = \left[\left(q_0 + 10q_2 + \frac{10q_4}{2}\right) - \left(\frac{10}{2}q_1 + 10q_3\right)\right].$$

II. Evaluate

$$y_5 = y_3 + \tfrac{1}{3}h[(q_5)_1 + 4q_4 + q_3].$$

III. Check and correct $(q_5)_1$ by means of the differential equation $(q_5)_2 = f(x_5, y_5)$, and continue the integration using this value of q_5.

As regards the actual integration, it is desirable to halve each value of q and insert it at the same time as q, thus all the terms required in I are at once available.

If it be found that $\tfrac{1}{3}h[(q_5)_1 - (q_5)_2]$ is of an order significant for the last figure in y which it is desired to retain, then the interval h must be reduced. Thus, if this method is to be continued after any stage using half the interval, a value of q must be interpolated midway between two consecutive pairs of values. Let q_0, q_1, q_2, q_3 be four consecutive values of q; to insert a term midway between q_1 and q_2 Bessels' interpolation formula gives at once

$$q_{1\frac{1}{2}} = \tfrac{1}{2}(q_1 + q_2) - \tfrac{1}{16}(\Delta^2 q_0 + \Delta^2 q_1) + \tfrac{3}{256}[\Delta^4 q_{-1} + \Delta^4 q_0].$$

This without the term in fourth differences is in error by $< \tfrac{1}{40}$ of fourth differences, and may therefore in practice be taken as correct to that order. In this case the expression may be rewritten as

$$q_{1\frac{1}{2}} = \tfrac{1}{16}[9(q_1 + q_2) - (q_0 + q_3)]$$

when one-fortieth of fourth differences does not have any influence on the accuracy required.

Having inserted $q_{1\frac{1}{2}}$ and $q_{2\frac{1}{2}}$, the integration may be continued as before, using half of the previous interval in x. If full benefit is to be obtained by the use of the formulæ, it should be observed that the last figure retained in the values of q, multiplied by $3h$, should not effect the accuracy required in the values of q. The table on p. 138 shows the arrangement in a particular example.

Example.—Integration of $\dfrac{dy}{dx} = y + x^2$ continued from $x = 0 \cdot 5$ to $x = 1$.

$y.$	$(q)_1.$	$(q)_2.$	$\frac{1}{2}(q)_2.$
1·69616	1·94595	1·94616	0·97308
1·90635	2·26651	2·26635	1·133175
2·15125	2·64105	2·64125	1·320625
2·43662	3·07663	3·07662	1·53831
2·76880	3·57876	3·57880	1·78940
3·15484	4·15471	4·15484	

Every value required in the formulæ is at once available in this table. The value 3·15484 is 0·000005 in deficiency, showing clearly that the method is effectively maintaining the required accuracy.

12.11. METHOD VI.—A second method of forward integration not requiring a difference table.

If it be required to perform a rapid integration ahead, and an error of order h^4 is allowable, then the formula of Heun may be used

$$(y_3)_1 = y_0 + \tfrac{3}{4}h[q_0 + 3q_2] \quad . \quad . \quad . \quad (5)$$

This errs in deficiency by $\tfrac{3}{8}h\Delta^3 q_0$. When this value of y_3 is substituted in the differential equation and q_3 is found, the integration may be continued.

It should be noticed that if the value of q_3 which has now been calculated is substituted in the expression

$$(y_3)_2 = y_1 + \tfrac{1}{3}h[q_1 + 4q_2 + (q_3)_1] \quad . \quad . \quad (5.1)$$

a corrected value of y_3 is obtained. A correspondingly better value of $(q_3)_2$ is now derived from the differential equation, and the process may be repeated using

$$(y_3)_3 = (y_3)_2 + \tfrac{1}{3}h[(q_3)_2 - (q_3)_1]$$

until this latter expression no longer influences y to the desired degree of accuracy. The process of successive approximation is obviously not as convenient as that described in the last method, unless the process converges rapidly and the calculation of q is easily carried out.

12.12. METHOD VII.—The method of Milne.

If in place of formula (5) above the formula

$$(y_n)_1 = y_{n-4} + \tfrac{4}{3}h[2q_{n-1} - q_{n-2} + 2q_{n-3}]$$

is used, a more accurate first value of y is obtained, which errs in excess by $\tfrac{1}{3}h\Delta^4 q_{n-1}$. If this value of $(y_n)_1$ is now substituted in the differential equation, $(q_n)_1$ is obtained, and hence substituting in the formula (5.1) above a corrected value of $(y_n)_2$ follows, whose error is $\tfrac{1}{90}h\Delta^4 q_{n-1}$ in excess.

Clearly if $\tfrac{1}{29}[(y_n)_2 - (y_n)_1]$ is so large as to affect the accuracy adversely, the value of h must be reduced (see first method of this type on p. 136); otherwise the process must be repeated until two values of y agree to the desired number of figures. The integration ahead should then be continued.

12.2. Comparison of the methods of integration of first-order equations.

The final degree of accuracy which is attainable by those methods which use Simpson's Rule,

$$y_{n+1} - y_{n-1} = h[2q_n + \tfrac{1}{3}\Delta^2 q_{n-1}] = \tfrac{1}{3}h[q_{n+1} + 4q_n + q_{n-1}]$$

in the checking of integrations is naturally the same, therefore the difference between such methods lies in the forward integration formulæ used in conjunction with the above rule. Let us suppose that the substitution of x and y in the differential equation to obtain the corresponding value of $\dfrac{dy}{dx}$ involves so much calculation that unnecessary repetition of the process must be avoided. In this case the forward integration formula recommended is that used in the example on p. 129. In general, the correction to be applied to y when this formula is used in conjunction with Simpson's Rule is too small to make necessary the recalculation of $\dfrac{dy}{dx}$

using the corrected y. This is one important advantage of using the method recommended, which, however, is possessed by the two methods which precede it. The use of Simpson's Rule as a check in place of the more complicated formula used in the two previous methods is an advantage over them, and, in addition, the checking of values by Simpson's Rule requires the calculation of a difference term which is used in subsequent calculations (see p. 131). If the calculation of $\frac{dy}{dx}$ by substitution in the differential equation is a simple and rapid one, then the process of successive approximation is made correspondingly easier, and it is then not as important as in the case above that the first forward integration should be carried out with a degree of accuracy which requires only one substitution in the differential equation. In this case the method which follows that discussed above is thoroughly satisfactory, and possesses the advantage that three accurate initial function values only are required to start the process. This method is clearly one which can be used to give approximate integrations within fairly wide limits of accuracy, according to the number of corrections made, and it is therefore a very convenient method, and one which is very simple in application. The Adams–Bashforth process, together with the check added to it, is equivalent to that of the method which follows it so far as forward integration is concerned. It is felt, however, that, although thoroughly sound methods, they are a little tedious in application when compared with other methods described in this chapter. The methods of forward integration without the use of a difference table all have the same final accuracy, but the first and third yield the more accurate forward integrations, and in this order. These have been added as alternatives to the difference methods, and are capable of giving precisely the same accuracy.

CHAPTER V

SIMULTANEOUS EQUATIONS AND EQUATIONS OF THE SECOND AND HIGHER ORDERS

The extension of the methods of Chapter IV to simultaneous equations and equations of the second and higher orders is a very simple one, and requires little explanation beyond that which is given by a study of worked examples. It may be remarked that the importance of checking and correcting calculations is even more important in the examples of this section than in the case of first-order equations, since the processes are somewhat more lengthy and a little more complicated. Hence, checking processes have been introduced which in some cases bear no relation to the actual forward integration. The processes have been systematised wherever possible, so that their application may be regarded as a mechanical process of a definite precision.

13. Simultaneous equations.

Let the given system be

$$\frac{dy}{dx} = f(x, y, z)$$

$$\frac{dz}{dx} = g(x, y, z)$$

in which x is regarded as the independent variable and y and z are the dependent variables.

If $x = x_0$, $y = y_0$, $z = z_0$ be the initial values of the variables, then the first increments in y and z due to an increment Δx_1, in x are given by Euler's method approximately.

Thus $\qquad \Delta y_1 = \left(\frac{dy}{dx}\right)_0 . \Delta x_1$

$$= f(x_0, y_0, z_0) . \Delta x_1$$

$$y_1 = y_0 + \Delta y_1.$$

Similarly $\qquad \Delta z_1 = g(x_0, y_0, z_0)\Delta x_1$

$$z_1 = z_0 + \Delta z_1.$$

Each of these values y, and z, may be corrected for

$$\left(\frac{dy}{dx}\right)_1 = f(x_1, y_1, z_1)$$

$$\Delta y_{11} = \frac{1}{2}\left[\left(\frac{dy}{dx}\right)_0 + \left(\frac{dy}{dx}\right)_1\right] . \Delta x_1$$

$$= \tfrac{1}{2}[f(x_0, y_0, z_0) + f(x_1, y_1, z_1)] . \Delta x_1.$$

Similarly $\qquad \Delta z_{11} = \tfrac{1}{2}[g(x_0, y_0, z_0) + g(x_1, y_1, z_1)]\Delta x_1.$

When the process has been repeated until the same values of Δy and Δz are obtained in two consecutive operations, the next interval may be treated. In this way the initial values necessary to begin the more accurate process by finite differences are obtained.

These preliminary values may be found more accurately by the application of one of the formulæ of Runge, Kutta or Heun. If the Simpson's Rule of Kutta is chosen, then on p. 105 will be found the sets of formulæ required, and by direct substitution in these formulæ as described in the worked example the initial values may at once be found.

Picard's method may also be used or the solution may be begun by direct expansion. Thus

$$\frac{dy}{dx} = f(x, y, z)$$

therefore
$$\frac{d^2y}{dx^2} = F\left(x, y, z, \frac{dy}{dx}, \frac{dz}{dx}\right)$$

and
$$\frac{d^3y}{dx^3} = \phi\left(x, y, z, \frac{dy}{dx}, \frac{dz}{dx}, \frac{d^2y}{dx^2}, \frac{d^2z}{dx^2}\right)$$

$$\cdots \cdots \cdots \cdots$$

and similarly for $\dfrac{dz}{dx}, \dfrac{d^2z}{dx^2}, \dfrac{d^3z}{dx^3}, \cdots$

Now, since y and z are assumed capable of expansion in powers of x, the above values calculated at the initial point (x_0, y_0, z_0) are substituted in the Taylor's expansions for y and z, and the increments in y and z are calculated. Thus

$$y_1 = y(x + \Delta x) = y_0 + \Delta x \cdot y_0' + \frac{1}{2!} \Delta x^2 \cdot y_0''$$
$$+ \frac{1}{3!} \Delta x^3 \cdot y_0''' + \cdots$$

in which Δx is known and

$$y_0' = f(x_0, y_0, z_0)$$
$$y_0'' = F\left(x_0, y_0, z_0, \left(\frac{dy}{dx}\right)_0, \left(\frac{dz}{dx}\right)_0\right)$$
$$y_0''' = \phi\left(x_0, y_0, z_0, \left(\frac{dy}{dx}\right)_0, \left(\frac{dz}{dx}\right)_0, \left(\frac{d^2y}{dx^2}\right)_0, \left(\frac{d^2z}{dx^2}\right)_0\right)$$

$$\cdots \cdots \cdots \cdots \cdots \cdots$$

and similarly for z_1.

When the successive differential coefficients are obtained without great labour, this is the most suitable method. In other cases either of the two previous methods may be used. Examples illustrating these methods are described in Chapter III.

14. Equations of higher order than the first.

Any differential equation of the second or higher order can be reduced to a system of simultaneous equations by the introduction of new variables.

Let the general differential equation of the nth order be written

$$\frac{d^ny}{dx^n} = f(x, y, y', y'', \ldots y^{n-1})$$

in which $\frac{dy}{dx} = y'$, $\frac{d^2y}{dx^2} = y''$, etc.

The equation may be reduced to the system

$$y_1 = \frac{dy}{dx}$$

$$y_2 = \frac{dy_1}{dx}$$

$$y_3 = \frac{dy_2}{dx}$$

$$\cdots \cdots$$

$$y_{n-1} = \frac{dy_{n-2}}{dx}$$

$$y_n = \frac{dy_{n-1}}{dx} = f(x, y, y_1, y_2, \ldots y_{n-1}).$$

The solution may be commenced if x, y, $y_1 \ldots y_{n-1}$ are known initially, that is, if x, y, $\frac{dy}{dx}$, $\frac{d^2y}{dx^2} \ldots \frac{d^{n-1}y}{dx^{n-1}}$ are given at some initial point; thus if the method of Euler is chosen,

$$\frac{dy_{n-1}}{dx} = f.$$

therefore $\qquad \Delta y_{n-1} = f \cdot \Delta x$

therefore the new value of y_{n-1} is given by

$$(y_{n-1})_1 = (y_{n-1})_0 + \Delta y_{n-1}.$$

Again $\qquad \frac{dy_{n-2}}{dx} = y_{n-1}$

therefore as above $\quad (y_{n-2})_1 = (y_{n-2})_0 + \Delta y_{n-2}.$

When the new values of $y_{n-3}, \ldots y_1$, y have been found by Euler's method, these may be corrected as already explained, using $\frac{1}{2}\left[\left(\frac{dy_{n-1}}{dx}\right)_0 + \left(\frac{dy_{n-1}}{dx}\right)_1\right]$ in place of $\left(\frac{dy_{n-1}}{dx}\right)_0$. The student should have no difficulty in following the process. These values, in turn, may be corrected by processes which have been described, or are described later.

The method of finite differences may be applied once the solution has been started, the number of initial values required depends upon the method chosen for forward integration.

15. An important check to be applied to the solutions of second-order differential equations when solved as a pair of simultaneous equations of the first order.

The approximate equation

$$\Delta^2 y_{r-1} = h^2[y_r'' + \tfrac{1}{12}\Delta^2 y_{r-1}'']$$

has a first error term of $\dfrac{h^6}{240} y_r{}^{\text{VI}}$, and the equation is therefore sufficiently accurate to act as a valuable check. When a second-order equation is integrated by resolving it into the equivalent pair of simultaneous first-order equations, there are two tables of differences, those of $\dfrac{dy}{dx}$ and $\dfrac{d^2y}{dx^2}$. The above equation enables us at any stage of the integration to check the value of y_{r+1} by using quantities already calculated in a very simple but effective manner.

Consider the example which is worked immediately below. Let it be required to check the value of $y_7 = 2 \cdot 55602$.

$$y_6'' = 6 \cdot 15225$$
$$\Delta^2 y_5'' = - 0 \cdot 00315.$$

Hence
$$\Delta^2 y_{r-1} = 0 \cdot 01[6 \cdot 15225 - 0 \cdot 00026]$$
$$= 0 \cdot 01[6 \cdot 15199]$$

and
$$\Delta y_r = \Delta y_{r-1} + \Delta^2 y_{r-1}$$
$$= 0 \cdot 34423 + 0 \cdot 06152$$
$$= \underline{0 \cdot 40575.}$$

This agrees exactly with the entry in the table.

Note.—The equation forms the basis of an effective method of integrating the equation $\dfrac{d^2y}{dx^2} = f(x, y)$ to be described later.

Example.—Given $\dfrac{d^2y}{dx^2} + 3x \dfrac{dy}{dx} - 6y = 0$ and that when

$x = 0$, $\dfrac{dy}{dx} = 0 \cdot 1$, $y = 1$, find the values of y at intervals of $0 \cdot 1$ in x up to $x = 1$.

$$\frac{d^2y}{dx^2} = 6y - 3x\frac{dy}{dx} \quad . \quad . \quad . \quad . \quad . \quad \text{(i)}$$

Let $\qquad\quad \dfrac{dy}{dx} = z$

then $\qquad\quad \dfrac{dz}{dx} = 6y - 3xz$ $\left. \begin{array}{c} \\ \\ \end{array} \right\}$ $\quad . \quad . \quad . \quad . \quad . \quad \text{(ii)}$

The simultaneous equations (ii) are equivalent to the single differential equation (i), and the solution of the latter equation may be found by solving the simultaneous system (ii) by the method applied to simultaneous equations of the first order. The numerical calculation may be set out as below. First of all the initial values of y and z are calculated by using Kutta's Simpson's Rule, and on p. 107 the actual calculation of y_1 and z_1 is carried through completely. The remaining values are found in precisely the same manner. Since the error in using these formulæ is of the order h^5, when $h = 0 \cdot 1$ over four intervals it may be assumed that the fifth decimal place in the values of z should be suspect, but that for y a further integration being required, the values correct to the fifth decimal place should be much more accurate. In point of fact, this forecast of the accuracy is fully justified, since only the final value of y, viz. y_4, needs to be changed by one unit in the fifth decimal place. The following table contains the results of applying Kutta's formula.

x.	y.	z.
0	1	$0 \cdot 1$
$0 \cdot 1$	$1 \cdot 04005$	$0 \cdot 70146$
$0 \cdot 2$	$1 \cdot 14040$	$1 \cdot 30587$
$0 \cdot 3$	$1 \cdot 30133$	$1 \cdot 91310$
$0 \cdot 4$	$1 \cdot 52312$	$2 \cdot 52295$

In order that the solution over a wider range of x may be obtained with these values, they will be checked, corrected, and the new set of values used. Should these differ sufficiently from the present values, a second correction would be necessary.

Correction of first sets of values of z and y.

Using the values of y and z in the foregoing table, and substituting in the differential equation

$$\frac{dz}{dx} = 6y - 3xz$$

$$\left(\frac{dz}{dx}\right)_0 = 6 \times 1 - 3 \times 0 \times 0 \cdot 1 = 6$$

$$\left(\frac{dz}{dx}\right)_1 = 6 \cdot 24030 - 0 \cdot 210438 = 6 \cdot 02986$$

similarly

$$\left(\frac{dz}{dx}\right)_2 = 6 \cdot 05886$$

$$\left(\frac{dz}{dx}\right)_3 = 6 \cdot 08619$$

$$\left(\frac{dz}{dx}\right)_4 = 6 \cdot 11118.$$

Forming the difference table

$\frac{dz}{dx}$.	Δ.	Δ².	Δ³.	Δ⁴.
6				
	2986			
6·02986		− 86		
	2900		− 81	
6·05886		− 167		14
	2733		− 67	
6·08619		− 234		
	2499			
6·11118				

Applying the formula of correction for the last interval

$$(\Delta z)_{-1} = \Delta x\left[\left(\frac{dz}{dx}\right)_0 - \frac{1}{2}\Delta\left(\frac{dz}{dx}\right)_{-1} - \frac{1}{12}\Delta^2\left(\frac{dz}{dx}\right)_{-2}\right.$$
$$\left. - \frac{1}{24}\Delta^3\left(\frac{dz}{dx}\right)_{-3} - \frac{19}{720}\Delta^4\left(\frac{dz}{dx}\right)_{-4} \cdots\right]$$

$$= 0\!\cdot\!1[6\!\cdot\!11118 - 0\!\cdot\!012495 + 0\!\cdot\!000195 + 0\!\cdot\!000028$$
$$- 0\!\cdot\!000004]$$
$$= 0\!\cdot\!60989.$$

Similar corrections applied to the other intervals $(\Delta z)_{-2}$ $= 0\!\cdot\!60727$, $(\Delta z)_{-3} = 0\!\cdot\!60445$, $(\Delta z)_{-4} = 0\!\cdot\!60150$. The corrected values of z are therefore $0\!\cdot\!1$, $0\!\cdot\!70150$, $1\!\cdot\!30595$, $1\!\cdot\!91322$, $2\!\cdot\!52311$. Using the values of z just found, the corresponding values of y are calculated in an exactly similar manner. The following is the table of results.

y.	Δy.	$z = \dfrac{dy}{dx}$.	Δ.	Δ^2.	Δ^3	Δ^4.
1		0·1				
	0·04005		60,150			
1·04005		0·70150		295		
	0·10035		60,445		− 13	
1·14040		1·30595		282		− 7
	0·16093		60,727		− 20	
1·30133		1·91322		262		
	0·22180		60,989			
1·52313		2·52311				

The values obtained for y are little different from those already obtained, so that if the fourth decimal place determines the degree of accuracy ultimately required, the process of forward integration may now be commenced, the values of y in the table being correct to a unit in the fifth decimal place at present.

Forward integration.

(1) Using the formula

$$\Delta z_1 = h\!\left[\left(\frac{dz}{dx}\right)_0 + \frac{1}{2}\Delta\!\left(\frac{dz}{dx}\right)_{-1} + \frac{5}{12}\Delta^2\!\left(\frac{dz}{dx}\right)_{-2} \right.$$
$$\left. + \frac{3}{8}\Delta^3\!\left(\frac{dz}{dx}\right)_{-3} + \frac{251}{720}\Delta^4 q_{-4}\right]$$

$$\Delta z_4 = 0\!\cdot\!1[6\!\cdot\!11105 + \tfrac{1}{2} \times 0\!\cdot\!02497 - \tfrac{5}{12} \times 0\!\cdot\!00228$$
$$- \tfrac{3}{8} \times 0\!\cdot\!00055 + \tfrac{251}{720} \times 0\!\cdot\!00031]$$

$$= 0\!\cdot\!61225.$$

The new value of z is therefore 3·13536, and substituting in the above table of z's and its differences, the new line of differences becomes

z.	Δz.	$\Delta^2 z$.	$\Delta^3 z$.	$\Delta^4 z$.
3·13536	0·61225	236	−26	−6

(2) Using the formula

$$\Delta y_{-1} = h\left[\left(\frac{dy}{dx}\right)_0 - \frac{1}{2}\Delta\left(\frac{dy}{dx}\right)_{-1} - \frac{1}{12}\Delta^2\left(\frac{dy}{dx}\right)_{-2} \right.$$
$$\left. - \frac{1}{24}\Delta^3\left(\frac{dy}{dx}\right)_{-3} - \frac{1}{36}\Delta^4\left(\frac{dy}{dx}\right)_{-4}\right]$$

$$\Delta y_4 = 0·1[3·13536 - 0·306125 - 0·000197 + 0·000011$$
$$+ 0·000002]$$
$$= 0·28291.$$

Hence

$$\underline{y_5 = 1·80604.}$$

(3) With this value of y the corresponding value of $\dfrac{dz}{dx}$ is obtained by substituting in the equation

$$\frac{dz}{dx} = 6y - 3xz \qquad\qquad \left.\begin{array}{l} y = 1·80604 \\ x = 0·5 \\ z = 3·13536 \end{array}\right\}$$

$$\underline{\left(\frac{dz}{dx}\right)_5 = 6·13320}$$

Construct the new line of differences for $\dfrac{dz}{dx}$.

(4) Check $(\Delta z)_4$ using the formula similar to that in (2),

$$(\Delta z)_4 = 0·1[6·13320 - 0·011075 + 0·000235 + 0·000046]$$
$$= \underline{0·61224.}$$

The correction is too small to affect the integration for y.

(5) Check the integration for y using the formula

$$\Delta^2 y_{r-1} = h^2 \cdot \left[\left(\frac{dz}{dx}\right)_r + \frac{1}{12}\Delta^2\left(\frac{dz}{dx}\right)_{r-1}\right]$$

$$\Delta^2 y_3 = 0·01[6·11105 - \tfrac{1}{12} \times 0·00282]$$
$$= 0·01[6·11105 - 0·000235]$$
$$= 0·06111$$

$$\Delta y_4 = 0·22180 + 0·06111$$
$$= \underline{0·28291.}$$

This is in exact agreement with the value in the table, and the integration may therefore be continued a stage further. The terms required in using the formulæ for Δy_{-1} and Δz_{-1} may be included in the table. One such line is included in the table on p. 151, which embodies all the results.

The value of y at $x = 1\cdot0$ given by the above integrations is 4·14386, or correct to the fourth decimal place 4·1439. The forward integrations maintain the accuracy of the initial values calculated by Kutta's formula, and although these were corrected before the integration was begun, the corrections were very small, and little error would have been introduced if the forward integration had been begun with these initial values before correction.

The combination of Kutta's formulæ with this process of integration is thus very effective indeed. We may note that every value of y in the above table is correct to the fourth decimal place. The estimate of the total error derived from the term $\frac{1}{3}h\Delta^4 q_{-5}$ is clearly too small to affect the required accuracy in the given range.

Note.—The series solution for the foregoing example is

$$y = 1 + 0\cdot1x + 3x^2 + \frac{1}{20}x^3 - \frac{3}{400}x^5 + \frac{9}{5600}x^7 - \frac{45}{134{,}400}x^9 + \frac{9 \times 45}{52 \times 134{,}400} \cdot x^{11} + \text{etc.}$$

16. Systematic methods of integrating and correcting.

(A) $$\frac{d^2y}{dx^2} = f(x, y)$$

(B) $$\frac{d^2y}{dx^2} = f\left(x, y, \frac{dy}{dx}\right)$$

(C) $$\left.\begin{array}{l} \dfrac{dy}{dx} = f(x, y, z) \\[2mm] \dfrac{dz}{dx} = g(x, y, z) \end{array}\right\}$$

Methods of integrating the above equations are set out below in step by step form, so that the whole procedure may be followed out systematically.

x	Δx	y	Δy	$z = \dfrac{dy}{dx}$	Δz	$\Delta^2 z$	$\Delta^3 z$	$\Delta^4 z$	$\left(\dfrac{dz}{dx}\right)$	$\Delta\left(\dfrac{dz}{dx}\right)$	$\Delta^2\left(\dfrac{dz}{dx}\right)$	$\Delta^3\left(\dfrac{dz}{dx}\right)$	$\Delta^4\left(\dfrac{dz}{dx}\right)$
0	0·1	1		0·1					6·00000				
			0·04005							2,985			
0·1	0·1	1·04005		0·70150					6·02985		− 87		
			0·10035		0·60445					2,898		− 86	
0·2	0·1	1·14040		1·30595		282			6·05883		− 173		31
			0·16093		0·60727		− 20			2,725		− 55	
0·3	0·1	1·30133		1·91322		262		− 7	6·08608		− 228		1
			0·22180		0·60989		− 26 1·1			2,497		− 54 + 2·3	
0·4	0·1	1·52313		2·52311		236 19·7		− 6 0·1	6·11105		− 282 + 23·5		+ 26
			0·28291		0·61225 30612·5		− 32			2,215 1,107·5		− 28	
0·5	0·1	1·80604		3·13536		204		− 6	6·13320		− 310		+ 23
			0·34423		0·61429		− 28			1,905		− 5	
0·6	0·1	2·15027		3·74965		176		+ 4	6·15225		− 315		25
			0·40575		0·61605		− 32			1,590		+ 20	
0·7	0·1	2·55602		4·36570		144		− 4	6·16815		− 295		
			0·46744		0·61749		− 28			1,295			
0·8	0·1	3·02346		4·98319		116		+ 4	6·18110				
			0·52924		0·61865								
0·9	0·1	3·55270		5·60184									
			0·59116										
1·0		4·14386											

(A) $$\frac{d^2y}{dx^2} = f(x, y).$$

Let the equivalent system of simultaneous equations be

$$\frac{dy}{dx} = q \quad \cdots \cdots \quad \text{(i)}$$

$$r = \frac{dq}{dx} = f(x, y) \quad \cdots \cdots \quad \text{(ii)}$$

Let y_0, q_0, $r_0 : \ldots y_4$, q_4, r_4 be the sets of corresponding values obtained by one of the previously described processes for the early stages of the solution.

Checking and correcting initial values.

(i) Correct y_1 by the formula
$$y_1 - y_0 = h[q_0 + \tfrac{1}{2}\Delta q_0 - \tfrac{1}{12}\Delta^2 q_0 + \tfrac{1}{24}\Delta^3 q_0 - \tfrac{1}{40}\Delta^4 q_0]$$

Error, $\dfrac{h}{720}\Delta^4 q_0$.

(ii) Calculate r_1 by using equation (ii).

(iii) Correct q_2 by
$$q_2 - q_0 = \tfrac{1}{3}h[r_2 + 4r_1 + r_0] \qquad \text{Error, } \dfrac{h}{90}\Delta^4 q_0.$$
$$= h(2r_1 + \tfrac{1}{3}\Delta^2 r_0).$$

(iv) Correct y_2 by
$$y_2 - y_0 = \tfrac{1}{3}h[q_2 + 4q_1 + q_0] = h(2q_1 + \tfrac{1}{3}\Delta^2 q_0).$$

(v) Calculate r_2 by using equation (ii).

The above process may be repeated with the corrected values and stopped when the same values are repeated.

Forward integration.

(i) Evaluate y_5 by using formula (i), viz.
$$(y_5)_1 - y_3 = h[2q_4 + \tfrac{1}{3}\Delta^2 q_0 + \Delta^3 q_1].$$

Error, $\dfrac{h}{90}\Delta^4 q_3 - \dfrac{31h}{90}\Delta^5 q_3$.

(ii) Calculate r_5.

(iii) Calculate q_5 using
$$(q_5 - q_3) = h[2r_4 + \tfrac{1}{3}\Delta^2 r_3].$$

(iv) Correct $(y_5)_1$ using
$$(y_5)_2 - y_3 = h[2q_4 + \tfrac{1}{3}\Delta^2 q_3]$$

and therefore
$$(y_5)_2 = (y_5)_1 + h[\tfrac{1}{3}\Delta^2 q_3 - (\tfrac{1}{3}\Delta^2 q_0 + \Delta^3 q_1)]$$

(iii) and (iv) may be repeated if necessary in exceptional cases.

(v) Evaluate y_6, then repeat the process outlined above.

Note.—No forward integration is required for the q's.

Example.—Solution of $\dfrac{d^2y}{dx^2} - 2(2x^2 - 1)y = 0$.

Initial conditions
$$\left.\begin{array}{l} x = 0 \\ y = 1 \\ q = 0 \end{array}\right\}$$

x.	y.	q.	Δ.	Δ^2.	Δ^3.	r.	Δ.	Δ^2.
0	1	0				-2		
			$-19{,}801$				$5{,}950$	
0·1	0·99005	$-0·19801$		$1{,}170$		$-1·94050$		$11{,}315$
			$-18{,}631$	390	$1{,}057$		$17{,}265$	$3{,}772$
0·2	0·96079	$-0·38432$		$2{,}227$		$-1·76785$		$9{,}635$
			$-16{,}404$	742	842		$26{,}900$	$3{,}212$
0·3	0·91393	$-0·54836$		$+3{,}069$		$-1·49885$		$7{,}093$
			$-13{,}335$	$1{,}023$	556		$33{,}993$	$2{,}364$
0·4	0·85214	$-0·68171$		$3{,}625$		$-1·15892$		$+4{,}017$
	0·77880		$-9{,}710$	$1{,}208$	245		$+38{,}010$	$1{,}339$
0·5	0·77882	$-0·77881$		$3{,}870$		$-0·77882$		802
	0·69767		$-5{,}840$	$1{,}290$	-77		$38{,}812$	267
0·6	0·69768	$-0·83721$		$+3{,}793$		$-0·39070$		$-2{,}193$
	0·61263		$-2{,}047$	$1{,}264$	-344		$36{,}619$	-731
0·7	0·61263	$-0·85768$		$+3{,}449$		$-0·02451$		$-4{,}641$
	0·52729		$+1{,}402$	$1{,}100$	-559		$31{,}978$	$-1{,}547$
0·8	0·52727	$-0·84366$		$2{,}890$		$+0·29527$		$-6{,}345$
	0·44486		$+4{,}292$	963	-683		$25{,}633$	$-2{,}115$
0·9	0·44484	$-0·80074$		$2{,}207$		$+0·55160$		$-7{,}223$
	0·36788		$+6{,}499$	736	-734		$18{,}410$	$-2{,}408$
1·0	0·36785	$-0·73575$		$1{,}473$		$+0·73570$		$-7{,}297$
	0·29820		$+7{,}972$	491			$11{,}113$	$-2{,}432$
1·1	0·29818	$-0·65603$		$+768$		$+0·84683$		$-6{,}722$
	0·23693		$+8{,}740$	256			$4{,}391$	$-2{,}241$
1·2	0·23690	$-0·56863$				$+0·89074$		

It should be remarked that no third differences are required in the difference table for the r's, and that no alteration is made in the tables. The correction applied to the y's is very rapidly carried out, and is too small to make it necessary to recalculate the values of r. The interval in x can readily be chosen so that this is the case, since at each integration ahead the accuracy in this value of y is carried to the r's by means of the differential equation. Thus, since the accuracy of the r's need not be that required for the y's, the process maintains its standard of accuracy throughout.

In the foregoing example the final value of $y = 0 \cdot 23693$ is correct to five significant figures, and every other value of y has this same accuracy.

Typical forward integration and correction.

$$(y_9)_1 - y_7 = 0 \cdot 1[- 1 \cdot 68732 + (0 \cdot 01290 - 0 \cdot 00344)]$$
$$= 0 \cdot 16779$$

therefore

$$(y_9)_1 = 0 \cdot 44484$$
$$(y_9)_2 = 0 \cdot 44484 + 0 \cdot 1[0 \cdot 00963 - 0 \cdot 00946]$$
$$= \underline{0 \cdot 44486}$$

$$r_9 = 0 \cdot 55160 \text{ from the differential equation}$$

and

$$q_9 = q_7 + 0 \cdot 1[0 \cdot 59054 - 0 \cdot 02115]$$
$$= - \underline{0 \cdot 80074}.$$

16.1. A method of integrating equations of the type

$$\frac{d^2y}{dx^2} = f(x, y)$$

subject to $x = x_0$, $y = y_0$, $\dfrac{dy}{dx} = \left(\dfrac{dy}{dx}\right)_0$ to be used when the values of $\dfrac{dy}{dx}$ are not required.

The methods of integrating the above equation which have been described necessitate the determination of $\dfrac{dy}{dx}$ at each stage of the integration. If the value of $\frac{dy}{dx}$ is not required, then the present method, following lines similar to those explained for a first order differential equation on p. 132, will be found convenient and accurate. The method has the important advantage that it is necessary to have only three function values before the integration can be systematically continued. Consider the approximate equation for forward integration

$$y_{r+1} - 2y_r + y_{r-1} = h^2[y_r'' + \tfrac{1}{12}\Delta^2 y_{r-2}''].$$

If the terms are expanded, the equation has a first error term of $-\dfrac{h^5}{12} y_r^{\text{v}}$ on the right-hand side. Hence to the degree of accuracy governed by the magnitude of this error term the equation may be regarded as one expressing y_{r+1} in terms of known values of y_r, y_{r-1}, y_r'' and $\Delta^2 y_{r-2}''$.

Let y_0, y_1, and y_2 be determined by expanding y as a Taylor's series, h having been chosen so that the error term, $\tfrac{1}{240} h^6 y_r^{\text{vi}}$ (see later), is too small to affect the accuracy required over the range of integration. Using the above approximate equation, y_3 is determined, and hence y_3'' may be calculated by using the differential equation. The next step provides a check upon the calculated value of y_3, and at the same time a correction.

Now $y_{r+1} - 2y_r + y_{r-1} = h^2[y_r'' + \tfrac{1}{12} \Delta^2 y_{r-1}'']$

is a more accurate equation than the first approximate equation, its first error term being $\dfrac{h^6}{240} y_r^{\text{vi}}$. The value of y_3 is recalculated by means of this equation, and it should differ from the previously calculated value by only a few units in the last figure kept for the y's. If there is a wider divergence in the two values of y, consideration must be given to reducing the interval, for this almost certainly means that the error $\dfrac{h^6}{240} y_r^{\text{vi}}$ is accumulating sufficiently rapidly to affect the accuracy of the last figure in the y's.

The value of y_3'' need not be corrected, however, for a slightly lower degree of accuracy is allowable in the y''''s as compared with the y's. It follows that the tables of differences for y and y'' are being systematically built up, the y table from the second difference column to the y column, and the y'' table in the opposite direction.

The steps in the integration.

1. Form the differences for y_0, y_1, y_2, and y_0'', y_1'', y_2''.

2. Calculate $y_2'' + \frac{1}{12}\Delta^2 y_0'' = 2\cdot39411 - 0\cdot00037 = 2\cdot39374$; column IV.

3. Insert $h^2(y_2'' + \frac{1}{12}\Delta^2 y_0'') = 0\cdot0239374$ in column IX, and hence by adding to $0\cdot132324$ obtain $\Delta_1 y_2 = 0\cdot156261$; column VII. Add $\Delta_1 y_2$ to y_2 to give the first approximation to y_3; first entry (a).

4. Calculate y_3'' by substitution in the differential equation and form the differences in columns II, III, and IV.

5. Recalculate y_3 as in (3) using the formula

$$\Delta^2 y_1 = h^2(y_2'' + \tfrac{1}{12}\Delta^2 y_1''),$$

see columns V (2·39329), X, VIII, and entry (b) in column VI, the latter being the corrected value of y_3.

The above process is repeated for each integration. In the example comparatively large steps in x have been taken, and six significant figures have been kept throughout the calculations. The accuracy demanded from such an arrangement should not be more than five significant figures, and that this is maintained is clear from the fact that, correct to six significant figures, the value of y_6 is $1\cdot02885$, whereas the value found is $1\cdot02886$.

Estimate of the approximate error over the range of integration.

The first error term in the equation used in the successive approximation for the value of y_{r+1} is

$$\frac{h^6}{240} \cdot y_r^{\mathrm{vi}} \backsimeq \frac{h^2}{240} \cdot \Delta^4 y_{r-2}''$$

$$= \frac{0\cdot01}{240} \times 0\cdot00099.$$

This term, although increasing to

$$\frac{0\cdot01}{240} \times 0\cdot00215$$

at the end of the integration, clearly does not affect the accuracy required in six integrations, but the manner in which the error term may grow to several times its initial value should be noted and allowed for.

Example.—*Integration of* $y'' = 2\sqrt{e^{2x} - y^2}$ *subject to* $y = 0$, $y' = 1$, $x = 0$.

	I.	II.	III.	IV.	V.
x.	y''.	Δ.	Δ^2.	$y_r'' + \frac{1}{12}\Delta^2 y_{r-2}''$.	$y_r'' + \frac{1}{12}\Delta^2 y_{r-1}''$.
0	2				
		0·19930			
0·1	2·19930		$-\frac{449}{12} = -37$		
		0·19481			
0·2	2·39411		$-\frac{978}{12} = -82$	2·39374	2·39329
		0·18503			
0·3	2·57914		$-\frac{1606}{12} = -134$	2·57832	2·57780
		0·16897			
0·4	2·74811		$-\frac{2332}{12} = -194$	2·74684	2·74617
		0·14565			
0·5	2·89376		$-\frac{3173}{12} = -264$	2·89182	2·89128
		0·11392			
0·6	3·00768				

	VI.	VII.	VIII.	IX.	X.
x.	y.	Δ_1.	Δ_2.	$\Delta_1{}^2$.	$\Delta_2{}^2$.
0	0				
		0·110332			
0·1	0·110332			0·021992	
		0·132324			
0·2	0·242656			0·0239374	0·0239329
	a 0·398917	0·156261	0·156257		
0·3	b 0·398913			0·0257832	0·0257780
	a 0·580953	0·182040	0·182037		
0·4	b 0·580950			0·0274684	0·0274617
	a 0·790454	0·209504	0·209499		
0·5	b 0·790449			0·0289182	0·0289112
	a 1·028866	0·238417	0·238410		
0·6	b 1·028859				

Modification of the above method.

In a recent paper (Vol. 77, Memoirs and Proc. of Manchester Literary and Phil. Soc., 1932–33) the above method has been modified, in that the value of $\Delta^2 y_{r-1}$ in the formula

$$\Delta^2 y_{r-1} = h^2[y_r'' + \tfrac{1}{12}\Delta^2 y_{r-1}'']$$

is estimated in the first place, and then, having found the value of y_{r+1}, the value of y_{r+1}'' is calculated by using the differential equation, and hence the value of $\Delta^2 y_{r-1}''$ is corrected. This is an extremely effective procedure when carefully executed, and the method is strongly recommended where the estimate of $\Delta^2 y_{r-1}''$ is easily made.

(B)
$$\frac{d^2 y}{dx^2} = f\left(x, y, \frac{dy}{dx}\right).$$

Let the equivalent systems of simultaneous differential equations be

$$\frac{dy}{dx} = q \quad . \quad . \quad . \quad . \quad . \quad . \quad \text{(i)}$$

$$r = \frac{dq}{dx} = f(x, y, q) \quad . \quad . \quad . \quad . \quad \text{(ii)}$$

Checking and correcting initial values.

   (i) Correct y_1 by the formula

$$y_1 - y_0 = h[q_0 + \tfrac{1}{2}\Delta q_0 - \tfrac{1}{12}\Delta^2 q_0 + \tfrac{1}{24}\Delta^3 q_0 - \tfrac{1}{40}\Delta^4 q_0].$$

   (ii) Correct q_1 by formula above.

   (iii) Substitute new values of y_1 and q_1 in equation (ii) and calculate r_1.

   (iv) Correct q_2 by the formula

$$(q_2)_1 - q_0 = \tfrac{1}{3}h[r_2 + 4r_1 + r_0] = h[2r_1 + \tfrac{1}{3}\Delta^2 r_0].$$

   (v) Correct y_2 by the formula

$$y_2 - y_0 = \tfrac{1}{3}h[(q_2)_1 + 4q_1 + q_0] = h[2q_1 + \tfrac{1}{3}(\Delta^2 q_0)_1].$$

using the corrected values of q_2.

   (vi) Calculate r_2.

   If necessary, check q_2 and y_2 again.

   (vii) Correct q_3 as at stage (iv), and repeat the process.

   Stop the process when repeated values are obtained.

Forward integration.

(i) Calculate q_5, using the formula

$$(q_5)_1 - q_3 = h[2r_4 + \tfrac{1}{3}\Delta^2 r_0 + \Delta^3 r_1].$$

(ii) Calculate y_5, using the formula

$$(y_5)_1 - y_3 = h[2q_4 + \tfrac{1}{3}(\Delta^2 q_3)_1].$$

(iii) Calculate r_5 from the differential equation, using the values from (i) and (ii).

(iv) Correct $(q_5)_1$ by the formula

$$(q_5)_2 - q_3 = h[2r_4 + \tfrac{1}{3}\Delta^2 r_3].$$

(v) Correct y_5 by the formula

$$(y_5)_2 - y_3 = h[2q_4 + \tfrac{1}{3}(\Delta^2 q_3)_2].$$

$$\text{i.e.}\quad (y_5)_2 = (y_5)_1 + h \cdot \tfrac{1}{3}[(\Delta^2 q_3)_2 - (\Delta^2 q_3)_1]$$

$$= (y_5)_1 + \frac{h}{3}[(q_5)_2 - (q_5)_1].$$

(vi) Apply the check

$$\Delta^2 y_{n-1} = h^2[r_n + \tfrac{1}{2}\Delta^2 r_{n-1}].$$

(**C**) Systematic method of integrating and correcting the simultaneous equations

$$\frac{dy}{dx} = f(x, y, z) \quad . \quad . \quad . \quad . \quad . \quad \text{(i)}$$

$$\frac{dz}{dx} = g(x, y, z) \quad . \quad . \quad . \quad . \quad . \quad \text{(ii)}$$

We write f_n and g_n for $f(x_n, y_n, z_n)$ and $g(x_n, y_n, z_n)$, respectively.

Checking and correcting initial values.

With the usual notation.

(i) Correct y_1 and z_1 by the difference formulæ

$$y_1 - y_0 = h[f_0 + \tfrac{1}{2}\Delta f_0 - \tfrac{1}{12}\Delta^2 f_0 + \tfrac{1}{24}\Delta^3 f_0 - \tfrac{1}{40}\Delta^4 f_0]$$
$$z_1 - z_0 = h[g_0 + \tfrac{1}{2}\Delta g_0 - \tfrac{1}{12}\Delta^2 g_0 + \tfrac{1}{24}\Delta^3 g_0 - \tfrac{1}{40}\Delta^4 g_0].$$

(ii) Calculate f_1 and g_1.

(iii) Correct y_2 and z_2, using the formulæ
$$y_2 - y_0 = \tfrac{1}{3}h[f_2 + 4f_1 + f_0] = h(2f_1 + \tfrac{1}{3}\Delta^2 f_0)$$
$$z_2 - z_0 = \tfrac{1}{3}h[g_2 + 4g_1 + g_0] = h(2g_1 + \tfrac{1}{3}\Delta^2 g_0).$$

(iv) Calculate $(f_2)_2$ and $(g_2)_2$. Hence make the corrections
$$\tfrac{1}{3}h[(f_2)_2 - (f_2)_1] \text{ and } \tfrac{1}{3}h[(g_2)_2 - (g_2)_1]$$
to y_2 and z_2 respectively.

(v) Correct y_3 and z_3 as in (iii).

(vi) Calculate f_3 and g_3 as in (iv), and make the corrections as indicated there.

(vii) Correct y_4 and z_4 as above.

The whole process may be repeated if necessary.

Forward integration.

(i) Evaluate $(y_5)_1$ and $(z_5)_1$ using the formulæ
$$(y_5)_1 - y_3 = h[2f_4 + \tfrac{1}{3}\Delta^2 f_0 + \Delta^3 f_1]$$
$$(z_5)_1 - z_3 = h[2g_4 + \tfrac{1}{3}\Delta^2 g_0 + \Delta^3 g_1].$$

(ii) Calculate f_5 and g_5 and correct $(y_5)_1$ and $(z_5)_1$ by the formulæ
$$(y_5)_2 - (y_3) = h[2f_4 + \tfrac{1}{3}\Delta^2 f_3] \text{ or}$$
$$(y_5)_2 = (y_5)_1 + h[\tfrac{1}{3}\Delta^2 f_3 - (\tfrac{1}{3}\Delta^2 f_0 + \Delta^3 f_1)].$$
$$(z_5)_2 - z_3 = h[2g_4 + \tfrac{1}{3}\Delta^2 g_3] \text{ or}$$
$$(z_5)_2 = (z_5)_1 + h[\tfrac{1}{3}\Delta^2 z_3 - (\tfrac{1}{3}\Delta^2 z_0 + \Delta^3 z_1)].$$

If necessary recalculate f_5 and g_5. The corresponding corrections to y_5 and z_5 are
$$\tfrac{1}{3}h[(f_5)_2 - (f_5)_1] \text{ and } \tfrac{1}{3}h[(g_5)_2 - (g_5)_1].$$

(iii) Integrate ahead and repeat the above process.

Alternative process for forward integration.

(i) Evaluate $(y_5)_1$ and $(z_5)_1$ using the formulæ
$$(y_5)_1 - y_3 = h[2f_4 + \tfrac{1}{3}\Delta^2 f_2]$$
$$(z_5)_2 - z_3 = h[2g_4 + \tfrac{1}{3}\Delta^2 g_2].$$

(ii) Calculate $(f_5)_1$ and $(g_5)_1$ and correct $(y_5)_1$ and $(z_5)_1$ by the formulæ
$$(y_5)_2 - y_3 = h[2f_4 + \tfrac{1}{3}\Delta^2 f_3]$$
$$(z_5)_2 - z_3 = h[2g_4 + \tfrac{1}{3}\Delta^2 g_3].$$

(iii) Recalculate $(f_5)_2$ and $(g_5)_2$ and apply the corrections

$$(y_5)_3 = (y_5)_2 + \frac{h}{3}[(f_5)_2 - (f_5)_1]$$

$$(z_5)_3 = (z_5)_2 + \frac{h}{3}[(g_5)_2 - (g_5)_1].$$

(iv) Repeat above process for y_6 and z_6.

Note.—This alternative process may be started with four initial pairs of values of y and z.

Examples.

1. Determine corresponding values of x and y for the range $0 < t < 0.5$ at intervals of $t = 0.05$ to satisfy the equation

$$\frac{dx}{dt} = x + y, \frac{dy}{dt} = x^2 - y^2;$$

$$x = 0, y = 0, t = 0.$$

2. Tabulate the solutions for x and y, at intervals of 0.05 in t for the range $0 < t < 0.5$, to satisfy

$$\frac{dx}{dt} = (x + y)t, \frac{dy}{dt} = (x - t)y$$

where $\qquad x = 0, y = 1, t = 0.$

3. If $y\frac{dx}{dt} = 2x - y$, $\frac{dy}{dt} = y^2 - x + t$ and if $x = 0$, $y = -1$, when $t = 0$ tabulate x and y at intervals of 0.1 from $t = 0$ to $t = 0.5$.

4. Tabulate y and $\frac{dy}{dx}$ to satisfy the equation

$$\frac{d^2y}{dx^2} = x\left[1 + \left(\frac{dy}{dx}\right)^2\right]$$

subject to $x = 0$, $\frac{dy}{dx} = 1$, $y = 0$ at intervals of 0.05 in x in the range $0 < x < 0.5$ correct to four decimal places.

5. Tabulate y and $\frac{dy}{dx}$ at intervals of 0.1 in x for the range $0 < x < 0.8$ correct to four decimal places to satisfy the equation

$$\frac{d^2y}{dx^2} + 4x\frac{dy}{dx} - 4y = 0$$

subject to $x = 0$, $y = 0.5$, $\frac{dy}{dx} = 0.2$.

6. Integrate the equation in 5, giving only the values of y by making the substitution $y = v \cdot e^{-x^2}$ and integrating the resulting equation in normal form for v.

7. Integrate the following equations correct to four decimal places giving y at intervals of 0·05 in x.

$\begin{cases} (a)\ \dfrac{d^2y}{dx^2} = (x^2 + 1)y, \text{ where } x = 0,\ y = 0,\ \dfrac{dy}{dx} = 1, \qquad 0 < x < 0\cdot 5. \\[2ex] (b)\ \dfrac{d^2y}{dx^2} = (y^2 + 1)x, \text{ where } x = 0,\ y = 0,\ \dfrac{dy}{dx} = 1, \qquad 0 < x < 0\cdot 5. \end{cases}$

17. Integration of differential equations of the types

$$\frac{d^2y}{dx^2} + \phi(x, y) = 0$$

$$\frac{d^2y}{dx^2} = f\!\left(x,\, y,\, \frac{dy}{dx}\right)$$

subject to $x = x_0,\ y = y_0;\ x = x_1,\ y = y_1.$

In the practical application of differential equations of the type

$$\frac{d^2y}{dx^2} + \phi(x, y) = 0 \quad . \quad . \quad . \quad . \quad (1)$$

it is very frequently the case that a numerical solution is required, subject to boundary conditions of the type: $x = x_0,\ y = y_0;\ x = x_1,\ y = y_1;$ error in y everywhere less than some given small number. A direct solution by expansion in a power series may fail because the range $(x_0,\ x_1)$ may be greater than the radius of convergence of the series, while an application of the process of continuation, where the number representing the slope at $(x_0,\ y_0)$ is carried forward from series to series, is burdensome and inconvenient.

The simplest method of approach to a graphical solution would be by means of the sequence

$$y_{r+1} = -\int_{x_0}^{x} dt \int_{x_0}^{t} dt\,\phi(t,\, y_r) + Ax + B. \quad . \quad (2)$$

where A and B are determined at each stage by making y_{r+1} conform to the required boundary conditions. This can best be effected graphically by sketching in any first approximation y_r satisfying the required conditions. Using the sequence (2) in the form

$$\frac{d^2 y_{r+1}}{dx^2} = - \chi(x, y_r) \quad . \quad . \quad . \quad . \quad (3)$$

$d^2 y_{r+1}/dx^2$ is then sketched in on an x base. Integrating this curve by means of a planimeter or otherwise, the shape of the curve dy_{r+1}/dx in the range (x_0, x_1) is determined, but its position is not. To make dy_{r+1}/dx conform to the required boundary conditions, any one possible curve for dy_{r+1}/dx is integrated between x_0 and x_1, and the displacement of this curve parallel to the y axis required to make this integral equal $y_1 - y_0$ is easily calculated. The next approximation y_{r+1} is thus definitely determined, and the process may be repeated until the difference between two successive approximations is less than the error initially postulated as allowable. If an error of $\frac{1}{2}$ per cent. is permissible in the final result, this may be attained graphically with comparative rapidity (see p. 54); but if greater accuracy is desirable it is usually necessary to compute the values of the integrals arithmetically. A suitable method is described later on p. 164.

A process similar to the above is clearly applicable to equations of the type

$$\frac{d^2 y}{dx^2} = f\left(x, y, \frac{dy}{dx}\right)$$

the sequence used being

$$y_{r+1}'' = f(x, y_r, y_r')$$

i.e. $$y_{r+1} = \int_{x_0}^{x_1} dt \int_{x_0}^{t} f(t, y_r, y_r') dt + Ax + B.$$

An examination of the conditions under which this sequence of steps is convergent leads, however, to the conclusion that it is subject to restrictions in application similar to those referred to in the case of an attempted solution by expansion in a power series, viz. that the sequence is convergent only over a limited range (see p. 58).

Equations of the above type are readily integrated by processes already described when x_0, y_0, and $\left(\dfrac{dy}{dx}\right)_0$ are given, by step-by-step forward integration, a process which can be carried out with almost any desired precision. The difficulty with the boundary conditions in the above form is to find the particular value of $\left(\dfrac{dy}{dx}\right)_0$ which yields the value of $y = y_1$ when $x = x_1$ after integration. If an equation with boundary conditions of this type arises in the course of a scientific investigation, it is probable that the general form of the solution in the given range is known ; if, however, nothing whatsoever is known of the solution except that it passes through the two end-points, then a preliminary evaluation of $f(x, y)$ in the region between the two boundary points will indicate how the curve must lie, since $\dfrac{d^2y}{dx^2}$ indicates the sign of the curvature.

Having found the general trend of the solution, the integration is begun by assuming a tentative value of $\dfrac{dy}{dx}$ initially. The first integration over the range need not be carried out very accurately, but this first solution will usually indicate how to approach a more accurate second solution satisfying the boundary conditions, demonstrating, as it does, how the required solution probably behaves in the region considered. The approximation can be adjusted to suit this behaviour. This will lead to an approximate solution for which the final ordinate is closer to y_1 than before. Plot $\left(\dfrac{dy}{dx}\right)_0$ against y_1 in the two cases, and inter- polate a better value of $\left(\dfrac{dy}{dx}\right)_0$. The succeeding solutions may now be made more accurate, and the above process of interpolating a better value of $\left(\dfrac{dy}{dx}\right)_0$ continued until a solution is obtained which is sufficiently accurate. An important method of obtaining an accurate solution when an approximate solution is found as above is given after the following two examples.

Example.—Consider the equation

$$\frac{d^2y}{dx^2} + 2 \cdot \sqrt{(e^{-2x} - y^2)} = 0$$

subject to
$$\begin{matrix} x = 0 \\ y = 0 \end{matrix} \Bigg\} \qquad \begin{matrix} x = 0.5 \\ y = 0.25 \end{matrix} \Bigg\}$$

$\frac{d^2y}{dx^2} = -2$ at $x = 0$, $y = 0$, and is less than this at all other possible values of x and y in the range. As x changes from 0 to 0·5, the greatest possible value of y is 1.

The solution for $\left(\frac{dy}{dx}\right)_0 = 0.5$ is first obtained, and then the solution for $\left(\frac{dy}{dx}\right)_0 = 1$. From these the value of $\left(\frac{dy}{dx}\right)_0$ is interpolated as

$$0.5 + \frac{1 - 0.5}{0.2907 - 0.0564} \times 0.1936$$
$$= 0.5 + 0.413$$
$$= 0.913.$$

The differential equation is again integrated, and the values are corrected until an accuracy of four figures is obtained. The three corresponding pairs of values of $\left(\frac{dy}{dx}\right)_0$ and y_1 are now plotted to see how the values of y_1 are varying with those of $\left(\frac{dy}{dx}\right)_0$, and it is found that a linear interpolation from the last two solutions for $\left(\frac{dy}{dx}\right)_0$ would probably give four-figure accuracy in the next solution. This gives $\left(\frac{dy}{dx}\right)_0 = 0.9207$, and the subsequent integration shows that the accuracy is everywhere within $\frac{1}{2,500}$.

The following are the tabulated results.

x.	x.	0.	0·1.	0·2.	0·3.	0·4.	0·5.
$\dfrac{d^2y}{dx^2}$	1st soln.	-2	$-1\cdot812$	$-1\cdot642$	$-1\cdot476$	$-1\cdot339$	$-1\cdot209$
	2nd ,,	-2	$-1\cdot800$	$-1\cdot610$	$-1\cdot414$	$-1\cdot235$	$-1\cdot066$
	3rd ,,	-2	$-1\cdot803$	$-1\cdot612$	$-1\cdot432$	$-1\cdot268$	$-1\cdot119$
	4th ,,	-2	$-1\cdot802$	$-1\cdot611$	$-1\cdot430$	$-1\cdot260$	$-1\cdot105$
$\dfrac{dy}{dx}$	(1)	0·5000	0·3100	0·1370	$-0\cdot0185$	$-0\cdot1591$	$-0\cdot2865$
	(2)	1	0·810	0·640	0·488	0·356	0·240
	(3)	0·913	0·723	0·552	0·400	0·265	0·146
	(4)	0·9207	0·7306	0·5601	0·5081	0·2737	0·1556
y	(1)	0·0000	0·0407	0·0626	0·0687	0·0594	0·0564
	(2)	0·0000	0·0904	0·1627	0·2190	0·2611	0·2907
	(3)	0·0000	0·0816	0·1452	0·1926	0·2258	0·2461
	(4)	0·0000	0·0824	0·1468	0·1950	0·2290	0·2501

The method of solution indicated above can clearly be extended to differential equations of the type

$$\frac{d^2y}{dx^2} + f\left(x,\, y,\, \frac{dy}{dx}\right) = 0.$$

Example.—Solution of

$$\frac{d^2y}{dx^2} + x^2y\,\frac{dy}{dx} + x\log_{10}(2+y) + x^2 + 2x = 0$$

subject to the end conditions

$$\left.\begin{array}{c} x = 0 \\ y = 0 \end{array}\right\} \qquad \left.\begin{array}{c} x = 0\cdot4 \\ y = 0\cdot5 \end{array}\right\}$$

The equation is first written in the form

$$\frac{dz}{dx} = -\,[x^2yz + x\log_{10}(2+y) + x^2 + 2x]$$

$$\frac{dy}{dx} = z$$

Beginning with $\left(\dfrac{dy}{dx}\right)_0 = 1$, the first solution is found, and following this the solution for $\left(\dfrac{dy}{dx}\right)_0 = 1\cdot2$.

Interpolating from these two solutions, the third solution is found with $\left(\dfrac{dy}{dx}\right)_0 = 1\cdot322$. The result is to give the required solution correct to approximately $\frac{1}{500}$ everywhere. The solutions obtained are tabulated below.

x.		0.	0·1.	0·2.	0·3.	0·4.
$\dfrac{d^2y}{dx^2}$	(1)	0	−0·243	−0·516	−0·821	−1·158
	(2)	0	−0·244	−0·521	−0·836	−1·189
	(3)	0	−0·2446	−0·5243	−0·8456	−1·2092
$\dfrac{dy}{dx}$	(1)	1	0·988	0·950	0·883	0·780
	(2)	1·2	1·881	1·1509	1·0835	0·9834
	(3)	1·3220	1·3101	1·2719	1·2038	1·1014
y	(1)	0	0·0994	0·1963	0·2879	0·3711
	(2)	0	0·1196	0·2368	0·3488	0·4524
	(3)	0	0·1318	0·2611	0·3852	0·5007

17.1. To obtain a more accurate solution of the foregoing differential equations.

It is proposed to use the sequence

$$[\Delta^2 y_{r-1}]_{n+1} = h^2[y_r'' + \tfrac{1}{12}\Delta^2 y_{r-1}]_n$$

to improve the accuracy of the solution of the equation

$$\frac{d^2y}{dx^2} = -2\sqrt{(e^{-2x} - y^2)}$$

already integrated above.

Referring to the table of values of y'' on p. 166, and quoted again below,

$$\Delta^2 y_0 = 0{\cdot}01[-1{\cdot}802 + \tfrac{1}{12} \times -0{\cdot}007]$$
$$= -0{\cdot}018026.$$

In a similar manner the table below is completed.

$\dfrac{d^2y}{dx^2}$.	Δ.	Δ^2.	$\Delta^2 y$.	
−2				
	198			
−1·802		− 7	−0·01826	× 4 = − 0·072104
	191			
−1·611		−10	−0·016118	× 3 = − 0·048354
	181			
−1·430		−11	−0·014309	× 2 = − 0·028618
	170			
−1·260		−15	−0·012613	× 1 = − 0·012613
	155			
−1·105				Total 0·161689

Since the values of $\Delta^2 y$ have all been determined, it remains to insert one value of Δy, and the table may be completed. In general, it is better to insert this value at the centre of the range, and, by using it, build up the complete table of values as linear functions of this entry. Now make the solution satisfy the end conditions, and the value of Δy inserted may be calculated. Let $\Delta y_0 = k$ then in this manner it may readily be seen that

$$k = \tfrac{1}{6}[(4\Delta^2 y_0 + 3\Delta^2 y_1 + 2\Delta^2 y_2 + \Delta^2 y_3) + 0.25]$$
$$= \tfrac{1}{6} \times (0.25 + 0.161689). \quad \text{See above table.}$$
$$= 0.082338.$$

The new table of values of y is therefore

$y.$	$y''.$			$\Delta^2 y.$	$y.$
0	-2				0
		19,783			
0.082338	-1.80217		$-\frac{648}{12} = -54$	-0.018027	0.0823366
		19,135			
0.146650	-1.61082		$-\frac{1001}{12} = -83.4$	-0.016117	0.1466462
		18,134			
0.194844	-1.42948		$-\frac{1204}{12} = -100.3$	-0.014305	0.1948388
		16,930			
0.228729	-1.26018		$-\frac{1434}{12} = -119.5$	-0.012614	0.2287264
		15,496			
0.250001	-1.10522				0.2500000

From the above table of values of y the values of y'' are recalculated and $\Delta^2 y$ is again determined, and the table of y's is built up as already described. The values are incorporated in the table, and from these results the final values of y are determined correct to five significant figures. It should be noticed that the above more accurate sequence method is only applied after the solution has been determined to a degree of accuracy which justifies its use, and is described here as especially applicable to equations of this type. If a more accurate solution of the second example is desired, the sequence method is used, but the integrations are carried out by a different process, such as have been described, and the boundary conditions are satisfied by making the solution pass through the initial and final points by adding $Ax + B$ to the values of y. A approaches a limiting value as the solution becomes more accurate.

The case of linear differential equations.

In the case of linear differential equations of any order the difficulty already referred to, regarding the terminal conditions when these refer to points further apart than the legitimate range of integration, can be avoided in a very simple manner. The method is quite general, but may be illustrated without any real restriction by the case of a linear equation of the second order, viz.

$$\frac{d^2y}{dx^2} + P(x)\frac{dy}{dx} + Q(x)y = 0 \quad . \quad . \quad . \quad (1)$$

Let the terminal conditions be of the form

$$L_1\left[y_1, y_2 \ldots \left(\frac{dy}{dx}\right)_1, \left(\frac{dy}{dx}\right)_2 \ldots\right] = 0 \quad . \quad . \quad (2)$$

$$L_2\left[y_1, y_2 \ldots \left(\frac{dy}{dx}\right)_1, \left(\frac{dy}{dx}\right)_2 \ldots\right] = 0 \quad . \quad . \quad (3)$$

two relations connecting the ordinates and differential coefficients at a finite series of positions.

By any of the methods already developed determine any two numerical solutions of (1) covering at least the whole range of x involved in (2) and (3), and subject to *any* simple terminal conditions; for example, $x = 0$, $y = 1$, $\frac{dy}{dx} = 0$, and $x = 0$, $y = 0$, $\frac{dy}{dx} = 1$. Then, if these be

$$y = u \quad \text{and} \quad y = v,$$

any other solution of (1) from the general theory of linear differential equations may be written

$$y = Au + Bv,$$

where A and B are definite constants to be determined.

Both these constants can immediately be found from conditions (2) and (3), for each of the numbers

$$\ldots y_1, y_2 \ldots \left(\frac{dy}{dx}\right)_1, \left(\frac{dy}{dx}\right)_2 \ldots$$

are either known explicitly or as linear functions of A and B, and consequently (2) and (3) provide two relations to determine A and B. When the relations (2) and (3) are linear in the elements A and B, the final solution will be unique.

73.2. A sequence method applicable over a wide range to equations of the type

$$\frac{d^2y}{dx^2} + \phi(x, y) = 0$$

subject to $x = x_0, y = y_0; x = x_1, y = y_1$.

If (x_0, x_1) be greater than the range of convergence of the sequence method which has been described, there does not appear to be any simple modification of the process that will enable the solution to be constructed. It is eminently desirable for practical purposes that a process be derived which will lead to a solution subject to the given boundary conditions, and whose convergence is independent of the range (x_0, x_1).

Consider the equation

$$\frac{d^2y}{dx^2} + n^2\phi(x, y) = 0 \quad . \quad . \quad . \quad . \quad (1)$$

and let the solution be required to satisfy the conditions

$$x = 0, y = a; x = l, y = b \quad . \quad . \quad . \quad (2)$$

Writing (4) in the form

$$(D^2 + n^2)y = n^2[y - \phi(x, y)]$$

the differential equation is directly transformable into the integral equation

$$y = A \sin nx + B \cos nx + n\int_0^x dt[y - \phi(t, y)] \sin n(t - x) \quad (3)$$

where A and B are arbitrary constants.
To satisfy conditions (2) we require

$$\left. \begin{array}{l} A \sin nl = b - a \cos nl - n\int_0^l dt[y - \phi] \sin n(t - l) \\ B = a \end{array} \right\} \quad . \quad (4)$$

and (3) takes the form

$$y = \frac{b \sin nx + a \sin (l - x)}{\sin nl}$$
$$+ \frac{n \sin n(x - l)}{\sin nl} \int_0^x dt \sin nt(y - \phi)$$
$$+ \frac{n \sin nx}{\sin nl} \int_x^l dt \sin n(t - l)(y - \phi) \quad . \quad (5)$$

Consider the sequence

$$y_{r+1} = \frac{b \sin nx + a \sin (l - x)}{\sin nl}$$
$$+ \frac{n \sin n(x - l)}{\sin nl} \int_0^x dt \sin nt[y_r - \phi(t, y_r)]$$
$$+ \frac{n \sin nx}{\sin nl} \int_x^l dt \sin n(t - l)[y_r - \phi(t, y_r)] \quad . \quad (6)$$

It is clear that at each stage y_{r+1} satisfies the conditions

$$x = 0, \ y_{r+1} = a; \quad x = l, \ y_{r+1} = b.$$

Let $\epsilon_{r+1} = y_{r+1} - y$, $\epsilon_r = y_r - y, \ldots$, where y is defined by the integral equation (5), then, from (5) and (6),

$$\epsilon_{r+1} = - n \sin nx \int_x^l dt \, \epsilon_r \left[1 - \left(\frac{\partial \phi}{\partial y} \right)_\mu \right] \cos nt$$
$$- n \cos nx \int_0^x dt \, \epsilon_r \left[1 - \left(\frac{\partial \phi}{\partial y} \right)_\mu \right] \sin nt$$
$$+ n \cot nl \sin nx \int_0^l dt \, \epsilon_r \left[1 - \left(\frac{\partial \phi}{\partial y} \right)_\mu \right] \sin nt \quad . \quad (7)$$

provided ϕ is continuous over the range (y_r, y) and $(\partial\phi/\partial y)_\mu$ is a value of $\partial\phi/\partial y$ at some value of y in that range for each value of x.

Let $$J_r(x) \equiv \epsilon_r \left[1 - \left(\frac{\partial \phi}{\partial y} \right)_\mu \right]; \quad \cdots \quad (8)$$

then since $y_{r+1} = y$ at $x = 0$ and $x = l$, $\epsilon_r = 0$ at these points, and, therefore, if $\partial\phi/\partial y$ is finite,

$$J_r(0) = 0 \quad \text{and} \quad J_r(l) = 0.$$

Let there be a finite number p of maxima and minima in $J_r(x)$ between $x = 0$ and $x = l$ occurring at

$$x = x_t \quad (t = 1, 2, \ldots, p),$$

then in the successive ranges

$$(0, x_1), (x_1, x_2) \ldots (x_t, x), (x, x_{t+1}), \ldots, (x_p, l),$$

$J_r(x)$ is monotonic.

Consider the first integral in the expression for ϵ_{r+1}, viz.

$$K = \int_x^l J_r(t) \cos nt \, dt$$
$$= \int_x^{x_{t+1}} + \int_{x_{t+1}}^{x_{t+2}} + \ldots + \int_{x_p}^l.$$

Since $J_r(t)$ is monotonic within each one of the successive ranges,

$$nK = J_r(x)[\sin n\xi_1 - \sin nx] \\
\qquad\qquad + J_r(x_{t+1})[\sin nx_{t+1} - \sin n\xi_1] \\
+ J_r(x_{t+1})[\sin n\xi_2 - \sin nx_{t+1}] \\
\qquad\qquad + J_r(x_{t+2})[\sin nx_{t+2} - \sin n\xi_2] \\
+ \quad . \qquad . \qquad . \qquad . \qquad . \\
+ J_r(x_p)[\sin n\xi_{p-t+1} - \sin nx_p] \\
\qquad\qquad + J_r(l)[\sin nl - \sin n\xi_{p-t+1}],$$

where $\qquad\qquad x_{t+s-1} < \xi_s < x_{t+s}.$

Similarly, for the second integral in the expression for ϵ_{r+1}, viz.

$$L = \int_0^x J_r(t) \sin nt \, dt$$
$$= \int_0^{x_1} + \int_{x_1}^{x_2} + \ldots + \int_{x_t}^x.$$

Since $J_r(t)$ is monotonic within the range of each subintegral,

$$nL = J_r(0)[1 - \cos n\eta_1] + J_r(x_1)[\cos n\eta_1 - \cos nx_1] \\
+ J_r(x_1)[\cos nx_1 - \cos n\eta_2] \\
\qquad\qquad + J_r(x_2)[\cos n\eta_2 - \cos nx_2] \\
+ \quad . \qquad . \qquad . \qquad . \qquad . \\
+ J_r(x_t)[\cos nx_t - \cos n\eta_{t+1}] \\
\qquad\qquad + J_r(x)[\cos n\eta_{t+1} - \cos nx],$$

where $\qquad\qquad x_s > \eta_s > x_{s-1}.$

If M be the greatest absolute value of $J_r(x)$ which can occur in the range $(0, l)$, it follows that

$$|nK \sin nx + nL \cos nx| < M(2p + 1).$$

In the same manner it will readily be seen that the third integral in the expression for ϵ_{r+1} is less than $2pM/n$. Hence

$$|\epsilon_{r+1}| < M(2p + 1 + 2p\lambda) \quad . \quad . \quad . \quad (9)$$

where

$$\lambda = |\cot nl| \quad . \quad . \quad . \quad . \quad (10)$$

Since $J_r(x) = \epsilon_r \left[1 - \left(\dfrac{\partial \phi}{\partial y} \right)_\mu \right]$, from the definition of M, it follows that

$$M < \epsilon_r' \left| 1 - \dfrac{\partial \phi}{\partial y} \right|_{\text{max.}},$$

where ϵ_r' is the maximum value of ϵ_r that occurs in the range $(0, l)$.

Thus from (9),

$$|\epsilon_{r+1}| < \epsilon_r' \left| 1 - \dfrac{\partial \phi}{\partial y} \right|_{\text{max.}} \{1 + 2p(1 + \lambda)\},$$

where $|\epsilon_{r+1}|$ is, of course, a function of x.
In particular therefore,

$$\epsilon_{r+1}' < \epsilon_r' \left| 1 - \dfrac{\partial \phi}{\partial y} \right|_{\text{max.}} \{1 + 2p(1 + \lambda)\},$$

$$\epsilon_r' < \epsilon_{r-1}' \left| 1 - \dfrac{\partial \phi}{\partial y} \right|_{\text{max.}} \{1 + 2p(1 + \lambda)\}$$

$$. \quad . \quad . \quad . \quad . \quad .$$

$$\epsilon_2' < \epsilon_1' \left| 1 - \dfrac{\partial \phi}{\partial y} \right|_{\text{max.}} \{1 + 2p(1 + \lambda\}.$$

Hence $\epsilon_{r+1}' < \epsilon_1'\{1 + 2p(1 + \lambda)\}^r \left| 1 - \dfrac{\partial \phi}{\partial y} \right|_{\text{max}}^r \quad . \quad . \quad (11)$

all the numbers involved being positive.

Provided $\quad \{1 + 2p(1 + \lambda)\} \left| 1 - \dfrac{\partial \phi}{\partial y} \right|_{\text{max.}} < 1, \quad . \quad (12)$

there exists a number ρ, such that for $r > \rho$, ϵ_{r+1}', and *a fortiori* $|\epsilon_{r+1}|$ can be made less than any given positive number, however small, no matter what (finite) quantity ϵ_1' (*i.e.* what finite function of x, ϵ_1) may be. Hence the sequence (6) converges, provided

$$1 - \frac{1}{1 + 2p(1 + \lambda)} < \frac{\partial \phi}{\partial y} < 1 + \frac{1}{1 + 2p(1 + \lambda)} \quad . \quad (13)$$

within the range $(0, l)$. In this condition the only number explicitly involving l is $\lambda = |\cot nl|$, and with this we shall deal presently.

Differentiate the sequence (6) twice with respect to x, then

$$\frac{d^2 y_{r+1}}{dx^2} = -n^2 y_{r+1} + n^2[y_r - \phi(x, y_r)] \quad . \quad . \quad (14)$$

i.e. $\quad \dfrac{d^2 y_{r+1}}{dx^2} + n^2 \phi(x, y_{r+1})$

$$= n^2[y_r - y_{r+1} - \phi(x, y_r) + \phi(x, y_{r+1})]$$

$$= n^2(\epsilon_r - \epsilon_{r+1})\left[1 - \left(\frac{\partial \phi}{\partial y}\right)_r\right] \quad . \quad . \quad (15)$$

where $(\partial \phi / \partial y)_r$ is a value of $\partial \phi / \partial y$ at a value of y intermediate between y_r and y_{r+1}, and is therefore finite. Hence from (11) and (13) a number σ can be found, such that for $r > \sigma$ the right-hand side of (15) can be made less than any given positive number τ, however small. Hence the value of y derived from the sequence (6) can be made to approach the solution of the differential equation

$$\frac{d^2 y}{dx^2} + n^2 \phi(x, y) = 0 \quad . \quad . \quad . \quad . \quad (1)$$

to any desired degree of closeness, and satisfy the boundary conditions

$$x = 0, y = a, x = l, y = b.$$

It remains to consider how far the convergence depends on the range, as implied by (13).

Consider the differential equation

$$\frac{d^2 y}{dx^2} + \chi(x, y) = 0 \quad . \quad . \quad . \quad . \quad (16)$$

This may be written in the form

$$\frac{d^2y}{dx^2} + n^2 \frac{\chi(x, y)}{n^2} = 0, \quad . \quad . \quad . \quad (17)$$

where n is arbitrary. Condition (13) then states that the present method of solution will certainly be valid, if M and m being the maximum and minimum values (positive) of $\partial\chi/\partial y$ which can occur in the range, it is possible to find a real number n such that

$$M < n^2 + \frac{n^2}{1 + 2p(1 + |\cot nl|)} \quad . \quad . \quad (18)$$

$$m > n^2 - \frac{n^2}{1 + 2p(1 + |\cot nl|)} \quad . \quad . \quad (19)$$

p being some unknown positive integer.

In practice, none of the numbers in (18) and (19), except l, are known exactly; but M and m can usually be estimated roughly, and a suitable value of n selected intermediate between $\sqrt{M}$ and $\sqrt{m}$. Moreover, the range of variation of $\partial\chi/\partial y$ permissible may be in point of fact much greater than that specified by (18) and (19), which are merely conditions sufficient to ensure convergence. For reasons apparent, however, from these conditions, care must be taken to avoid choosing n in the immediate neighbourhood of $s\pi/l$, where s is an integer. If it is convenient to choose $n = (2s + 1)\pi/2l$, the sequence solution for (1), convergent over the whole range takes the simpler form

$$y_{r+1} = (-1)^s b \sin (2s + 1) \frac{\pi x}{2l} + a \cos (2s + 1) \frac{\pi x}{2l}$$

$$- (2s + 1) \frac{\pi}{2l} \left[\sin \frac{(2s + 1)\pi x}{2l} \int_x^l dt[y_r - \phi(t, y_r)] \cos \frac{(2s + 1)\pi t}{2l} \right.$$

$$\left. + \cos (2s + 1) \frac{\pi x}{2l} \int_0^x dt[y_r - \phi(t, y_r)] \sin \frac{(2s + 1)\pi t}{2l} \right] \quad . \quad (20)$$

and (4) becomes

$$\frac{d^2y}{dx^2} + \frac{(2s + 1)^2 \pi^2}{4l^2} \phi(x, y) = 0 \quad . \quad . \quad (21)$$

For practical convenience in calculation it is better to use the sequence (6) in the form

$$y_{r+1} = A_r \sin nx + a \cos nx$$
$$+ n \sin nx \int_0^x dt[y_r - \phi(t, y_r)] \cos nt$$
$$- n \cos nx \int_0^x dt[y_r - \phi(t, y_r)] \sin nt,$$

where
$$A_r = \frac{b - a \cos nl}{\sin nl} - n \int_0^l dt[y_r - \phi(t, y_r)] \cos nt$$
$$+ n \cot nl \int_0^l dt[y_r - \phi(t, y_r)] \sin nt.$$

The two integrals in the expression for y_{r+1} can be evaluated graphically or arithmetically for any approximate solution y_r, and in doing so, the evaluation of the two integrals in the expression for A_r is incidentally accomplished.

It may be remarked that the same method may be applied, subject to corresponding restrictions, to equations of the type

$$\frac{d^2y}{dx^2} + \phi\left(x, y, \frac{dy}{dx}\right) = 0,$$

and even to equations of higher order.

In the simpler case, where the boundary conditions refer to one point only, the process here explained may be applied with equal success.

Let the differential equation be

$$\frac{d^2y}{dx^2} + n^2\phi(x, y) = 0 \quad \cdot \quad \cdot \quad \cdot \quad \cdot \quad (1)$$

subject to the conditions

$$x = 0, \quad y = A, \quad \frac{dy}{dx} = B.$$

Consider the sequence

$$y_{r+1} = A \cos nx + B \sin nx$$
$$+ n \sin nx \int_0^x \cos nt[y_r - \phi(t, y_r)]dt$$
$$- n \cos nx \int_0^x \sin nt[y_r - \phi(t, y_r)]dt \quad \cdot \quad (22)$$

A and B being now given constants.

We note that when

$$x = 0, \quad y_{r+1} = A, \quad \text{and} \quad \frac{dy_{r+1}}{dx} = B.$$

As before, defining y by equation (22), when y has been substituted for y_{r+1} and y_r, we have

$$\epsilon_{r+1} = n \sin nx \int_0^x \epsilon_r \left[1 - \left(\frac{\partial \phi}{\partial y} \right)_\mu \right] \cos nt \, dt$$
$$- n \cos nx \int_0^x \epsilon_r \left[1 - \left(\frac{\partial \phi}{\partial y} \right)_\mu \right] \sin nt \, dt$$

where $(\partial \phi / \partial y)_\mu$ is the value of $\partial \phi / \partial y$ at some value of y intermediate between y and y_r for each value of t.

Thus $\qquad \epsilon_{r+1} = n \int_0^x J_r(t) \sin n(x - t) dt,$

where $\qquad J_r(x) = \epsilon_r \left[1 - \left(\frac{\partial \phi}{\partial y} \right)_\mu \right],$

since $\epsilon_{r+1} = 0$ when $x = 0$, $J_r(0) = 0$.

Let the successive maxima and minima of $J_r(x)$ occur at $x_1, x_2, \ldots, x_p$; $J_r(x)$ is monotonic in the ranges $(0, x_1)$, $(x_1, x_2), \ldots, (x_p, x)$.

Therefore $\qquad \epsilon_{r+1} = n[I_1 + I_2 + \ldots + I_p + I_x],$

where

$$nI_1 = n \int_0^{x_1} J_r(t) \sin n(x - t) dt$$
$$= nJ_r(0) \int_0^{\xi_1} \sin n(x - t) dt + nJ_r(x_1) \int_{\xi_1}^{x_1} \sin n(x - t) dt$$
$$= J_r(x_1)[\cos n(x - x_1) - \cos n(x - \xi_1)]$$
$$nI_2 = J_r(x_1)[\cos n(x - \xi_2) - \cos n(x - x_1)]$$
$$+ J_r(x_2)[\cos n(x - x_2) - \cos n(x - \xi_2)]$$
$$nI_3 = J_r(x_2)[\cos n(x - \xi_3) - \cos n(x - x_2)]$$
$$+ J_r(x_3)[\cos n(x - x_3) - \cos n(x - \xi_3)]$$

$$\qquad \cdot \qquad \cdot \qquad \cdot \qquad \cdot \qquad \cdot \qquad \cdot$$

$$nI_p = J_r(x_{p-1})[\cos n(x - \xi_p) - \cos n(x - x_{p-1})]$$
$$+ J_r(x_p)[\cos n(x - x_p) - \cos n(x - \xi_p)]$$
$$nI_x = J_r(x_p)[\cos n(x - \xi_{p+1}) - \cos n(x - x_p)]$$
$$+ J_r(x)[1 - \cos n(x - \xi_{p+1})].$$

Hence if M be the maximum absolute value of $J_r(x)$ which can occur in the range $(0, x)$

$$|\epsilon_{r+1}| < 2M(p+1).$$

Now since $\quad J_r(x) = \epsilon_r\left[1 - \left(\dfrac{\partial\phi}{\partial y}\right)_\mu\right],$

it follows as before that

$$\epsilon_{r+1} < 2(p+1)\epsilon_r'\left|1 - \left(\dfrac{\partial\phi}{\partial y}\right)\right|_{\text{max.}}$$

Hence $\quad \epsilon_r' < 2(p+1)\epsilon_{r-1}'\left|1 - \dfrac{\partial\phi}{\partial y}\right|_{\text{max.}}$

$$\cdot \quad \cdot \quad \cdot \quad \cdot \quad \cdot \quad \cdot \quad \cdot \quad \cdot \quad \cdot \quad \cdot$$

$$\epsilon_2' < 2(p+1)\epsilon_1'\left|1 - \dfrac{\partial\phi}{\partial y}\right|_{\text{max.}}$$

Thus $\quad \epsilon_{r+1}' < 2^r(p+1)^r\left|1 - \dfrac{\partial\phi}{\partial y}\right|_{\text{max.}}^r \epsilon_1' \quad . \quad . \quad . \quad$ (23)

where ϵ_r' is the maximum absolute value of ϵ_r that occurs in the range $(0, x)$.

Hence provided $2(p+1)\left|1 - \dfrac{\partial\phi}{\partial y}\right|_{\text{max.}} < 1 \quad . \quad .$ (24)

there exists a quantity ρ such that for $r > \rho$, ϵ_{r+1}' can be made less than any assigned positive number, however small, no matter what (finite) value ϵ_1' may have.

It follows that, subject to the restriction (24), the sequence (22) converges. It converges, moreover, to the solution of equation (1), for from (22)

$$\frac{d^2y_{r+1}}{dx^2} = -n^2y_{r+1} + n^2y_r - n^2\phi(x, y_r).$$

Thus

$$\frac{d^2y_{r+1}}{dx^2} + n^2\phi(x, y_{r+1})$$
$$= n^2[\phi(x, y_{r+1}) - \phi(x, y_r) - y_{r+1} + y_r]$$
$$= n^2(\epsilon_{r+1} - \epsilon_r)\left[\left(\frac{\partial\phi}{\partial y}\right)_v - 1\right] \quad . \quad . \quad . \quad (25)$$

where $(\partial\phi/\partial y)_v$ is the value of $\partial\phi/\partial y$ at some value of y intermediate between y_{r+1} and y_r for each value of x.

From (24), $\partial\phi/\partial y - 1$ always remains finite, and from (23) $\epsilon_{r+1} - \epsilon_r$ can be diminished without limit by suitably increasing r.   Hence y_{r+1}, as derived from the sequence (22), can be made to approach as closely as we require to the solution of

$$\frac{d^2y}{dx^2} + n^2\phi(x, y) = 0 \quad . \quad . \quad . \quad . \quad (4)$$

$$x = 0, \quad y = A, \quad \frac{dy}{dx} = B.$$

There is no restriction on the range of validity of this sequence other than that implied by the inequality (24). This is equivalent to the requirement that $\partial\phi/\partial y$ shall be positive, and

$$1 - \frac{1}{2(p+1)} < \frac{\partial\phi}{\partial y} < 1 + \frac{1}{2(p+1)},$$

$$p \gg 0.$$

This condition, it should be noted, is independent of the number n^2.

If the equation for solution is

$$\frac{d^2y}{dx^2} + \chi(x, y) = 0,$$

the condition merely requires that a quantity n^2 shall be chosen, such that

$$\left.\begin{array}{l} M < n^2 + \dfrac{n^2}{2(p+1)} \\[3mm] m > n^2 - \dfrac{n^2}{2(p+1)} \end{array}\right\} \quad . \quad . \quad . \quad (26)$$

where M and m are the maximum and minimum values of $\partial\chi/\partial y$ in the range over which the solution is required. M and m can usually be estimated roughly at the commencement of the operation and a value of n^2 chosen midway between them.   Should it appear, after the integration has been effected over a portion of the range required, that the values of y are such as to cause a violation of the conditions (26), an adjusted value of n may be adopted from that

x	y_1	$(0.02 - xe^{-10x}) \times y_1 \cos x$	$(0.02 - xe^{-10x}) \times y_1 \sin x$	$\int_1$	$\int_2$	$\sin x \times \int_1$	$-\cos x \times \int_2$	$A_1 \sin x \int_2$	y_2	Col. 3 corrected.	Col. 4 corrected.	y_3
				$\times 10^{-4}$	$\times 10^{-4}$	$\times 10^{-4}$	$\times 10^{-4}$					
0·0	0·00	0·0000	0	0	0	0	0	0	0	0	0	0
0·1	0·10	−0·0017	−0·0002	−6	−1	−1	+1	0·0991	0·0991	−0·0017	−0·0002	0·0991
0·2	0·20	−0·0015	−0·0003	−25	−4	−5	+4	0·1971	0·1971	−0·0015	−0·0003	0·1971
0·3	0·30	+0·0015	+0·0004	−26	−4	−8	+4	0·2931	0·2931	+0·0014	−0·0004	0·2931
0·4	0·39	+0·0046	+0·0019	+4	+7	+2	−6	0·3862	0·3862	+0·0045	+0·0019	0·3862
0·5	0·48	+0·0070	+0·0038	+62	+36	+30	−32	0·4755	0·4755	+0·0070	+0·0038	0·4755
0·6	0·56	+0·0086	+0·0058	+130	+85	+73	−70	0·5601	0·5601	+0·0086	+0·0059	0·5601
0·7	0·64	+0·0095	+0·0080	+223	+155	+144	−119	0·6390	0·6392	+0·0096	+0·0081	0·6392
0·8	0·72	+0·0100	+0·0102	+322	+247	+231	−172	0·7116	0·7122	+0·0099	+0·0102	0·7122
0·9	0·78	+0·0096	+0·0122	+421	+361	+330	−224	0·7770	0·7781	+0·0097	+0·0122	0·7781
1·0	0·84	+0·0091	+0·0141	+515	+491	+433	−265	0·8347	0·8364	+0·0091	+0·0141	0·8364
1·1	0·89	+0·0081	+0·0158	+607	+641	+541	−291	0·8840	0·8865	+0·0081	+0·0159	0·8865
1·2	0·93	+0·0067	+0·0173	+682	+807	+636	−292	0·9245	0·9279	+0·0067	+0·0173	0·9279
1·3	0·96	+0·0052	+0·0185	+742	+987	+715	−264	0·9558	0·9603	+0·0052	+0·0186	0·9603
1·4	0·99	+0·0034	+0·0195	+785	+1177	+774	−200	0·9775	0·9832	+0·0033	+0·0194	0·9832
1·5	1·00	+0·0014	+0·0200	+809	+1375	+807	−97	0·9894	0·9965	+0·0014	+0·0200	0·9965
π/2	1·00	+0·0000	+0·0200	+814	+1575	+814	0	0·9919	1·00	+0·0000	+0·0200	1·00

point onwards, and by this process the integration may be effected over as wide a range as desired, provided only that $\partial\chi/\partial y$ remains positive.

A similar process may, of course, be adopted for the solution of the equation

$$\frac{d^2y}{dx^2} + \phi\left(x, y, \frac{dy}{dx}\right) = 0,$$

and, indeed, the whole method is capable of simple extension to differential equations of higher order.

Example.—The following numerical example will provide a fair indication of the rapidity of convergence of the sequence and the amount of labour involved in arriving at a solution.

$$\frac{d^2y}{dx^2} + (0.98 + xe^{-10x})y = 0,$$

$$x = 0, \ y = 0; \ x = \pi/2, \ y = 1.$$

Taking $n = 1$ the sequence solution is

$$y_{r+1} = A_r \sin x + \sin x \int_0^x y_r(0.02 - te^{-10t}) \cos t \, dt$$

$$- \cos x \int_0^x y_r(0.02 - te^{-10t}) \sin t \, dt,$$

$$A_r = 1 - \int_0^{\pi/2} y_r(0.02 - te^{-10t}) \cos t \, dt.$$

The first approximation is taken as $y_1 = \sin x$, tabulated on p. 180 to two places of decimals only. The two integrals in y_{r+1} were evaluated graphically by means of a planimeter, A_r being determined incidentally in the course of evaluating the first integral. It is to be noted that the second and third approximations y_2 and y_3 agree to four places, and therefore represent the solution to the degree of accuracy obtainable by means of a planimeter.

CHAPTER VI

SPECIAL METHODS APPLICABLE TO LINEAR DIFFERENTIAL EQUATIONS OF THE SECOND ORDER

In the previous chapters the methods of numerical solution that have been explained are in the main applicable to differential equations of any order and of all types. Many problems in mathematical physics, however, depend for their solution on differential equations of a much simpler kind. This arises from the fact that in seeking for special forms of solution of the partial differential equations of mathematical physics, the possibility of finding such solutions turns usually on the discovery of solutions of certain types of Ordinary Linear Differential Equations of the second order. Among such types may be cited, for example, the equations of Bessel, Legendre, Hill, Mathieu, and Emden. It is not the purpose of this chapter to discuss the general properties of the solutions of such equations, for each of these would occupy a volume in itself. We restrict ourselves rather to such general properties of differential equations of the second order as may assist us in arriving at a numerical solution by the easiest and most direct route.

We begin by showing that where any tabulated solution $y = y_1$ has already been found to any such equation, any other solution may be immediately derived by a straightforward process of numerical integration.

18. Properties of Linear Differential Equations of the Second Order.

Consider the equation

$$\frac{d^2y}{dx^2} + P(x)\frac{dy}{dx} + Q(x)y = R(x) \quad . \quad . \quad (1)$$

and let $y = y_1$ be any solution of the equation in which $R(x)$ is absent.   Then

$$\frac{d^2y_1}{dx^2} + P(x)\frac{dy_1}{dx} + Q(x)y_1 = 0.$$

Multiplying these two equations by y_1 and y, respectively, and subtracting

$$\left(y_1\frac{d^2y}{dx^2} - y\frac{d^2y_1}{dx^2}\right) + P(x)\left(y_1\frac{dy}{dx} - y\frac{dy_1}{dx}\right) = R(x)y_1,$$

or $$\frac{d}{dx}\left(y_1\frac{dy}{dx} - y\frac{dy_1}{dx}\right) + P(x)\left(y_1\frac{dy}{dx} - y\frac{dy_1}{dx}\right) = R(x)y_1.$$

This is a linear differential equation of the first order in $y_1\frac{dy}{dx} - y\frac{dy_1}{dx}$ and its integrating factor is $e^{\int(x)dx}$.   It follows that

$$\left(y_1\frac{dy}{dx} - y\frac{dy_1}{dx}\right)e^{\int Pdx} = A + \int_0^x R(x) \cdot y_1 e^{\int Pdx}\, dx,$$

or $$\frac{d}{dx}(y/y_1) \cdot y_1{}^2 e^{\int Pdx} = A + \int_0^x R(x)y_1 e^{\int Pdx}\, dx,$$

or

$$y/y_1 = A\int_0^x \frac{e^{-\int Pdx}}{y_1{}^2}\, dx + \int_0^x \frac{e^{-\int Pdx}}{y_1{}^2}\left[\int_0^x R(x) \cdot y_1 e^{\int Pdx}\, dx\right]dx + B.$$

It follows that if any solution $y = y_1$ of the differential equation (1) be determined when $R \equiv 0$, the two fundamental solutions of (1) may be taken as

$$y = y_1 \text{ and } y = y_1\int_0^x \frac{e^{-\int Pdx}dx}{y_1{}^2},$$

and the particular integral is

$$y = y_1 \int_0^x \frac{e^{-\int P dx}}{y_1{}^2} \left[\int_0^x R(x) y_1 e^{\int P dx} \, dx \right] dx.$$

Numerically, therefore, the original differential equation may be completely solved in all cases where integrals exist, for by the methods already developed a solution $y = y_1$ can be derived to any required degree of accuracy, and the determination of the remaining expressions involves nothing more than the tabulation of simple numerical functions, and their numerical integration. For the determination of any special solution or series of solutions satisfying given terminal conditions, the methods already developed may then be immediately applied.

If the equation is in the Normal Form (see § **18.1.**)

$$\frac{d^2y}{dx^2} + I(x)y = S(x)$$

the two fundamental integrals are

$$y = y_1, \quad y_2 = y_1 \int_0^x \frac{dx}{y_1{}^2},$$

and the particular integral is

$$y = y_1 \int_0^x \frac{dx}{y_1{}^2} \left[\int_0^x S(x) y_1 dx \right].$$

The complete solution can thus be derived from any particular numerical solution $y = y_1$ by three integrations.

In the special case where $S(x) \equiv 0$, the solution takes the form

$$y = Ay_1 + B \int_0^x \frac{dx}{y_1{}^2}.$$

If the boundary conditions are $x = 0$, $y = y(0)$; $x = x_0$, $y = y(x_0)$ then

$$A = y(0)/y_1(0); \quad B = \frac{y(x_0)y_1(0) - y(0)y_1(x_0)}{y_1(0) \displaystyle\int_0^{x_0} \frac{dx}{y_1{}^2}}.$$

In the following example the equation to be solved is
$$y'' - 2(1 + 2x^2)y = 0,$$
subject to three different sets of boundary conditions. It is assumed that *a* solution has already been found by any of the earlier methods, and this is tabulated in column I. The following table should then be self explanatory.

Example.
$$y'' - 2(1 + 2x^2)y = 0.$$

To find solutions with end conditions

(i) $x = 0,\ y = 1$ (ii) $x = 0,\ y = 1$ (iii) $x = 0,\ \ y = 1$
$\quad x = \tfrac{1}{2},\ y = 1$ $\qquad x = 1,\ y = 1$ $\qquad x \to \infty,\ \ y \to 0$

one solution $y = Y$, tabulated below, already having been found.

The general solution is
$$y = AY + BY \int_0^x \frac{dx}{Y^2}.$$

x.	Y.	$1/Y^2$.	$\int_0^x \frac{dx}{Y^2}$	$Z = Y\int_0^x \frac{dx}{Y^2}$	$Y - 0{\cdot}51705Z$.	$Y - 1{\cdot}056805Z$.	$Y - 1{\cdot}59577Z$.
0·0	1	1	0	0	1·00000	1·00000	1·00000
0·1	1·01005	0·980199	0·099337	0·100335	0·95817	0·90402	0·84994
0·2	1·04081	0·923118	0·194792	0·202741	0·93598	0·82655	0·71728
0·3	1·09417	0·835277	0·282931	0·309575	0·93410	0·76701	0·60016
0·4	1·17351	0·726150	0·361136	0·423797	0·95439	0·72564	0·49723
0·5	1·28403	0·606526	0·427812	0·549323	1·00000	0·70350	0·40744
0·6	1·43333	0·486752	0·482439	0·69149	1·07580	0·70256	0·32987
0·7	1·63232	0·375309	0·525443	0·85769	1·18885	0·72591	0·26364
0·8	1·89648	0·278038	0·557976	1·05819	1·34934	0·77818	0·20785
0·9	2·24791	0·197898	0·581625	1·30744	1·57190	0·86620	0·16154
1·0	2·71828	0·135335	0·598144	1·62592	1·87760	1·00000	0·12369
1·1	3·35348	0·088922	0·609232	2·04305	2·29712	1·19437	0·09325
1·2	4·22070	0·056135	0·616383	2·60157	2·87556	1·47135	0·06920
1·3	5·41948	0·034047	0·620815	3·36449			0·05052
1·4	7·09933	0·019841	0·623455	4·42611			0·03628
1·5	9·4878	0·011109	0·624965	5·9295			0·02562
1·6	12·9358	0·005976	0·625796	8·0952			0·01777
1·7	17·9933	0·003089	0·626235	11·2680			0·0121
1·8	25·5337	0·001534	0·626458	15·9958			0·0081
1·9	36·9661	0·000732	0·626566	23·1617			0·0054
2·0	54·5982	0·000335	0·626617	34·2122			0·0035
2·1	82·2696	0·000148	0·626640	51·5534			0·0022
2·2	126·470	0·000063	0·626650	79·252			(0·0014)
2·3	198·344	0·000025	0·626654	124·293			(0·0009)
2·4	317·348	0·000010	0·626656	198·868			(0·0004)
2·5	518·015	0·000004	0·626657	324·618			(0·0001)
2·6	862·64	0·000001	0·626657	540·48			(0·0000)
2·7		0·000000	0·626657				

For each solution

$$A = y(0), \ B = \frac{y(x_0) - Ay(x_0)}{y(x_0) \int_0^{x_0} \frac{dx}{y^2}}.$$

Thus here $A = 1$ in all cases.   Hence it follows that

(i) $B = \dfrac{1 - 1 \cdot 28403}{0 \cdot 549323} \ \ = - \ 0 \cdot 51705,$

(ii) $B = \dfrac{1 - 2 \cdot 71828}{1 \cdot 62592} \ \ = - \ 1 \cdot 056805,$

(iii) $B = - \ 1/0 \cdot 626657 = - \ 1 \cdot 59577.$

These values of A and B enable the solutions in the last three columns to be tabulated.

In the foregoing example the equation is in the Normal Form.   Every linear differential equation of the second order may be transformed to this type by a simple change of dependent or independent variable.

Transforming linear equations of the second order into Normal Form.

18.1. Method I.—The equation

$$\frac{d^2y}{dx^2} + P\frac{dy}{dx} + Qy = 0$$

may be thrown into the normal form by a change of dependent variable.   For example, let $y = uv$, where v is the new dependent variable and u is some function of x to be determined.   Then

$$\frac{dy}{dx} = u\frac{dv}{dx} + v\frac{du}{dx}$$

$$\frac{d^2y}{dx^2} = u\frac{d^2v}{dx^2} + 2\frac{du}{dx}\frac{dv}{dx} + v\frac{d^2u}{dx^2}.$$

On inserting these expressions for $\dfrac{dy}{dx}$ and $\dfrac{d^2y}{dx^2}$ into the original equation, it takes the form

$$u\frac{d^2v}{dx^2} + \frac{dv}{dx}\Big(2\frac{du}{dx} + Pu\Big) + v\Big(\frac{d^2u}{dx^2} + P\frac{du}{dx} + Qu\Big) = 0.$$

Now let u be chosen to ensure that

$$2\frac{du}{dx} + Pu = 0$$

i.e.
$$u = e^{-\frac{1}{2}\int Pdx}$$

If this value be inserted in the transformed equation, the latter becomes

$$\frac{d^2v}{dx^2} + \rho(x)v = 0$$

where
$$\rho(x) = Q - \frac{1}{2}\frac{dP}{dx} - \frac{1}{4}P^2.$$

Consider the equation

$$\frac{d^2y}{dx^2} + 3x\frac{dy}{dx} - 6y = 0$$

which has already been integrated numerically on p. 145 by resolving the equation into two simultaneous equations of the first order.

If
$$u = e^{-3x^2/4}$$
then
$$\rho(x) = -6 - \tfrac{3}{2} - \tfrac{9}{4}x^2$$
$$= -\tfrac{15}{2} - \tfrac{9}{4}x^2.$$

The required solution of the differential equation is

$$y = v \cdot e^{-3x^2/4}$$

subject to $x = 0$, $\frac{dy}{dx} = 0{\cdot}1$, $y = 1$.

Hence v is to be the solution of the equation

$$\frac{d^2v}{dx^2} = \tfrac{1}{4}(30 + 9x^2)v$$

that is, subject to $x = 0$, $\frac{dv}{dx} = 1{\cdot}6$, $v = 1$.

This transformation is particularly suited to this type of equation provided the values of y only are required and not the values of $\frac{dy}{dx}$ (see p. 154).

Example.—Tabulate the solution of the differential equation

$$\frac{d^2y}{dx^2} + 3x\frac{dy}{dx} - 6y = 0$$

subject to $x = 0$, $\frac{dy}{dx} = 0.1$, $y = 1$ at intervals of 0.1 in x in the range $0 < x < 1$ correct to four decimal places by transforming to normal form and using the method on p. 154.

This transformation is usually assumed to be applicable only to equations in which the coefficients P and Q are functions expressed literally in terms of the independent variable x. This is, of course, not necessarily the case. The functions P and Q may be presented in tabular form, and $\rho(x)$ can then be calculated also in the same form once $\frac{dP}{dx}$ has been numerically evaluated.

For the determination of $\frac{dP}{dx}$ either the formula

$$hf_0' = \tfrac{1}{2}[\Delta f_0 + \Delta f_{-1}] - \tfrac{1}{12}[\Delta^3 f_{-1} + \Delta^3 f_{-2}] + \tfrac{1}{60}[\Delta^5 f_{-2} + \Delta^5 f_{-3}] + \cdots$$

or the central difference formula

$$hf_0' = \mu\delta f_{\frac{1}{2}} - \tfrac{1}{6}\mu\delta^3 f_{\frac{1}{2}} + \tfrac{1}{30}\mu\delta^5 f_{\frac{1}{2}} - \cdots$$

may be used.

Example.—In the equation

$$y'' + Py' + Qy = 0$$

P and Q are tabulated as follows

x .	0	0·1	0·2	0·3	0·4	0·5	0·6	0·7	0·8	0·9	1·0
P .	1	0·9091	0·8333	0·7692	0·7143	0·6667	0·6250	0·5882	0·5556	0·5263	0·5000
Q .	0·7500	0·7934	0·8264	0·8521	0·8724	0·8889	0·9023	0·9135	0·9228	0·9307	0·9375

Tabulate the function $\rho(x)$ in the equation

$$\frac{d^2v}{dx^2} + \rho(x)v = 0,$$

where

$$y = ve^{-\frac{1}{2}\int_0^x P\,dx}$$

18.2. Method II.—Any equation of the form

$$y'' + Py' + Qy = 0$$

where P and Q are functions of x can be reduced to the standard form

$$y'' + \rho(x)y = 0$$

by a change of independent variable.

Change the independent variable x to z—thus

$$\frac{dy}{dx} = \frac{dy}{dz} z', \quad \frac{d^2y}{dx^2} = z'^2 \frac{d^2y}{dz^2} + \frac{dy}{dz} z''.$$

The equation then transforms to

$$\frac{d^2y}{dz^2} z'^2 + \frac{dy}{dz} \cdot z'' + Pz' \frac{dy}{dz} + Qy = 0.$$

The term in $\dfrac{dy}{dz}$ may be made to vanish if

$$z'' + Pz' = 0$$

i.e. if

$$z' = e^{-\int P dx}$$

or

$$z = \int e^{-\int P dx} . \, dx.$$

The normal form is then

$$\frac{d^2y}{dz^2} + Q \cdot e^{2\int P dx} . \, y = 0$$

where $Qe^{2\int P dx}$, which is a function of x, has to be replaced by its equivalent function of z by using the relation

$$z = \int e^{-\int P dx} \, dx.$$

Example.—Reduction of the equation

$$y'' + Py' + Qy = 0$$

to normal form, where $P(x)$ and $Q(x)$ are given by

x .	0	0·1	0·2	0·3	0·4	0·5	0·6	0·7	0·8	0·9	1·0
P .	0	0·2	0·4	0·6	0·8	1·0	1·2	1·4	1·6	1·8	2·0
Q .	1	1·2	1·4	1·6	1·8	2·0	2·2	2·4	2·6	2·8	3·0

The numerical process is clearly outlined in the table below, the new equation being

$$\frac{d^2y}{dz^2} + \rho(z)y = 0.$$

$\int_0^x P\,dx$	0	0·01	0·04	0·09	0·16	0·36
$\exp. 2\int_0^x P\,dx$ . .	1	1·0202	1·0833	1·1980	1·377	1·6490
$\varrho(x) = Q\exp. 2\int_0^x P\,dx$.	1	1·2242	1·5166	1·9168	2·4786	3·2980
$\exp. -\int_0^x P\,.\,dx$ . .	1	0·9900	0·9608	0·9139	0·8521	0·7787
$z = \int_0^x (\exp. -\int_0^x P\,dx)dx$.	0	0·0997	0·1972	0·2910	0·3790	0·4612

$\int_0^x P\,dx$	0·36	0·49	0·64	0·81	1·0	
$\exp. 2\int_0^x P\,dx$ . .	2·054	2·665	3·596	5·054	7·389	
$\varrho(x) = Q\exp. 2\int_0^x P\,dx$.	4·5188	6·396	9·3496	14,1512	22·167	
$\exp. -\int_0^x P\,.\,dx$ . .	0·6977	0·6127	0·5272	0·4448	0·3679	
$z = \int_0^x (\exp. -\int_0^x P\,dx)dx$.	0·5350	0·6000	0·6570	0·7050	0·7463	

19. Further General Theorems dealing with the solutions of equations of the type

$$\frac{d^2y}{dx^2} + \rho(x)y = 0.$$

In Chapter I we considered a number of comparison theorems which enabled us to set upper and lower bounds within which the solution of a differential equation of the first order lies. The theorems that follow are rather akin to these, and suggest corresponding bounds to the solutions of differential equations of the second order. At the same time, they provide a valuable insight into certain general properties of such solutions, linking them up with the simple properties of the sine and cosine solutions of the elementary periodic equation

$$y'' + y = 0.$$

Let $\rho(x)$ be positive in the range

so that $\qquad\qquad 0 < m \le \rho(x) \le M$

m and M being the upper and lower bounds of $f(x)$ in the range.

19.1. Theorem I.—Let $y = y_1$ and $y = y_2$ be two independent solutions of the equation

$$y'' + \rho(x)y = 0 \quad . \quad . \quad . \quad . \quad \text{(i)}$$

Then between every two zeros of y_1 there must be at least one zero of y_2.

For
$$\left.\begin{array}{l} y_1'' + \rho(x)y_1 = 0 \\ y_2'' + \rho(x)y_2 = 0 \end{array}\right\} \quad . \quad . \quad . \quad . \quad \text{(ii)}$$

therefore $\qquad y_1y_2'' - y_2y_1'' = 0 \quad . \quad . \quad . \quad . \quad \text{(iii)}$

Let $x = \xi$ and $x = \eta$ be two zeros of $y = y_1$.

Integrating (iii)

$$y_1y_2' - y_2y_1' = A,$$

therefore $\qquad [y_1(x)y_2'(x) - y_2(x)y_1'(x)]_\xi^\eta = 0$

and

$$[y_1(\eta)y_2'(\eta) - y_2(\eta)y_1'(\eta)] - [y_1(\xi)y_2'(\xi) - y_2(\xi)y_1'(\xi)] = 0.$$

Since $\qquad\qquad y_1(\xi) = 0$ and $y_1(\eta) = 0$

therefore $\qquad y_2(\xi) \cdot y_1'(\xi) - y_2(\eta) \cdot y_1'(\eta) = 0 \quad . \quad . \quad \text{(iv)}$

Assume that $y_1(x)$ is $+ve$ between $x = \xi$ and $x = \eta$, therefore $y_1'(\xi) > 0$ and $y_1'(\eta) < 0$

From (iv) $\qquad y_2(\eta) = \dfrac{y_2(\xi)y_1'(\xi)}{y_1'(\eta)} < 0$ if $y_2(\xi)$ is $+ve$

$$\text{and} > 0 \text{ if } y_2(\xi) \text{ is } -ve$$

Thus $\qquad\qquad y_2(\eta)$ is $-ve$ if $y_2(\xi)$ is $+ve$

and $\qquad\qquad y_2(\eta)$ is $+ve$ if $y_2(\xi)$ is $-ve$.

$y_2(x)$ therefore changes sign between the two zeros $x = \xi$ and $x = \eta$ of $y_1(x)$.

Thus there must be 1, 3, 5, ... zeros of $y_2(x)$ between two consecutive zeros of $y_1(x)$.

It follows that if any one solution of $y'' + \rho(x)y = 0$ crosses and recrosses the axis of x, so also does every other solution, and each such solution interlaces with every other. An elementary illustration is

$$y'' + y = 0, \quad y_1 = \sin x, \quad y_2 = \cos x.$$

Example.—Show that each member of the system of curves $y = Ae^{-x}\cos x(1 + B\int_0^x e^{2x}\sec^2 x\,dx)$, where A and B are arbitrary constants, has an infinite number of zeros, and that the zeros of any one member separate the zeros of any other.

19.2. Theorem II.—If in the differential equations

$$\left.\begin{array}{l} y'' + \rho(x)y = 0 \quad . \,. \,. \, A \\ z'' + \sigma(x)z = 0 \quad . \,. \,. \, B \end{array}\right\} \quad . \quad . \quad . \quad \text{(v)}$$

$M \geq \sigma(x) \geq \rho(x)$ in the range $b \geq x \geq a$, and if $y = z$ and $y' = z'$ at $x = x_0$ in the range, then equation (A) has the greater integral, throughout the range $b > x > x_0$.

Let $y(x)$ and $z(x)$ both commence at the common zero $x = x_0$ at which also let $y'(x_0) = z'(x_0)$.

By multiplying the equations A and B by z and y and subtracting

$$y''z - z''y = (\sigma - \rho)yz \quad . \quad . \quad . \quad \text{(vi)}$$

and hence $\quad y'z - z'y = \int_{x_0}^x (\sigma - \rho)\,.\,yz\,.\,dx \quad . \quad . \quad \text{(vii)}$

the constant vanishing.

Since $\sigma - \rho$ is $+ve$, if y and z are both $+ve$

$$y'z - z'y > 0$$

hence $\qquad (y'z - z'y)/z^2 > 0$

$$\frac{d}{dx}\left(\frac{y}{z}\right) > 0.$$

Thus y/z is an increasing function and $y > z$ for $x > x_0$ up to the next zero.

It may therefore be deduced that the zeros of the integral

of the differential equation with the larger y-coefficient must lie closer than those of the equation with the smaller y-coefficient.

19.3. Theorem III.—Comparison of the solution of

$$y'' + \rho(x)y = 0$$

with
$$z'' + \lambda^2 z = 0$$

where at $x = x_0$ $y = z = 0$ and $z_0' = y_0'$.

Clearly $z = A \sin \lambda(x - x_0) = (y_0'/\lambda) \sin \lambda(x - x_0)$.

Suppose that $0 < m < \rho < M$ in the interval $a < x < b$.

Comparing
$$y'' + \rho(x)y = 0$$

with
$$z'' + Mz = 0$$

by the previous theorem the solution of

$$y'' + \rho(x)y = 0$$

with the given boundary conditions, is greater than that of

$$z'' + Mz = 0.$$

Therefore $\quad y > (y_0'/\sqrt{M}) \sin \sqrt{(M)}(x - x_0)$

up to the zero value of y *next after that given by* $x = x_0$, *i.e.* up to that given by $x_0 + \pi/\sqrt{M}$, unless $b < x_0 + \pi/\sqrt{M}$, in which case only up to the value $\underline{x = b}$.

Thus the next zero x_1 of y must be greater than

$$x_0 + \pi/\sqrt{M}, \quad i.e. \ x_1 - x_0 \geq \pi/\sqrt{M}.$$

Similarly, comparing the two following equations

$$y'' + \rho(x)y = 0$$
$$z'' + mz = 0$$

it may be shown that $y < (y'_0/\sqrt{m}) \sin \sqrt{m} . (x - x_0)$.

And as before, x_1 the next root of y is such that

$$x_1 - x_0 \leq \pi/\sqrt{m}.$$

We note that the interval between the two successive zeros $x = x_0$ and $x = x_1$ lies between $\dfrac{\pi}{\sqrt{m}}$ and $\dfrac{\pi}{\sqrt{M}}$.

Example (i)—Consider

$$y'' + y/(1 + x^2) = 0$$

where $y = 0$ and $y' = 1$ when $x = 0$.   It is required to find the value of y at $x = 0.5$.

Now $$1 \geq \frac{1}{1 + x^2} \geq \tfrac{4}{5} \qquad \underline{0 \leq x \leq 0.5}$$

<u>For $M = 1$</u> $\qquad\qquad y_1'' + y_1 = 0,$

the solution is $\qquad\qquad y_1 = \sin x.$

<u>For $m = \tfrac{4}{5}$</u> $\qquad\qquad y_2'' + \tfrac{4}{5}y_2 = 0,$

the solution is $\qquad\qquad y_2 = 1.12 \sin 0.894\, x.$

Thus at $x = 0.5$, y lies between

$$\sin 0.5 = \sin 28° \ 39' = 0.480$$

and $1.12 \sin (0.894 \times 0.5) = 1.12 \sin 25° \ 37'$

$$= 0.484.$$

Hence the value lies between

$$y_1(0.5) = 0.480$$
and $\qquad\qquad y_2(0.5) = 0.484.$

If the average of these values be taken, viz. $y(0.5) = 0.482$ the error is approximately 0.4 per cent.

Example (ii).—
$$y'' = y/(1 + x^2).$$

Conditions as above.

The value of $y(0.5)$ lies between y_1 and y_2, such that

$$y_1'' = y_1, \text{ and hence } y_1 = \sinh x$$
and $\qquad\quad y_2'' = (0.9^2)y_2 \,; \text{ hence } y_2 = 1.11 \sinh 0.9x$
$$y_1(0.5) = \sinh (0.5) = 0.521$$
$$y_2(0.5) = 1.11 \sinh (0.45) = 0.516$$

Therefore $\qquad\quad 0.516 < y(0.5) < 0.521.$

Thus $\qquad\qquad\quad y(0.5) = 0.518,$

where the error is less than 1 per cent.

The following two examples are illustrations of a simple generalisation of Theorem II.

Example (iii).—

$$y'' = x \sinh \frac{y}{x} \quad . \quad . \quad . \quad . \quad . \quad (1)$$

where $\qquad x = 0; \ y = 0; \frac{dy}{dx} = 1.$

Now $\qquad x \sinh \frac{y}{x} > x \cdot \frac{y}{x}, \ i.e. \ > y.$

Hence if we compare (1) with

$$z'' = z \quad . \quad . \quad . \quad . \quad . \quad . \quad (2)$$

where $\qquad x = 0, \ z = 0, \ \frac{dz}{dx} = 1$

$$z < y.$$

The solution of (2) is $z = \sinh x.$

Hence $\qquad y > \sinh x.$

Thus $\sinh x$ is a lower bound to the solution.

An upper bound can also be found as follows :

Since $\qquad y > \sinh x$

$$\frac{y}{x} > \frac{\sinh x}{x}$$

$$x \sinh \frac{y}{x} > x \sinh \left(\frac{\sinh x}{x} \right).$$

Thus the solution of the equation

$$y'' = x \sinh \left(\frac{\sinh x}{x} \right)$$

with the same boundary conditions is less than the solution of the original equations.

Accordingly,

$$x + \int_0^x dx \int_0^x dx \ x \sinh \left(\frac{\sinh x}{x} \right) > y > \sinh x,$$

giving upper and lower bounds to the solution of the equation, explicitly in terms of x.

Example.—Find upper and lower bounds to the solution of the equation

$$y'' + x \sinh \frac{y}{x} = 0,$$

where $y = 0, \dfrac{dy}{dx} = 1$ when $x = 0$.

19.4. By comparing the equation with one of simpler type, the foregoing theorems may be used to find an approximation to the position of the first root of y the solution of the equation,

$$y'' + \rho(x)y = 0$$

with given boundary conditions—say $x = 0$, $y = 0$, $y' = a$.

The root being unknown, the range is also unknown, and M and m may therefore be taken in the first instance as the maximum and minimum values of $\rho(x)$ for the range

$$0 < x < \infty.$$

The method is best illustrated by an example.

Example.—

$$y'' + \frac{x^2 + 4}{x^2 + 9}y = 0$$

$$x = 0, y = 0, y' = 1.$$

Here $M = 1$ and $m = \frac{4}{9}$. Thus the solution of the equation lies between those of

$$y_1'' + y_1 = 0$$

and $$y_2'' + \tfrac{4}{9}y_2 = 0.$$

Subject to the boundary condition, the solutions are

$$y_1 = \sin x$$

and $$y_2 = \tfrac{3}{2} \sin \tfrac{2}{3}x,$$

and accordingly the required zero of y lies between $x = \dfrac{3\pi}{2}$ and $x = \pi$. This enables us to readjust our value of M, for the range is now less than $x = 0$ to $x = \dfrac{3\pi}{2}$.

Therefore $M = \dfrac{(9\pi^2/4) + 4}{(9\pi^2/4) + 9} \doteq \dfrac{53}{63}$ say,

and $m = \dfrac{4}{9} \qquad\qquad = \dfrac{28}{63}$

The solution lies between

$$y = (\tfrac{6\,3}{5\,3})^{\frac{1}{4}} \cdot \sin (\tfrac{5\,3}{6\,3})^{\frac{1}{4}} x$$

and

$$y = \tfrac{3}{2} \sin \tfrac{2}{3}x.$$

Therefore the first zero lies between $\dfrac{3\pi}{2}$ and $\pi\sqrt{\left(\dfrac{63}{53}\right)}$.
The mean is 4·08, the error being certainly less than 0·63 (see below).

The following are the results of integrating the differential equation :

$$\frac{d^2y}{dx^2} + \frac{x^2 + 4}{x^2 + 9} \cdot y = 0$$

$$x = 0,\ y = 0,\ \left(\frac{dy}{dx}\right)_0 = 1.$$

x.	$\dfrac{d^2y}{dx^2}$.	$\dfrac{dy}{dx}$.	y.
0	0	1	0
0·5	−0·223	0·945	0·491
1	−0·457	0·775	0·931
1·5	−0·682	0·490	1·247
2	−0·845	0·103	1·404
2·5	−0·884	−0·334	1·342
3	−0·750	−0·752	1·073
3·5	−0·450	−1·057	0·609
4	−0·030	−1·182	0·046
4·5	+0·435	−1·080	−0·535

The zero is slightly greater than 4. To seek the interpolated zero, we use Newton's backward interpolation formula

$$f(4 + \xi \times 0\cdot5) = f(4) + \xi\Delta f(3\cdot5) + \frac{\xi(\xi + 1)}{2\,!} \Delta^2 f(3) + \ldots$$

Using this to find x for the left-hand side to vanish, as we easily find that $\xi = 0\cdot075$. Accordingly the zero is at $\underline{x = 4\cdot038}$, which may be compared with the mean 4·08 already found. Thus the error is actually 0·042.

Example.—Given

$$\frac{d^2y}{dx^2} + \lambda\frac{x^2 + 0\cdot245}{x^2 + 0\cdot552} \cdot y = 0$$

determine the value of λ which makes y vanish at $x = 0$ and $x = 1$.

Ans. $\lambda = 16\cdot3$.

Example.—

$$y'' + e^{2x} y = 0; \quad x = 0, y = 0, y' = 1.$$

For a range $0 < x < X$; $M = e^{2X}$, $m = 1$ and the solution lies between that of $y'' + y = 0$ and of $y'' + e^{2X} y = 0$,

i.e. $\qquad y = \sin x$ and $y = e^{-X} \sin (x \, e^{X})$.

Accordingly, the next zero lies between $x = \pi$ and $x = \pi \, e^{-X}$, and since $x = \pi$ is the upper bound to the zero, we can merely state that it lies between $x = \pi$ and $x = \pi \, e^{-\pi}$.

The foregoing example indicates that it is not always possible by the method we have so far developed to approximate with increasing accuracy to the position of the root. When, however, $\rho(x)$ is a function whose greatest and least values occur at the beginning and end of the range, respectively, the foregoing process may be repeated, so that the region within which the zero lies may be progressively narrowed.

Example.—

$$\frac{d^2y}{dx^2} + \pi^2 \Big(1 - \frac{1}{\pi} \tan^{-1} \frac{x}{\sqrt{2}} \Big) y = 0$$

where $\qquad 0 \le \tan^{-1} \dfrac{x}{\sqrt{2}} \le \dfrac{\pi}{2}.$

In this case $M = \pi^2$ occurring at $x = 0$

and $\qquad m = \dfrac{\pi^2}{2}$ when $x \longrightarrow \infty$.

Thus the solution which vanishes at $x = 0$ lies between

$$y = A \sin \pi x$$

and $\qquad y = A \sin \Big(\dfrac{\pi x}{\sqrt{2}} \Big)$

so that the next zero α lies between $x = 1$ and $x = \sqrt{2}$,

i.e. $\qquad 1 < \alpha < 1{\cdot}414.$

The limits of the range in x are now $0 < x < \sqrt{2}$, in which case

$$M = \pi^2, \; m = \pi^2 \Big(1 - \frac{1}{\pi} \tan^{-1} \frac{\sqrt{2}}{\sqrt{2}} \Big) = \frac{3\pi^2}{4}.$$

Thus the zeros of the solution which vanishes at $x = 0$ lies between those of

$$y = A \sin \pi x$$

and

$$y = A \sin \frac{\pi \sqrt{3}}{2} x$$

so that the next zero α lies between $x = 1$ and $x = \frac{2}{\sqrt{3}}$, *i.e.*

$$1 < \alpha < 1\cdot 15.$$

The process may be repeated—thus

$$M = \pi^2, \; m = \pi^2 \left(1 - \frac{1}{\pi} \tan^{-1} \sqrt{\frac{2}{3}} \right)$$

and the zero lies between $x = 1$ and

$$x = \left(1 - \frac{1}{\pi} \tan^{-1} \sqrt{\frac{2}{3}} \right)^{-\frac{1}{2}} = 1\cdot 13.$$

Hence $\qquad\qquad 1 < \alpha < 1\cdot 13.$

Alternative Method

The mean value of $1 - \dfrac{1}{\pi} \tan^{-1} \dfrac{x}{\sqrt{2}}$ for the range 0 to α is

$$\frac{1}{\alpha} \int_0^\alpha \left(1 - \frac{1}{\pi} \tan^{-1} \frac{x}{\sqrt{2}} \right) dx$$

$$= \frac{1}{\alpha} \left[\alpha - \frac{1}{\pi} \left(\alpha \tan^{-1} \frac{\alpha}{\sqrt{2}} - \frac{1}{\sqrt{2}} \log \frac{\alpha^2 + 2}{2} \right) \right]$$

$$= 1 - \frac{1}{\pi} \left[\tan^{-1} \frac{\alpha}{\sqrt{2}} + \frac{1}{\alpha \sqrt{2}} \log \left(1 + \frac{\alpha^2}{2} \right) \right].$$

Hence if we replace the original equation by

$$\frac{d^2 y}{dx^2} + \left[\pi^2 - \pi \left\{ \tan^{-1} \frac{\alpha}{\sqrt{2}} + \frac{1}{\alpha \sqrt{2}} \log \left(1 + \frac{\alpha^2}{2} \right) \right\} \right] y = 0$$

the solution will vanish at $x = \alpha$

if $\quad \alpha^2 \left[\pi^2 - \pi \tan^{-1} \dfrac{\alpha}{\sqrt{2}} - \dfrac{\pi}{\alpha \sqrt{2}} \log_e \left(1 + \dfrac{\alpha^2}{2} \right) \right] = \pi^2,$

i.e. $\quad \alpha^2 = 1 \Big/ \left[1 - \dfrac{1}{\pi} \tan^{-1} \dfrac{\alpha}{\sqrt{2}} - \dfrac{1}{\pi \alpha \sqrt{2}} \log_e \left(1 + \dfrac{\alpha^2}{2} \right) \right].$

Inserting $\alpha = \sqrt{2}$ on the right as a first approximation, we get

$$\alpha^2 = 1 \Big/ \Big[1 - \frac{1}{4} - \frac{1}{2\pi} \log_e 2 \Big],$$

i.e. $\alpha = 1{\cdot}25$ approx.   Reinserting this on the right gives again $1{\cdot}25$.

We may compare this with $1 < \alpha < 1{\cdot}13$ given by the previous method.

19.41. Application to the zeros of the Bessel Function.

By a change in the dependent variable Bessel's Equation of zero order, viz.

$$x \frac{d^2y}{dx^2} + \frac{dy}{dx} + xy = 0$$

can be transformed into

$$\frac{d^2u}{dx^2} + \Big(1 + \frac{1}{4x^2} \Big) u = 0$$

where $\qquad\qquad y = ux^{-\frac{1}{2}}.$

Let it be given that the smallest zero of u, and therefore of y, is at $x = 2{\cdot}405$. It is required to determine approximations to the higher roots.

Between $x = 2{\cdot}405$ and the next zero $x = x_1$

$$M = 1 + \frac{1}{4(2{\cdot}405)^2} = 1 + \frac{1}{23{\cdot}14} = 1{\cdot}0432$$

and $\qquad\qquad m = 1 + \frac{1}{4x_1^2}.$

Thus $\qquad\qquad u > A \sin{(\sqrt{M})}\,(x - 2{\cdot}405)$
$$u < B \sin{(\sqrt{m})}\,(x - 2{\cdot}405).$$

Thus the next root lies in the range

$$2{\cdot}405 + \frac{\pi}{\sqrt{m}} > x_1 > 2{\cdot}405 + \frac{\pi}{\sqrt{M}}$$

i.e. $\qquad\qquad\qquad > 2{\cdot}405 + 0{\cdot}98\,\pi$

i.e. $\qquad\qquad\qquad > 5{\cdot}485$

$$2{\cdot}405 + \pi\Big(1 - \frac{1}{8x_1^2} \Big) > x_1$$

$$x_1 + \frac{\pi}{8x_1^2} < 2{\cdot}405 + \pi < 5{\cdot}5478.$$

Now the root of

$$x + \frac{\pi}{8x^2} = 5{\cdot}5478$$

can be found from the sequence

$$x_{n+1} = 5 \cdot 5478 - \frac{\pi}{8x_n^2}$$

and leads to $\qquad x = 5 \cdot 534$.

Thus the next root x lies in the range

$$5 \cdot 485 < x_1 < 5 \cdot 534.$$

The mean of these values is $5 \cdot 51$, as compared with $5 \cdot 520$, the more accurate solution.

19.42. If $x = x_n$ be the nth positive root, then for the range

$$x_n < x < x_{n+1}$$

$$M = 1 + \frac{1}{4x_n^2} \text{ and } m = 1 + \frac{1}{4x_{n+1}^2}$$

and $\qquad B \sin(\sqrt{m}) \cdot (x - x_n) < u < A \sin(\sqrt{M})(x - x_n)$

Hence $\qquad x_{n+1} > x_n + \dfrac{\pi}{\sqrt{M}}$

and $\qquad x_{n+1} < x_n + \dfrac{\pi}{\sqrt{m}}.$

Writing $\qquad M^{-\frac{1}{2}} = 1 - \dfrac{1}{8x_n^2}, \quad m^{-\frac{1}{2}} = 1 - \dfrac{1}{8x_{n+1}^2}$

approximately it follows that

$$\pi - \frac{\pi}{8x_{n+1}^2} > x_{n+1} - x_n > \pi - \frac{\pi}{8x_n^2}.$$

The first two roots, x_1 and x_2, are $2 \cdot 405$ and $5 \cdot 520$. Thus for $n = 2$,

$$\pi - \frac{\pi}{8x_{n+1}^2} > x_{n+1} - 5 \cdot 52 > \pi - \frac{\pi}{8(5.52)^2}$$

i.e. $\qquad > 3 \cdot 1288$

$$x_{n+1} > 8 \cdot 6488$$

Now $\qquad x_{n+1} < 5 \cdot 52 + \pi - \dfrac{\pi}{8x_{n+1}^2}$

i.e. $\qquad < 8 \cdot 6616 - \dfrac{\pi}{8x_{n+1}^2}$

i.e. $\qquad < 8 \cdot 6616 - \dfrac{\pi}{8(8 \cdot 6616)^2}$

i.e. $\qquad < 8 \cdot 6564$

$$8 \cdot 649 < x_3 < 8 \cdot 656.$$

Taking the mean of these extremes gives

$$x_3 = 8 \cdot 652.$$

The more accurate value is $8 \cdot 654$.

20. The foregoing comparison theorems have practically been concerned with the changes that occur in the solution of the equation

$$y'' + \rho(x)y = 0$$

when $\rho(x)$ is replaced by a greater or a smaller function of x, simpler from the point of view of effecting a solution of the equation. There are, however, a variety of methods for the approximate representation of $\rho(x)$ suitable for our purpose, and we proceed to consider a number of these in detail.

20.1. Suppose $\rho(x)$ is expressed in the form

$$\rho(x) = a_0 + a_1 x + a_2 x^2 + \ldots$$

then a whole variety of forms of expansion may be found for the solution, depending on the precise values of a_0, a_1, $a_2 \ldots$ For example, the solution of the equation

$$\frac{d^2y}{dx^2} + \left(n + \frac{1}{2} - \frac{x^2}{4}\right)y = 0$$

is the function

$$(-1)^n\, e^{x^2/4}\, \frac{d^n}{dx^n}\left(e^{-x^2/2}\right),$$

known as the parabolic cylinder function. These and similar differential equations of this type arise from certain of the partial differential equations of Mathematical Physics. They will be dealt with in detail, therefore, in Vol. II. Apart from such cases and those that can be dealt with by the method of Frobenius (§ 6·3), the best method is undoubtedly to tabulate the function $a_0 + a_1 x + a_2 x^2 + \ldots$ over the range of x for which the solution is required and to proceed by any of the numerical methods detailed in the earlier chapters. If over the range of x for which the solution is required the series $a_0 + a_1 x + \ldots$ converges very rapidly, a simple method of successive approximation frequently suffices. The following example will illustrate this.

Example.—

$$y'' + \lambda^2\left(1 - \frac{x}{10}\right)y = 0.$$

Write $$y'' + \lambda^2 y = \frac{\lambda^2 xy}{10}$$

and as a first approximation let us try

$$y'' + \lambda^2 y = 0$$

i.e. $$y = A \sin \lambda x + B \cos \lambda x.$$

The expression on the right of (1) then takes the form (apart from the constants)

$$x \sin \lambda x \text{ and } x \cos \lambda x.$$

As typical of both consider $xe^{i\lambda x}$, then the particular integrals are involved in

$$\frac{e^{i\lambda x}}{4i\lambda} x^2 = \frac{x^2}{4\lambda} (- i \cos \lambda x + \sin \lambda x)$$

and are, in fact,

$$\frac{A\lambda^2}{10}\left(-\frac{x^2}{4\lambda} \cos \lambda x\right) \text{ and } \frac{B\lambda^2}{10} \cdot \frac{x^2}{4\lambda} \sin \lambda x.$$

Thus

$$y = A\left(\sin \lambda x - \frac{\lambda}{40} x^2 \cos \lambda x\right) + B\left(\cos \lambda x + \frac{\lambda x^2}{40} \sin \lambda x\right).$$

This provides a second approximation to the solution of the differential equation for a given value of λ, subject to any two compatible boundary conditions.

Examples.

Determine first and second approximations to the solutions of the following equations, indicating the range of x for which they are valid :

(i) $y'' + 4y = x^2 y$,
(ii) $y'' - y = ye^{-x}$,
(iii) $y'' - 2(1 + 2x^2)y = e^{-x^2}y$,

given that the expression on the right vanishes for $y = e^{x^2}$.

(iv) $y'' + \rho(x)y = 0$,

where

x . .	0	0·1	0·2	0·3	0·4	0·5
$\rho(x)$.	1·0	0·999	0·996	0·991	0·984	0·975

Express $\rho(x)$ in polynomial form.

20.2. Suppose $\rho(x)$ can be represented in the form of descending integral powers of x, convergent over a range $0 < a < x < \infty$, so that the equation takes the form :

$$\frac{d^2y}{dx^2} + \left(a_0 + \frac{a_1}{x} + \frac{a_2}{x^2} + \ldots\right)y = 0.$$

In Vol. II, we shall deal in detail with certain differential equations of this class that arise from problems of mathematical physics. An important equation of this type is, for example,

$$\frac{d^2y}{dx^2} + \left(-\frac{1}{4} + \frac{k}{x} + \frac{\frac{1}{4} - m^2}{x^2}\right)y = 0,$$

whose solution is the Whittaker W-function, related to a number of other functions such as the Abel ϕ-function and the Parabolic Cylinder function to which we have already referred in the preceding paragraph. These special forms do not concern us here.

In any particular case the first term in the expansion for $\rho(x)$ can always be reduced to unity by a simple change in the independent variable x. Thus we may write

$$\frac{d^2y}{dx^2} + \left(1 + \frac{a_1}{x} + \frac{a_2}{x^2} + \frac{a_3}{x^3} + \ldots\right)y = 0.$$

20.21. When x is very large, $\rho(x)$ tends to unity, and the equation takes the approximate form

$$y'' + y = 0.$$

The solution of this equation gives a first approximation, and this may be systematically refined. In order to arrive at a closer approximation to the solution, we follow a method closely analogous to that dealt with in the preceding paragraph. The process is best illustrated in the first instance by means of Bessel's Equation of order zero, viz.

$$x\frac{d^2y}{dx^2} + \frac{dy}{dx} + xy = 0$$

or

$$\frac{d}{dx}\left(x\frac{dy}{dx}\right) + xy = 0$$

Transform this to the normal form by a change of dependent variable

$$y = ux^{-\frac{1}{2}},$$

and it takes the form

$$\frac{d^2u}{dx^2} + \left(1 + \frac{1}{4x^2}\right)u = 0.$$

If x in the range required is so large that $\frac{1}{4x^2}$ is small compared with unity, we may write

$$\frac{d^2u}{dx^2} + u = -\frac{u}{4x^2},$$

and regarding

$$u_0 = A_0 \sin x + B_0 \cos x$$

as a first approximation, let us assume

$$u_1 = \left(A_0 + \frac{A_1}{x}\right)\sin x + \left(B_0 + \frac{B_1}{x}\right)\cos x.$$

Inserting into the differential equation,

$$-A_0 \sin x - B_0 \cos x$$
$$+ A_1\left(-\frac{\sin x}{x} - \frac{2\cos x}{x^2} + \frac{2\sin x}{x^3}\right) + \left(A_0 + \frac{A_1}{x}\right)\sin x$$
$$+ B_1\left(-\frac{\cos x}{x} + \frac{2\sin x}{x^2} + \frac{2\cos x}{x^3}\right) + \left(B_0 + \frac{B_1}{x}\right)\cos x$$
$$= -\left(A_0 + \frac{A_1}{x}\right)\frac{\sin x}{4x^2} - \left(B_0 + \frac{B_1}{x}\right)\frac{\cos x}{4x^2}.$$

The terms in x^0 and x^{-1} cancel.

Equating coefficients of $\frac{\sin x}{x^2}$ and $\frac{\cos x}{x^2}$ on both sides,

$$-2A_1 + \frac{B_0}{4} = 0, \qquad\qquad i.e.\ A_1 = B_0/8,$$

$$2B_1 + \frac{A_0}{4} = 0, \qquad\qquad i.e.\ B_1 = -A_0/8,$$

so that with the formula

$$u_1 = \left(A_0 + \frac{B_0}{8x}\right)\sin x + \left(B_0 - \frac{A_0}{8x}\right)\cos x,$$

the original equation is satisfied with error of order

$$\frac{\sin x}{x^3} \text{ and } \frac{\cos x}{x^3}.$$

Proceeding in this way, we easily find

$$u_2 = \left(A_0 + \frac{B_0}{8x} - \frac{9A_0}{2 \cdot 4^3 x^2}\right) \sin x$$

$$+ \left(B_0 - \frac{A_0}{8x} - \frac{9B_0}{2 \cdot 4^3 x^2}\right) \cos x$$

the error being of order $\dfrac{\sin x}{x^4}$ and $\dfrac{\cos x}{x^4}$, and this associated

with $y = ux^{-\frac{1}{2}}$ gives an approximation to the Bessel function

of order zero, provided x is sufficiently large to make $\dfrac{1}{x^4}$

negligible to the required accuracy.

Example.

Given that y is zero at $x = 5 \cdot 520$ and at $x = 8 \cdot 654$ determine A_0 and B_0. Compare the answer with the results of § **20.22**.

20.22. It remains to determine the constants A_0 and B_0 so that u does, in fact, approximate to $x^{\frac{1}{2}} J_0(x)$. Since the expansion is not valid in the region of $x = 0$, we proceed to rewrite it so that the general form of the series may stand out more clearly. It can then be compared with other approximations to $J_0(x)$ for large values of x.

Write $\quad A_0 \sin x + B_0 \cos x = C \cos (\alpha - x)$
$\qquad\quad A_0 \cos x - B_0 \sin x = C \sin (\alpha - x)$

$\qquad\quad C^2 = A_0{}^2 + B_0{}^2$ and $\tan \alpha = A_0 / B_0$

then $\qquad u = C\{P \cos (\alpha - x) + Q \sin (\alpha - x)\}$

whence it is easily found that

$$P = 1 - \frac{1^2 \cdot 3^2}{2! (8x)^2} + \frac{1^2 \cdot 3^2 \cdot 5^2 \cdot 7^2}{4! (8x)^4} - \cdots$$

$$Q = -\frac{1}{8x} + \frac{1^2 \cdot 3^2 \cdot 5^2}{3! (8x)^3} - \cdots$$

It remains to find α and C so that u approximates to $x^{\frac{1}{2}} J_0(x)$. Now, it is easily verified by differentiating under the integral sign, and integrating by parts, that

$$J_0(x) = \frac{1}{\pi} \int_0^\pi \cos (x \cos \phi) d\phi$$

satisfies the Bessel Equation.

Consider

$$U = \int_0^\pi \cos (x \cos \phi)d\phi = 2 \int_0^{\pi/2} \cos (x \cos \phi)d\phi.$$

Let $\cos \phi = 1 - \mu$ then $d\phi = \dfrac{d\mu}{\sqrt{(2\mu - \mu^2)}}$

Then

$$U = \int_0^\pi \cos (x - x\mu)d\phi = \int_0^\pi \cos x \cos \mu x \, d\phi + \int_0^\pi \sin x \sin \mu x \, d\phi$$

$$= U_1 \cos x + U_2 \sin x$$

where $U_1 = 2 \int_0^1 \dfrac{\cos \mu x}{\sqrt{(2\mu - \mu^2)}} \, d\mu$ and $U_2 = \int_0^1 \dfrac{\sin \mu x}{\sqrt{(2\mu - \mu^2)}} \, d\mu$

In U_1 let $t = \mu x$, then

$$U_1 = \sqrt{\left(\frac{2}{x}\right)} \int_0^x \frac{\cos t \cdot dt}{\sqrt{\left(t - \dfrac{t^2}{2x}\right)}} = \sqrt{\left(\frac{2}{x}\right)}\left\{\int_0^x \frac{\cos t}{\sqrt{t}} \, dt + \frac{1}{x} V\right\}$$

where $V = \int_0^x \dfrac{x \cos t \, dt}{\sqrt{t}} \left\{\left(1 - \dfrac{t}{2x}\right)^{-\frac{1}{2}} - 1\right\}.$

It may easily be proved that V is finite, however large x is, thus

$$U_1 \longrightarrow \underset{x \longrightarrow \infty}{\text{Lim.}} \sqrt{\left(\frac{2}{x}\right)} \int_0^x \frac{\cos t}{\sqrt{t}} \, dt = \frac{1}{\sqrt{x}} \Gamma\left(-\frac{1}{2}\right)$$

Similarly,
$$U_2 \longrightarrow \frac{1}{\sqrt{x}} \Gamma\left(-\frac{1}{2}\right)$$

Thus
$$U \longrightarrow \frac{\cos x + \sin x}{\sqrt{x}} \Gamma(-\tfrac{1}{2})$$

Hence $J_0(x) \longrightarrow \dfrac{\cos x + \sin x}{\pi\sqrt{x}} \Gamma\left(-\dfrac{1}{2}\right) = \sqrt{\left(\dfrac{2}{\pi x}\right)} \cos \left(\dfrac{\pi}{4} - x\right)$

It remains to determine C and α by identifying the expression for u with

$$x^{\frac{1}{2}}J_0(x) = \sqrt{\left(\frac{2}{\pi}\right)} \cos \left(\frac{\pi}{4} - x\right)$$

when x is large.

Now
$$u \longrightarrow C\{P \cos (\alpha - x) + Q \sin (\alpha - x)\}$$
$$\longrightarrow C\{\cos (\alpha - x)\}$$

Thus
$$C = \sqrt{\frac{2}{\pi}} \text{ and } \alpha = \frac{\pi}{4}$$

and we have finally

$$J_0(x) \longrightarrow \sqrt{\left(\frac{2}{\pi x}\right)}\left\{P \cos \left(\frac{\pi}{4} - x\right) + Q \sin \left(\frac{\pi}{4} - x\right)\right\}$$

where
$$P = 1 - \frac{1^2 \cdot 3^2}{2! (8x)^2} + \frac{1^2 \cdot 3^2 \cdot 5^2 \cdot 7^2}{4! (8x)^4} \cdots$$
$$Q = - \frac{1^2}{1! \cdot 8x} + \frac{1^2 \cdot 3^2 \cdot 5^2}{3! (8x)^3} \cdots$$

20.23. We are now in a position to determine the large roots of $J_0(x)$, for this is zero when

$$\tan\left(\frac{\pi}{4} - x\right) = -P/Q = \frac{1 - \dfrac{1^2 \cdot 3^2}{2! (8x)^2} + \dfrac{1^2 \cdot 3^2 \cdot 5^2 \cdot 7^2}{4! (8x)^4}}{\dfrac{1^2}{1! \, 8x} - \dfrac{1^2 \cdot 3^2 \cdot 5^2}{3! (8x)^3} + \cdots}$$

When x is exceedingly large, the right-hand side becomes large also. Thus the roots approach the values given by

$$\frac{\pi}{4} - x = (2n + 1)\frac{\pi}{2} = n\pi + \frac{\pi}{2}$$

i.e.
$$x = -n\pi - \frac{\pi}{4}$$

or
$$x = m\pi - \frac{\pi}{4}$$

where m is any integer.

A second approximation may be derived by expanding the right-hand side of the above expression in the form

$$\tan\left(\frac{\pi}{4} - x\right) = \frac{1}{8x}\left[1 + \frac{21}{2(8x)^2} \cdots\right]$$

and thus
$$x = \frac{\pi}{4} - \tan^{-1}\left(\frac{1}{8x}\right) \text{ approximately.}$$

20.24. We may illustrate the more general method by means of the equation

$$\frac{d^2y}{dx^2} - \left(a^2 + \frac{k}{x}\right)y = 0,$$

which corresponds to the case $m = \frac{1}{2}$ for the Whittaker W-functions.

When x is large the equation approximates to one whose solutions are e^{ax} and e^{-ax}. Accordingly, let us tentatively assume an expansion of the form

$$y = e^{-ax} x^r\left(1 + \frac{A_1}{x} + \frac{A_2}{x^2} + \cdots\right)$$

where r, A_1, A_2, . . . are to be determined. Inserting this into the differential equation, the term e^{-ax} can be everywhere removed, and we find

$$a^2(x^r + A_1 x^{r-1} + A_2 x^{r-2} + \ldots)$$
$$- 2a[rx^{r-1} + (r-1)A_1 x^{r-2} + (r-2)A_2 x^{r-3} + \ldots]$$
$$+ [r(r-1)x^{r-2} + A_1(r-1)(r-2)x^{r-3}$$
$$+ A_2(r-2)(r-3)x^{r-4} + \ldots]$$
$$- \left(a^2 + \frac{k}{x}\right)(x^r + A_1 x^{r-1} + A_2 x^{r-2} + \ldots) = 0.$$

Equating the coefficients of x^r, x^{r-1}, . . . in succession, to zero, we find the following relations to determine r, A_1, A_2, etc.

$$a^2 - a^2 = 0$$
$$A_1 a^2 - 2ar - k - A_1 a^2 = 0$$
$$A_2 a^2 - 2a(r-1)A_1 + r(r-1) - a^2 A_2 - kA_1 = 0$$
$$A_3 a^2 - 2a(r-2)A_2 + A_1(r-1)(r-2) - a^2 A_3 - kA_2 = 0$$
. . . .

From these it follows that :

$$r = -k/2a$$
$$A_1 = -k(k+2a)/(2a)^3$$
$$A_2 = k(k+2a)^2(k+4a)/2 \cdot (2a)^6$$
. . . .

and the terms in the expansion for one of the solutions are thereby determined. If in the above a be replaced by $-a$, the other solution is immediately found.

Example.—Tabulate for the range $4 \leq x \leq 10$ to four places of decimals, the solution of

$$y'' = \left(1 + \frac{1}{2x}\right)y$$

that is zero when x is infinite and has unit value when $x = 4$. The solution that is zero when x is infinite is that corresponding to the factor e^{-x}. In this case

$$k = \tfrac{1}{2},\ a = 1,\ r = -\tfrac{1}{4}$$
$$A_1 = -\tfrac{5}{32},\ A_2 = \tfrac{225}{2048}.$$

Thus
$$y = Ae^{-x}x^{-\frac{1}{4}}\left(1 - \frac{5}{32x} + \frac{225}{2048x^2} - \ldots\right).$$

Determine A, and then tabulate.

20.3. It has not been assumed in all the previous numerical work that $\rho(x)$ is necessarily a continuous function of x, except where the forms in which it has been presented imply this. For many practical purposes, however, $\rho(x)$ stands for a series of physical measurements that resemble a discontinuous function—for example, in the case of the flexure of a stepped strut, whose area of section may increase by finite increments at various positions along its length. For the study of such cases, either a purely numerical method may be applied, using one of the numerous processes described in the earlier chapters of this work, or $\rho(x)$ may be represented as a Fourier Series. The equation then takes the form (1) below, a type of equation that arises in various other physical problems.

Let $\rho(x)$ be represented in the form of a Fourier Series, thus

$$\rho(x) = a_0 + a_1 \cos x + a_2 \cos 2x + \ldots$$

so that

$$y'' + (a_0 + a_1 \cos x + a_2 \cos 2x + \ldots)y = 0 \quad . \quad (1)$$

This is Hill's Equation, which arises from a study of the departures from the periodic orbit due to the action of certain disturbing forces, x being the time variable and a_0, a_1, $a_2 \ldots$ numerical coefficients. Floquet * has shown that the general solution of this equation is of the form

$$y = C_1 e^{\lambda x} \phi_1(x) + C_2 e^{-\lambda x} \phi_2(x) \quad . \quad . \quad (2)$$

where C_1 and C_2 are arbitrary constants, and λ is a constant depending on the coefficients a_0, a_1, $\ldots$ in (1), while $\phi_1(x)$ and $\phi_2(x)$ are periodic functions of period equal to that of $\rho(x)$, viz. 2π.

Now (2) is a very simple case of the representation of $y(x)$ in terms of quasi-periodic function. It follows that if *any* particular solution of (1) can be determined, say in numerical form, then by an analysis of these tabulated values it should be possible to determine λ, $\phi_1(x)$ and $\phi_2(x)$, the latter two as periodic functions, and hence to find the *general* solution of the differential equation in terms of the two arbitrary constants. To find the periodic forms of the

* *Annales de l'Ecole Normale Superieure*, (2), **12**, (1883), 47–88.

functions ϕ_1 and ϕ_2 it would be necessary merely to express the tabulated values as Fourier Series.

It remains, therefore, to show how λ, ϕ_1 and ϕ_2 can be determined numerically, once some one numerical solution of the equation has been found over a wide enough range.

Let a be the period of the functions $\phi_1(x)$ and $\phi_2(x)$, in the present case a being equal to 2π.

Let E represent the operation of increasing x by a, so that

$$E\phi(x) = \phi(x + a)$$

Then

$$(E - e_{\lambda a})e^{\lambda x}\phi_1(x) = e^{\lambda(x + a)}\phi_1(x + a) - e^{\lambda(x + a)}\phi_1(x) = 0$$

since

$$\phi_1(x + a) = \phi_1(x)$$

Also

$$\begin{aligned}
(E - e^{\lambda a})e^{-\lambda x}\phi_2(x) &= e^{-\lambda(x + a)}\phi_2(x + a) - e^{-\lambda(x - a)}\phi_2(x) \\
&= (e^{-\lambda a} - e^{\lambda a})e^{-\lambda x}\phi_2(x) \\
&= -2\sinh \lambda a \, e^{-\lambda x}\phi_2(x).
\end{aligned}$$

Moreover,

$$(E - e^{-\lambda a})e^{-\lambda x}\phi_2(x) = 0.$$

Accordingly, from (2)

$$(E - e^{\lambda a})(E - e^{-\lambda a})y(x) = 0,$$

i.e.

$$(E^2 - 2\cosh \lambda a + 1)y(x) = 0$$

i.e. $\quad y(x + 2a) - 2\cosh \lambda a \,.\, y(x + a) + y(x) = 0 \quad$. (3)

It appears then that $y(x)$ the general solution of the differential equation must satisfy the functional equation (3).

Thus $\quad \cosh \lambda a = \tfrac{1}{2}[y(x + 2a) + y(x)]/y(x + a).$

Since $a = 2\pi$ and x may have any value, it follows that we may write

$$\cosh 2\lambda\pi = \tfrac{1}{2}[y(4\pi) + y(0)]/y(2\pi),$$

so that λ is determined at once if *any* solution of the differential equation has been evaluated over a range $0 - 4\pi$. This, of course, can be done by any of the numerous methods already outlined in previous chapters. Once λ is determined, the functions $\phi_1(x)$ and $\phi_2(x)$ follow easily as follows.

We have

$$(E - e^{-\lambda a})y(x)$$
$$= (E - e^{-\lambda a})[C_1 e^{\lambda x}\phi_1(x) + C_2 e^{-\lambda x}\phi_2(x)]$$
$$= (E - e^{-\lambda a}) \cdot C_1 e^{\lambda x}\phi_1(x)$$
$$= 2C_1 e^{\lambda x}\phi_1(x) \sinh \lambda a.$$

Thus

$$C_1\phi_1(x) = e^{-\lambda x}[y(x + 2\pi) - e^{-2\pi\lambda}y(x)]/2 \sinh 2\pi\lambda.$$

Similarly

$$C_2\phi_2(x) = - e^{\lambda x}[y(x + 2\pi) - e^{2\pi\lambda}y(x)]/2 \sinh 2\pi\lambda.$$

Since λ has now been determined, and a function $y(x)$ is presumed known in tabular form, the two functions $\phi_1(x)$ and $\phi_2(x)$ are here expressed in a form capable of direct tabulation over a full period $0 - 2\pi$. For this purpose C_1 and C_2 may be replaced by a constant, say, $\frac{1}{2} \sinh 2\pi\lambda$ and we can write

$$\phi_1(x) = e^{-\lambda x}[y(x + 2\pi) - e^{-2\pi\lambda}y(x)]$$
$$\phi_2(x) = e^{\lambda x}[e^{2\pi\lambda}y(x) - y(x + 2\pi)].$$

Once ϕ_1 and ϕ_2 have been so tabulated, they can be expressed as a Fourier Series in the ordinary way.

20.31. For simplicity we will apply the method to Mathieu's Equation, a particular case of Hill's Equation, viz. :

$$y'' + (a + b \cos 2x)y = 0.$$

Write, for example,

$$y'' + (1\cdot3158 + 0\cdot800 \cos 2x)y = 0.$$

The table opposite gives the values of y to five significant figures for the range $x = 0$ to $x = 6\pi$ at intervals of $\pi/6$.

Accordingly

$$\cosh 2\pi\lambda = [y(0) + y(4\pi)]/2y(2\pi)$$
$$= [0\cdot0080 - 0\cdot8542]/2 \times (- 0\cdot3524)$$
$$= 1\cdot2008$$

Hence $\lambda = 0\cdot0992.$

x.	y.	x.	y.	x.	y
0	$+0.0080$				
$\pi/6$	$+1.0449$	$13\pi/6$	$+0.9947$	$25\pi/6$	$+1.0337$
$\pi/3$	$+1.6486$	$7\pi/3$	$+1.9391$	$13\pi/3$	$+3.0078$
$\pi/2$	$+1.8553$	$5\pi/2$	$+2.4168$	$9\pi/2$	$+3.9480$
$2\pi/3$	$+1.7642$	$8\pi/3$	$+2.5093$	$14\pi/3$	$+4.2612$
$5\pi/6$	$+1.2214$	$17\pi/6$	$+1.9617$	$29\pi/6$	$+3.4892$
π	$+0.1644$	3π	$+0.5752$	5π	$+1.2168$
$7\pi/6$	-0.9723	$19\pi/6$	-1.1146	$31\pi/6$	-1.7042
$4\pi/3$	-1.7101	$10\pi/3$	-2.3579	$16\pi/3$	-3.9519
$3\pi/2$	-2.0365	$7\pi/2$	-3.0341	$11\pi/2$	-5.2492
$5\pi/3$	-2.0369	$11\pi/3$	-3.2270	$17\pi/3$	-5.7120
$11\pi/6$	-1.5175	$23\pi/6$	-2.5983	$35\pi/6$	-4.7222
2π	-0.3524	4π	-0.8542	6π	-1.6987

The following is an alternative method of deriving these results.

$$y(0) = C_1\phi_1(0) + C_2\phi_2(0)$$
$$y(2\pi) = e^{2\pi\lambda}\phi_1(0) + e^{-2\pi\lambda}\phi_2(0)$$
$$y(4\pi) = e^{4\pi\lambda}\phi_1(0) + e^{-4\pi\lambda}\phi_2(0)$$

and accordingly

$$\begin{vmatrix} y(0) & 1 & 1 \\ y(2\pi) & e^{2\pi\lambda} & e^{-2\pi\lambda} \\ y(4\pi) & e^{4\pi\lambda} & e^{-4\pi\lambda} \end{vmatrix} = 0$$

This gives the same result as before.

Now $\qquad e^{\lambda x}\phi_1(x) = y(x + 2\pi) - e^{-2\pi\lambda}y(x)$

and $\qquad e^{-\lambda x}\phi_2(x) = e^{2\pi\lambda}y(x) - y(x + 2\pi)$,

hence the calculation proceeds as below for a complete period.

x.	0.	$\pi/6$.	$\pi/3$.	$\pi/2$.	$2\pi/3$.	$5\pi/6$.	π.
$e^{\lambda x}\phi_1(x)$	-0.3568	$+0.4346$	$+1.0557$	$+1.4225$	$+1.5640$	$+1.3073$	$+0.4872$
$\phi_1(x)$	-0.3568	$+0.4126$	$+0.9515$	$+1.2173$	$+1.2705$	$+1.0083$	$+0.3568$
$e^{-\lambda x}\phi_2(x)$	$+0.3674$	$+0.9545$	$+1.1360$	$+1.0440$	$+0.7813$	$+0.3164$	-0.2687
$\phi_2(x)$	$+0.3674$	$+1.0054$	$+1.2604$	$+1.2200$	$+0.9618$	$+0.4103$	-0.3674

x.		$7\pi/6$.	$4\pi/3$.	$3\pi/2$.	$5\pi/3$.	$11\pi/6$.	2π.
$e^{\lambda x}\phi_1(x)$		-0.5934	-1.4416	-1.9429	-2.1357	-1.7857	-0.6655
$\phi_1(x)$		-0.4126	-0.9515	-1.2173	-1.2705	-1.0083	-0.3568
$e^{-\lambda x}\phi_2(x)$		-0.6991	-0.8318	-0.7644	-0.5722	-0.2317	$+0.1972$
$\phi_2(x)$		-1.0054	-1.2604	-1.2200	-0.9618	-0.4103	$+0.3674$

These results, when represented in periodic form, determine $\phi_1(x)$ and $\phi_2(x)$ as follows :

$$\phi_1(x) = 1{\cdot}2841 \sin x - 0{\cdot}3440 \cos x$$
$$+ 0{\cdot}0679 \sin 3x - 0{\cdot}0126 \cos 3x$$
$$+ 0{\cdot}0012 \sin 5x - 0{\cdot}0001 \cos 5x$$

· · · · · · · · ·

and
$$\phi_2(x) = 1{\cdot}2841 \sin x + 0{\cdot}3440 \cos x$$
$$+ 0{\cdot}0653 \sin 3x + 0{\cdot}0230 \cos 3x$$
$$+ 0{\cdot}0009 \sin 5x + 0{\cdot}0004 \cos 5x$$

· · · · · · · · ·

Thus the solution of Mathieu's equation is completely represented for *any* range of values of x.

20.4. A method closely related to that of the previous section can be applied when the equation can be written in the form

$$\frac{d^2y}{dx^2} - (a^2 + a_1 e^{-x} + a_2 e^{-2x} + \ldots)y = 0.$$

Here $\rho(x)$ may be presumed expressed in terms of exponentials by Prony's Method. When x is large, the equation limits to one whose solutions are e^{ax} and e^{-ax}.

Accordingly, write

$$y = e^{ax}(1 + A_1 e^{-x} + A_2 e^{-2x} + \ldots).$$

Inserting this in the equation, we get

$$0 = a^2 e^{ax} + (a-1)^2 A_1 e^{(a-1)x} + (a-2)^2 A_2 e^{(a-2)x} + \ldots$$
$$- (a^2 + a_1 e^{-x} + a_2 e^{-2x} + \ldots)(e^{ax} + A_1 e^{(a-1)x} + A_2 e^{(a-2)x} + \ldots).$$

Equating to zero coefficients of e^{ax}, $e^{(a-1)x}$, etc., we derive the following system of equations

$$a^2 - a^2 = 0$$
$$(a-1)^2 A_1 - a^2 A_1 - a_1 = 0$$
$$(a-2)^2 A_2 - a^2 A_2 - a_1 A_1 - a_2 = 0$$
$$(a-3)^2 A_3 - a^2 A_3 - a_1 A_2 - a_2 A_1 - a_3 = 0$$

· · · · · · · ·

It follows at once that

$$A_1 = \frac{a_1}{1 - 2a} \; ; \; A_2 = \frac{a_1{}^2 + a_2(1 - 2a)}{2(1 - 2a)(2 - 2a)} \; ; \; A_3 = \ldots$$

This provides one of the fundamental solutions of the equation. The other is immediately derived by replacing a by $-a$ in the expression.

Thus, approximately,

$$y = Ae^{ax}\left(1 + \frac{a_1}{1 - 2a}e^{-x} + \frac{a_1{}^2 + a_2(1 - 2a)}{2(1 - 2a)(2 - 2a)}e^{-2x} + \ldots\right)$$
$$+ Be^{-ax}\left(1 + \frac{a_1}{1 + 2a}e^{-x} + \frac{a_1{}^2 + a_2(1 + 2a)}{2(1 + 2a)(2 + 2a)}e^{-2x} + \ldots\right)$$

Examples.

(i) Derive the approximate solution

$$y = A[1 - e^{-x} + \tfrac{9}{40}e^{-2x} - \tfrac{3}{200}e^{-3x} + \ldots]$$

to the differential equation

$$(e^x - \tfrac{1}{10})y'' + y = 0$$

by writing the latter

$$y'' = -\frac{y}{e^x - \tfrac{1}{10}} = -ye^{-x}\left(1 - \frac{e^{-x}}{10}\right)^{-1}$$

How would you derive a second solution ?

(ii) Examine in detail the case $a^2 = \tfrac{1}{4}$.

(iii) Examine in detail the case

$$a_1 = a_2 = a_3 = \ldots = a^2.$$

20.41. When the equation is of the form

$$\frac{d^2y}{dx^2} + (a^2 + a_1e^{-x} + a_2e^{-2x} + \ldots)y = 0,$$

a solution can be found of the form

$$y = \sin ax(A_0 + A_1e^{-x} + A_2e^{-2x} + \ldots)$$
$$+ \cos ax(B_0 + B_1e^{-x} + B_2e^{-2x} + \ldots)$$

This follows at once from the previous case, but can be verified directly by insertion into the differential equation and equating to zero coefficients of $e^{-nx}\sin ax$ and $e^{-nx}\cos ax$ in the resulting expression.

Example.—Determine a solution of the equation

$$y'' + (1 - e^{-x})y = 0$$

as far as terms of the order $e^{-2x} \sin x$ and $e^{-2x} \cos x$

(i) by the above method,
(ii) by successive approximations, using the sequence

$$y_{n+1}'' + y_{n+1} = e^{-x}y_n$$

and taking $y_0 = A_0 \sin x + B_0 \cos x.$

21. Differential equations involving an unspecified constant.

In general, the dependent and independent variables in a differential equation that represents some physical problem stand for measures of physical quantities. Thus they have dimensions. Such an equation must therefore be dimensionally homogeneous. By a simple transformation of both these variables it is possible in general to reduce the equation to a relation between non-dimensional numbers, but in the process there usually appears in the equation as transformed a constant not previously apparent.

For example, the differential equation for the flexure of a strut is

$$EIy'' + Fy = 0.$$

If l be the length, then by writing

$$x = lx_1,\, y = ly_1$$

and

$$I = I_0 R(x_1)$$

the equation becomes

$$\frac{d^2y_1}{dx_1{}^2} + \frac{Fl^2}{EI_0} \cdot \frac{y_1}{R(x_1)} = 0,$$

where $\dfrac{Fl^2}{EI_0}$ is now itself a non-dimensional combination and all the other terms that occur in the equation are also pure numbers. Again the equation for a vibrating pendulum of length l is

$$l\frac{d^2\theta}{dt^2} + g\theta = 0.$$

Writing $t = Tt_1$, where T is the periodic time, this becomes

$$\frac{d^2\theta}{dt_1{}^2} + \frac{gT^2}{l}\,\theta = 0$$

and gT^2/l is now a non-dimensional constant.

These equations are both of the type

$$y'' + \lambda\rho(x)y = 0$$

and for many purposes what is required is a solution, not for a specified value of λ, but as an expression involving λ explicitly, so that the types of solution for a variety of values of the constant λ may be studied.

The most obvious method of seeking a solution in the first instance is to obtain an expansion of the dependent variable as a series of ascending powers of this constant.

21.1. Consider in illustration the differential equation

$$\frac{d^2y}{dx^2} + \lambda y = 0 \quad . \quad . \quad . \quad . \quad (1)$$

where λ is a constant, and let us assume that there exists a convergent solution in ascending powers of λ of the form

$$y = y_0 + \lambda y_1 + \lambda^2 y_2 + \ldots \quad . \quad . \quad (2)$$

where $y_0, y_1 \ldots$ are functions of x.

If such a convergent expansion can be found containing two arbitrary constants, it must be the solution of the equation.

Insert (2) in (1), we have :

$$y_0'' + \lambda y_1'' + \lambda^2 y_2'' + \ldots$$
$$+ \lambda y_0 + \lambda^2 y_1 + \ldots \qquad = 0$$

Equating coefficients of λ to zero, we have the following system of equations to determine $y_0, y_1, \ldots$

$$y_0'' = 0 \qquad \text{Hence} \quad y_0 = A + Bx$$

$$y_1'' = -y_0 \qquad ; \quad y_1 = -\frac{Ax^2}{2!} - \frac{Bx^3}{3!}$$

$$y_2'' = -y_1 \qquad ; \quad y_2 = \frac{Ax^4}{4!} + \frac{Bx^5}{5!}$$

$$. \quad . \quad . \quad . \quad ; \quad . \quad . \quad . \quad . \quad .$$

Thus the functions $y_0, y_1 \ldots$ are found, and they involve the two constants A and B. The expansion therefore takes the form,

$$y = A\left[1 - \frac{\lambda x^2}{2!} + \frac{\lambda^2 x^4}{4!} - \frac{\lambda^3 x^6}{6!} + \ldots\right] \quad \cdot \quad \cdot \quad (3)$$

$$+ B\left[x - \frac{\lambda x^3}{3!} + \frac{\lambda^2 x^5}{5!} - \frac{\lambda^3 x^7}{7!} \cdots\right]$$

$$= A \cos x\sqrt{\lambda} + \frac{B}{\sqrt{\lambda}} \sin x\sqrt{\lambda}$$

when λ is positive.   If λ be negative and written $-\mu$, then the solution of

$$\frac{d^2y}{dx^2} - \mu y = 0 \quad . \quad . \quad . \quad . \quad . \quad (4)$$

is $\qquad y = A \cosh x\sqrt{\mu} + \frac{B}{\sqrt{\mu}} \sinh x\sqrt{\mu}.$

Thus the two fundamental solutions of

$$\frac{d^2y}{dx^2} + n^2 y = 0$$

are $\qquad 1 - \frac{n^2 x^2}{2!} + \frac{n^4 x^4}{4!} - \ldots \qquad = \cos nx$

and $\qquad nx - \frac{n^3 x^3}{3!} + \frac{n^5 x^5}{5!} - \ldots \qquad = \sin nx$

while for the equation

$$\frac{d^2y}{dx^2} - n^2 y = 0$$

they are $\qquad 1 + \frac{n^2 x^2}{2!} + \frac{n^4 x^4}{4!} + \ldots \qquad = \cosh nx$

and $\qquad nx + \frac{n^3 x^3}{3!} + \frac{n^5 x^5}{5!} + \ldots \qquad = \sinh nx.$

These well-known expansions are uniformly convergent over any range of values of x.

21.2. Consider now the differential equation

$$\frac{d^2y}{dx^2} + \lambda\rho(x)y = 0$$

where $\rho(x)$ is a positive function of x in the range $a \leq x \leq b$ Thus, for this range $0 < m \leq \rho(x) \leq M$, where m and M are finite.

As before, assume that a solution exists in the form

$$y = y_0 + \lambda y_1 + \lambda^2 y_2 + \ldots$$

where y_0, y_1, y_2 ... are functions of x. We shall show immediately that such an expansion can be found, and that both it and its first differential coefficient are uniformly convergent. Accordingly it may be differentiated term by term. Inserting this expression for y into the differential equation we find

$$\frac{d^2y_0}{dx^2} + \lambda \frac{d^2y_1}{dx^2} + \lambda^2 \frac{d^2y_2}{dx^2} + \ldots$$
$$+ \lambda \rho(x) y_0 + \lambda^2 \rho(x) y_1 + \ldots \qquad = 0$$

Equating coefficients of powers of λ to zero, we have :

$$y_0'' = 0; \; y_0 = A + Bx$$
$$y_1'' = - \rho(x) y_0;$$
$$y_1 = - A \int_a^x dx \int_a^x \rho(x) dx - B \int_a^x dx \int_a^x x\rho(x) dx$$
$$y_2'' = - \rho(x) y_1;$$
$$y_2 = A \int_a^x dx \int_a^x \rho(x) dx \int_a^x dx \int_a^x \rho(x) dx -$$
$$- B \int_a^x dx \int_a^x \rho(x) dx \int_a^x dx \int_a^x x\rho(x) dx$$

$$\bullet \quad \bullet \quad \bullet \quad \bullet \quad \bullet \quad \bullet \quad \bullet \quad \bullet \quad \bullet \quad \bullet \quad \bullet$$

Inserting these expressions of y_1, y_2 ... into the expansion for y in powers of λ we obtain the solutions :

$$y = A \bigg[1 - \lambda \int_a^x dx \int_a^x \rho(x) dx$$
$$+ \lambda^2 \int_a^x dx \int_a^x \rho(x) dx \int_a^x dx \int_a^x \rho(x) dx - \ldots \bigg]$$
$$+ B \bigg[x - \lambda \int_a^x dx \int_a^x x\rho(x) dx$$
$$+ \lambda^2 \int_a^x dx \int_a^x \rho(x) dx \int_a^x dx \int_a^x x\rho(x) dx - \ldots \bigg]$$

where the series in square brackets are evidently generalized forms of the trigonometric functions, $\sin x$ and $\cos x$.

The boundary conditions are easily inserted.
Suppose

$$x = a, \; y = 0, \; y' = b$$

then $\quad 0 = A + Ba$

$$b = B.$$

Thus $\quad A = -ab, \; B = b.$

This leads to a rather important conclusion. We note that both A and B contain the factor b. Thus we may write:

$$y/b = -aC(\lambda, x) + S(\lambda, x).$$

Thus

(i) for any given value of λ and x the ordinate of y is directly proportional to the slope at $x = a$.

(ii) since the expression on the right is independent of b, the positions of the zeros of y are also independent of b. Thus all solutions of the differential equation that pass through the point $x = a$, $y = 0$ have the same zeros provided the expansions are valid over the range.

Examples.

(i) When λ is small, show that the zeros are given approximately by the equation

$$x - a = \lambda \int_a^x dx \int_a^x (x - 1) \cdot \rho(x) dx.$$

(ii) If y is zero at $x = 0$ and $x = 1$, show that λ must have one of an infinite set of values, and find an equation of infinite degree in λ from which they may be determined.*

21.21. Convergence of the expansions.

In illustration let us write $\lambda = 1$, and take the lower limit of the interval as zero. Writing

$$C(x) = 1 - \int_0^x dx \int_0^x \rho(x) dx$$
$$+ \int_0^x dx \int_0^x \rho(x) dx \int_0^x dx \int_0^x \rho(x) dx - \ldots$$

---

* These are the *characteristic* values of λ. We shall return to a discussion of such numbers in Vol. II.

$$S(x) = x - \int_0^x dx \int_0^x x\rho(x)dx$$

$$+ \int_0^x dx \int_0^x \rho(x)dx \int_0^x dx \int_0^x x\rho(x)dx - \ldots$$

Now $|C(x)|$ is less than the sum of all the terms in the expression for $C(x)$, each taken with the positive sign, and these again are less than the corresponding terms in which $\rho(x)$ in each integral is replaced by M. Accordingly

$$|C(x)| < 1 + M\frac{x^2}{2!} + M^2\frac{x^4}{4!} + \ldots$$

i.e. $\qquad\qquad\qquad < \cosh x\sqrt{M}$

which is finite for any finite range of x. A similar argument applies to $S(x)$.

Example—Show that

$$\cosh x\sqrt{m} - \cosh x\sqrt{M} + \cos x\sqrt{m} + \cos x\sqrt{M}$$
$$< 2C(x)$$
$$< \cosh x\sqrt{M} - \cosh x\sqrt{m} + \cos x\sqrt{M} + \cos x\sqrt{m}.$$

In most practical cases, depending on the solution of a differential equation of the foregoing type (*e.g.* the flexure of a strut) the function $\rho(x)$ in the multiple integral is provided in tabular form, and the integrals are easily evaluated numerically. We shall return to this subject in Vol. II when dealing with the determination of Characteristic Numbers and other critical constants of physical problems defined mathematically by differential equations of the second order.

Example.

$$y'' + \lambda\left(1 - \frac{x}{10}\right)y = 0$$

In this case

$$\rho(x) = 1 - \frac{x}{10}.$$

Accordingly

$$\int_0^x dx \int_0^x \left(1 - \frac{x}{10}\right)dx = \frac{x^2}{2} - \frac{x^3}{60}$$

$$\int_0^x dx \int_0^x \left(1 - \frac{x}{10}\right)dx \int_0^x dx \int_0^x \left(1 - \frac{x}{10}\right)dx = \frac{x^4}{24} - \frac{x^5}{300} + \frac{x^6}{18,000}.$$

Thus one fundamental solution is given approximately by

$$1 - \lambda\left(\frac{x^2}{2} - \frac{x^3}{60}\right) + \lambda^2\left(\frac{x^4}{24} - \frac{x^5}{300} + \frac{x^6}{18,000}\right) - \cdots$$

For the second fundamental solution we have

$$\int_0^x dx \int_0^x x\left(1 - \frac{x}{10}\right)dx = \frac{x^3}{6} - \frac{x^4}{120}$$

$$\int_0^x dx \int_0^x \left(1 - \frac{x}{10}\right)dx \int_0^x dx \int_0^x x\left(1 - \frac{x}{10}\right)dx$$

$$= \frac{x^5}{120} - \frac{x^6}{1200} + \frac{x^7}{50,400} \cdots$$

Finally therefore we have approximately

$$y = A\left[1 - \lambda\left(\frac{x^2}{2} - \frac{x^3}{60}\right) + \lambda^2\left(\frac{x^4}{24} - \frac{x^5}{300} + \frac{x^6}{18,000}\right) - \cdots\right]$$
$$+ B\left[x - \lambda\left(\frac{x^3}{6} - \frac{x^4}{120}\right) + \lambda^2\left(\frac{x^5}{120} - \frac{x^6}{1200} + \frac{x^7}{50,400}\right) - \cdots\right].$$

21.3. The same method of expansion may be applied directly to the equation

$$\frac{d}{dx}\left[\frac{1}{p(x)}\frac{dy}{dx}\right] + \lambda q(x)y = 0.$$

This is equivalent to writing $p(x)dx$ in place of dx and $q(x)/p(x)$ in place of $\rho(x)$ in each of the integrals. For example, $S(x)$ and $C(x)$ now take the form

$$C(x) = 1 - \int_0^x p(x)dx \int_0^x q(x)dx$$
$$+ \int_0^x p(x)dx \int_0^x q(x)dx \int_0^x p(x)dx \int_0^x q(x)dx - \cdots$$
$$S(x) = x - \int_0^x p(x)dx \int_0^x xq(x)dx$$
$$+ \int_0^x p(x)dx \int_0^x q(x)dx \int_0^x p(x)dx \int_0^x xq(x)dx - \cdots$$

Examples.

1. The equation
$$\frac{d^2}{dx^2}\left[p(x)\frac{d^2y}{dx^2}\right] + \lambda q(x)y = 0$$
arises from a consideration of the flexure of a rotating shaft. Find an expansion for y in a power series for λ.

2. Find an expression in ascending powers of λ for the general solutions of the equations

(i) $\dfrac{d}{dx}\left(\dfrac{1}{1+x^2}\dfrac{dy}{dx}\right) + \lambda y = 0$

(ii) $\dfrac{d}{dx}\left(e^x\dfrac{dy}{dx}\right) + \lambda e^x y = 0$

(iii) $\dfrac{d}{dx}\left(\dfrac{1}{1+x^2}\dfrac{dy}{dx}\right) + \lambda e^x y = 0$

21.4. Suppose $\rho(x) = p(x) - \epsilon q(x) - \epsilon^2 r(x) - \ldots$

where the equation

$$z'' + p(x)z = 0,$$

is completely soluble in terms of elementary functions, and ϵ is a small constant.

Let $\qquad z = Az_1(x) + Bz_2(x)$

be the solution of the equation in z then the equation

$$y'' + \rho(x)y = 0$$

may be written as

$$y'' + p(x)y = \epsilon q(x)y + \epsilon^2 r(x)y.$$

Let $\qquad y = y_1 + \epsilon y_2 + \epsilon^2 y_3 + \ldots$

as before, then inserting this into the foregoing equation and equating powers of ϵ to zero we have

$$y_1'' + p(x)y_1 = 0$$
$$y_2'' + p(x)y_2 = q(x)y_1$$
$$y_3'' + p(x)y_3 = q(x)y_2 + r(x)y_1$$

. . . .

These equations are now soluble in succession, so that the expression for y may be derived to any required order in ϵ. Since we can introduce the two arbitrary constants in the solution of the first equation, only the particular integrals (involving these same two constants) are required from the subsequent equations.

Example.

$$y'' - (1 + \epsilon e^{-x})y = 0.$$

The systems for solution are

$$y_1'' - y_1 = 0$$
$$y_2'' - y_2 = e^{-x}y_1$$
$$y_3'' - y_3 = e^{-x}y_2$$

. . . .

Thus $\qquad\qquad y_1 = Ae^x + Be^{-x}.$

Accordingly to determine y_2 we have

$$y_2'' - y_2 = A + Be^{-2x}$$

and therefore $\qquad y_2 = -A + \dfrac{B}{3}e^{-2x}.$

Thus $\qquad\qquad y_3'' - y_3 = -Ae^{-x} + \dfrac{B}{3}e^{-3x}$

so that $\qquad\qquad y_3 = -\dfrac{A}{2}xe^{-x} + \dfrac{B}{24}e^{-3x}.$

It follows that as far as terms in ϵ^2 the solution may be written

$$y = A\left(e^x - \epsilon - \frac{\epsilon^2 x}{2}e^{-x}\right) + B\left(e^{-x} + \frac{\epsilon}{3}e^{-2x} + \frac{\epsilon^2}{24}e^{-3x}\right).$$

Examples.

1. Tabulate the solution of the equation

$$y'' - (1 + e^{-x}/10)y = 0$$

where $x = 0$, $y = 0$; $x = 1$, $y = 1$ for the range $0 \le x \le 1$ correct to three decimal places.

2.   Solve the equations

(ii) $y'' + (25 - \cos x)y = 0$,
(iii) $y'' + (9 - \cos x)y = 0$,
(iv) $y'' + (4 - \cos x)y = 0$,

correct to two decimal places subject to the conditions

$$x = 0,\ y = 0,\ y' = 1.$$

Determine the range of x for which these approximations are valid.

(v) In the case of examples (ii), (iii) and (iv) find approximately the position of the next zero.

(vi) Solve

$$(x^2 + 9)y'' + y = 0$$

where $x = 0, y = 0, y' = 1$ correct to 1 per cent. for the range $0 \le x \le 1$.

(Rewrite the equation as

$$y'' + \frac{y}{9}\left(1 + \frac{x^2}{9}\right)^{-1} = 0$$

and expanding the binomial terms as far as is necessary for the desired accuracy, apply the method described in the foregoing paragraph.)

22. We turn now to a consideration of differential equations of the second order in which, the equation being in the normal form, the coefficient of y is a function of x and a constant, say h, that can assume large values. The problem is to find an approximate solution to the differential equation, the accuracy of the approximation depending on the magnitude of h.

Consider in the first instance the following simple case.

22.1. Let the equation be

$$\frac{d^2y}{dx^2} - h^2 \cdot \psi \cdot y = 0 \quad \ldots \quad \text{(i)}$$

where ψ is a function of x and h is capable of assuming an indefinitely large value.

Assume that a solution is possible in the following form

$$y = \phi \cdot e^{hw}\left(1 + \frac{f_1}{h} + \frac{f_2}{h^2} + \ldots\right) \quad \ldots \quad \text{(ii)}$$

where ϕ, w, f_1, f_2, etc., are functions of x alone. Substituting in (i) and equating coefficients of h^2, h and h^0 to zero, the following equations may readily be found

$$\psi = (w')^2 \quad \ldots \quad \ldots \quad \text{(iii)}$$

$$\frac{\phi'}{\phi} = -\frac{w''}{2w'} \quad \ldots \quad \ldots \quad \text{(iv)}$$

$$\frac{\phi''}{\phi} = -2w'f_1' \quad \ldots \quad \ldots \quad \text{(v)}$$

From (iii) $\qquad w = \int dx \cdot \psi^{\frac{1}{2}}$ taking the positive sign only.

From (v) $\quad \log \phi = -\frac{1}{2} \log w' + \text{const.}$

$$= \log (\psi^{-\frac{1}{4}}) + \text{const.}$$

Thus it is enough to take

$$\phi = \psi^{-\frac{1}{4}}.$$

Using this in (v)

$$f_1 = \frac{1}{8}\psi'\psi^{-\frac{3}{2}} + \frac{1}{32}\int (\psi')^2 \cdot \psi^{-\frac{5}{2}} \cdot dx.$$

The approximate solution is therefore

$$y = \psi^{-\frac{1}{4}} . (\exp . h \int \psi^{\frac{1}{2}} . dx) . \left[1 + \frac{1}{32h} (4\psi'\psi^{\frac{3}{2}} \right.$$
$$\left. + \int (\psi')^2 . \psi^{-\frac{5}{2}} . dx + . . . \right]$$

corresponding to the positive sign only in equation (iii).

The solution becomes invalid if ψ has a zero in the range over which the integral is required.

An approximate solution of

$$\frac{d^2y}{dx^2} - h^2 . \psi . y = 0$$

is therefore given by

$$y = \psi^{-\frac{1}{4}} . \exp.(\pm h \int^x \psi^{\frac{1}{2}} . dx)$$

when ψ is positive in the range, and if ψ is negative over the range the approximate solutions are given by

$$y = \psi^{-\frac{1}{4}} \cos (h \int^x \psi^{\frac{1}{2}} . dx)$$

and $$y = \psi^{-\frac{1}{4}} \sin (h \int^x \psi^{\frac{1}{2}} . dx).$$

Accordingly if in the equation

$$\frac{d^2y}{dx^2} - Ry = 0,$$

R is a positive function of x which does not vanish or become infinite over a specific range, and if it has, as a factor, a constant h^2 which may become large, then approximate solutions of the equation are

$$y = R^{-\frac{1}{4}} e^{\pm \int^x R^{\frac{1}{2}} . dx}.$$

If R is negative over the range, and $R = -T$, then

$$\frac{d^2y}{dx^2} + Ty = 0$$

and $$y = T^{-\frac{1}{4}}(A \cos L + B \sin L)$$

where $$L = \int^x T^{\frac{1}{2}} dx.$$

Examples.

(i) Consider

$$\frac{d^2y}{dx^2} + h^2 e^{-2x} y = 0.$$

Thus $L = \int^x T^{\frac{1}{2}} dx = \int^x h e^{-x} dx = - h e^{-x}$

and $y = e^{x/2}(A \cos h e^{-x} + B \sin h e^{-x}).$

Suppose $y \longrightarrow 0$ as $x \longrightarrow \infty$, then, since

$$e^{x/2} \sin h e^{-x} \longrightarrow e^{x/2} . h e^{-x} \longrightarrow h e^{-x/2} \longrightarrow 0$$

it follows that $A = 0$

$$y = B e^{x/2} \sin h e^{-x}.$$

This series of solutions therefore has zeros at

$$x = \log \frac{h}{n\pi}$$

where $n = 1, 2, 3, \ldots$

(ii) If $\qquad \dfrac{d^2y}{dx^2} - (x^2 + 100)^2 y = 0$

to determine an approximate expression for y over the range $0 < x < 10$.

Let $x = 10z$, then

$$\frac{d^2y}{dz^2} - 10^6 (z^2 + 1)^2 y = 0.$$

Thus $h = 1{,}000$ and $\psi = (z^2 + 1)^2$

$$\int^z \psi^{\frac{1}{2}} dz = \frac{z^3}{3} + z$$

and therefore an approximate solution

$$= (z^2 + 1)^{-\frac{1}{2}} e^{\pm 1000 \left(\frac{z^3}{3} + z \right)}$$

$$= \tfrac{1}{10} (x^2 + 100)^{-\frac{1}{2}} . e^{\pm \frac{x^3}{3} \pm 100x}.$$

Finally

$$y = (x^2 + 100)^{-\frac{1}{2}} \Big[A e^{\frac{x^3}{3} + 100x} + B e^{- \frac{x^3}{3} - 100x} \Big]$$

(iii) Show that if

$$\frac{d^2y}{dx^2} + (x^2 + 100)^2 y = 0,$$

where $x = 0$, $y = 0$, $y' = 1$, then, approximately

$$y = \tfrac{1}{10}(x^2 + 100)^{-\frac{1}{4}} \sin\left(\frac{x^3}{3} + 100x\right).$$

(iv)　　　　$$\frac{d^2y}{dx^2} + 25\left(1 - \frac{1}{25}\cos x\right)y = 0.$$

In this case

$$h^2 = 25, \quad \psi = \tfrac{1}{25}\cos x - 1.$$

Hence ψ is always negative and the approximate solutions are

$$(1 - \tfrac{1}{25}\cos x)^{-\frac{1}{4}}\cos 5\int^x (1 - \tfrac{1}{25}\cos x)^{\frac{1}{2}}dx$$

and　　　$$(1 - \tfrac{1}{25}\cos x)^{-\frac{1}{4}}\sin 5\int^x (1 - \tfrac{1}{25}\cos x)^{\frac{1}{2}}dx.$$

Expanding the binomial terms and carrying through the integration, these give approximately

$$\cos 5\int^x (1 - \tfrac{1}{25}\cos x)^{\frac{1}{2}}dx = \cos 5\left(x - \frac{\sin x}{50}\right)$$

$$= \cos 5x + \tfrac{1}{10}\sin x \sin 5x$$

$$\sin 5\int^x (1 - \tfrac{1}{25}\cos x)^{\frac{1}{2}} = \sin 5x - \tfrac{1}{10}\sin x \cos 5x.$$

Thus, correct to 1 per cent. at least the solution is

$$y = A\cos 5x + B\sin 5x + \frac{\sin x}{10}(A\sin 5x - B\cos 5x).$$

This should be compared with the result of example (ii) of the previous section.

(v) Approximate solution of

$$\frac{d^2y}{dx^2} + \frac{\lambda^2 y}{(c^2 - x^2)^2} = 0$$

where λ is large, and $|x| < |c|$.

The solutions by the method of this paragraph are

$$y_1 = (c^2 - x^2)^{\frac{1}{2}} \cdot \cos\left\{\lambda\int^x (c^2 - x^2)^{-1} \cdot dx\right\}$$

$$= (c^2 - x^2)^{\frac{1}{2}} \cdot \cos\left\{\frac{\lambda}{2c}\log\frac{c+x}{c-x}\right\} \quad . \quad . \quad \text{(i)}$$

and

$$y_2 = (c^2 - x^2)^{\frac{1}{2}} . \sin \left\{ \lambda \int^x (c^2 - x^2)^{-1} . dx \right\}$$

$$= (c^2 - x^2)^{\frac{1}{2}} . \sin \left\{ \frac{\lambda}{2c} \log \frac{c + x}{c - x} \right\} \quad . \quad . \quad \text{(ii)}$$

When λ is large the latter becomes

$$(c^2 - x^2)^{\frac{1}{2}} \left\{ A \left(\frac{c + x}{c - x} \right)^{\frac{i\lambda}{2c}} + B \left(\frac{c - x}{c + x} \right)^{\frac{i\lambda}{2c}} \right\}$$

$$= (c^2 - x^2)^{\frac{1}{2}} \left\{ A \exp \left(\frac{i\lambda}{2c} \log \frac{c + x}{c - x} \right) + B \exp \left(-\frac{i\lambda}{2c} . \log \frac{c + x}{c - x} \right) \right\}.$$

This gives at once the general solution in the form

$$y = (c^2 - x^2)^{\frac{1}{2}} \left\{ L \cos \left(\frac{\lambda}{2c} \log \frac{c + x}{c - x} \right) + M \sin \left(\frac{\lambda}{2c} \log \frac{c + x}{c - x} \right) \right\}$$

which is also the form obtained from (i) and (ii) above.

Examples.

Find approximate solutions to the following equations for positive and for negative values of x, indicating in each case for what ranges of x the form of solution is valid.

(1) $\dfrac{d^2y}{dx^2} - 9(x + 1)^4 y = 0.$

(2) $\dfrac{d^2y}{dx^2} + 9(x + 1)^3 y = 0.$

(3) $\dfrac{d^2y}{dx^2} + \dfrac{16y}{(x^2 + 1)^2} = 0.$

(4) $\dfrac{d^2y}{dx^2} - \dfrac{16y}{(x^3 + 1)^2} = 0.$

(5) $\dfrac{d^2y}{dx^2} + \dfrac{16y}{(x^3 - 2x + 4)^2} = 0.$

The method of approximation carried through in the previous paragraph may be extended without much elaboration to the more general case where the coefficient of y is a quadratic function of h whose coefficients are functions of x.

22.2. Consider the equation *

$$\frac{d^2y}{dx^2} - (h^2\psi_0 + h\psi_1 + \psi_2) \cdot y = 0 \quad . \quad : \quad \text{(i)}$$

ψ_0, ψ_1 and ψ_2 are functions of x, and h is a parameter independent of x but capable of assuming indefinitely large values.

As before, assume that a solution exists in the form

$$y = \phi \cdot e^{hw}\left(1 + \frac{f_1}{h} + \frac{f_2}{h^2} + \ldots\right) \quad . \quad . \quad \text{(ii)}$$

where $\phi, w, f_1, f_2 \ldots$ are functions of x alone.

From (ii)

$$\frac{dy}{dx} = e^{hw}\left[\phi'\left(1 + \frac{f_1}{h} + \frac{f_2}{h^2} + \ldots\right) + \phi\left(\frac{f_1'}{h} + \frac{f_2'}{h} + \ldots\right)\right.$$
$$\left. + hw'\phi\left(1 + \frac{f_1}{h} + \frac{f_2}{h^2} + \ldots\right)\right]$$
$$= e^{hw}\left[hw'\phi + (\phi' + w'\phi f_1)\right.$$
$$\left. + \frac{1}{h}(\phi'f_1 + \phi f_1' + w'\phi f_2) + \ldots\right]$$
$$= e^{hw}[hP + Q + h^{-1}R]$$
$$\frac{d^2y}{dx^2} = e^{hw}[w'Ph^2 + h(P' + wQ) + (Q' + w'R) + \ldots].$$

Hence, inserting this expression in the differential equation and equating coefficients of h^0, h and h^2 on the left-hand side of (i) to zero :

$$w'P - \psi_0\phi = 0$$
$$P' + w'Q - (\psi_1\phi + \phi f_1\psi_0) = 0$$
$$\text{and} \qquad Q' + w'R - (\psi_2\phi + f_1\psi_1\phi + f_2\psi_0\phi) = 0$$

where $P = w'\phi$; $Q = \phi' + w'\phi f_1$; $R = \phi f_1 + \phi f_1' + w'\phi f_2$.

Inserting these values for P, Q and R, the three above equations become

$$w'^2 = \psi_0$$
$$w''\phi + w'\phi' + w'\phi' + w'^2\phi f_1 = \psi_1\phi + \phi f_1\psi_0$$
$$\phi'' + w''\phi f_1 + 2w'\phi'f_1 + 2w'\phi f_1' + w'^2\phi f_2$$
$$= \psi_2\phi + f_1\psi_1\phi + f_2\psi_0\phi.$$

* The substance of the following paragraphs and of parapraph **18.1** is taken from a series of papers by H. Jeffreys (*Proc. Lond. Math. Soc.*, 2, **23**, Part 6).

These final equations reduce to

$$w'^2 = \psi_0 \quad . \quad . \quad . \quad . \quad . \quad \text{(iii)}$$

$$\frac{\phi'}{\phi} = \frac{\psi_1 - w''}{2w'} \quad . \quad . \quad . \quad . \quad \text{(iv)}$$

$$2w'f_1' = \psi_2 - \frac{\phi''}{\phi} \quad . \quad . \quad . \quad . \quad \text{(v)}$$

(iv) may be written in the form

$$\frac{\phi'}{\phi} + \frac{1}{2}\frac{w''}{w'} = \frac{\psi_1}{2w'}$$

and integrating

$$\phi = (w')^{-\frac{1}{2}} \cdot \exp. \int^x \frac{\psi_1}{2w'} \cdot dx$$

$$= \psi_0^{-\frac{1}{4}} \cdot \exp. \int^x \frac{\psi_1}{2w'} dx.$$

Thus the term $\phi \cdot e^{hw}$, to which the solution y approaches as h becomes indefinitely large, is

$$\phi e^{hw} = \phi e^{\pm h \int^x \psi_0^{\frac{1}{2}} dx}$$

$$= \psi_0^{-\frac{1}{4}} e^{\int^x \frac{\psi_1}{2w'} dx} e^{\pm h \int^x \psi_0^{\frac{1}{2}} dx}$$

$$= \psi_0^{-\frac{1}{4}} \cdot \exp. \left[\pm \int^x \{h\psi_0^{\frac{1}{2}} + (\psi_1/2\psi_0^{\frac{1}{2}})\} dx \right] \quad . \quad . \quad \text{(vi)}$$

the lower limit of the integral being arbitrary.

From (v) the function f_1 is determined in the form

$$f_1 = \int^x \frac{dx}{2w'} \left(\psi_2 - \frac{\phi''}{\phi} \right).$$

All the terms under the integral sign are now known, and therefore the following are approximate integrals of the equation :

$$y_1 = \psi_0^{-\frac{1}{4}} e^{\int^x [h\psi_0^{\frac{1}{2}} + (\psi_1/2\psi_0^{\frac{1}{2}})] dx} \cdot \left[1 + \frac{1}{h} \int^x \frac{dx}{2\psi_0^{\frac{1}{2}}} \left(\psi_2 - \frac{\phi''}{\phi} \right) \right] \quad \text{(vii)}$$

$$y_2 = \psi_0^{-\frac{1}{4}} e^{-\int^x [h\psi_0^{\frac{1}{2}} + (\psi_1/2\psi_0^{\frac{1}{2}})] dx} \cdot \left[1 - \frac{1}{h} \int^x \frac{dx}{2\psi_0^{\frac{1}{2}}} \left(\psi_2 - \frac{\phi''}{\phi} \right) \right] \quad \text{(viii)}$$

where in y_1, $\qquad \phi = \psi_0^{-\frac{1}{4}} \cdot \exp. \left(\int^x \frac{\psi_1}{2\psi_0^{\frac{3}{4}}} \, dx \right)$

and in y_2, $\qquad \phi = - \psi_0^{-\frac{1}{4}} \exp. \left(- \int^x \frac{\psi_1}{2\psi_0^{\frac{3}{4}}} \cdot dx \right).$

Returning to equation (vi), it may be easily seen that $h\psi_0^{\frac{1}{2}} + \frac{\psi_1}{2\psi_0^{\frac{1}{2}}}$ differs from $(h^2\psi_0 + h\psi_1 + \psi_2)^{\frac{1}{2}}$ by a quantity at most of order h^{-1}. Thus if the equation (i) is written in the form

$$\frac{d^2y}{dx^2} - Ry = 0$$

then the solution of the equation may be approximately written

$$y = h^{\frac{1}{2}} \cdot R^{-\frac{1}{4}} \cdot e^{\pm \int^x R^{\frac{1}{2}} dx}.$$

If R is positive throughout the range, this is the most convenient form.

If R is negative throughout the range, then

$$y = h^{\frac{1}{2}} T^{-\frac{1}{4}} \cdot \cos \int^x T^{\frac{1}{2}} \cdot dx$$

and $\qquad y = h^{\frac{1}{2}} \cdot T^{-\frac{1}{4}} \sin \int^x T^{\frac{1}{2}} dx$

are the real forms of the solution.

If T is an even function, it will be found to be convenient to take the lower limit in the integrals as zero.

Then if $\qquad L = \int_0^x T^{\frac{1}{2}} dx$
$$y = h^{\frac{1}{2}} T^{-\frac{1}{4}} \cdot (A \cos L + B \sin L).$$

The particular case of $\psi_1 = \psi_2 = 0$ has already been dealt with.

Example.—Examine the nature of the solution in the case where $\psi_1^2 = 4\psi_0\psi_2$.

22.3. Application to Bessel's equation of large order.

Consider Bessel's equation of order n

$$\frac{d^2y}{dx^2} + \frac{1}{x}\frac{dy}{dx} + \left(1 - \frac{n^2}{x^2}\right)y = 0$$

or
$$x \frac{d}{dx}\left(x \frac{dy}{dx}\right) + (x^2 - n^2).y = 0.$$

If $x = ne^{\xi}$, then this equation reduces to

$$\frac{d^2y}{d\xi^2} - n^2(1 - e^{2\xi})y = 0.$$

Comparing with

$$\frac{d^2y}{dx^2} - h^2\psi.y = 0$$
$$\psi = 1 - e^{2\xi}.$$

Consider the case when n is large and ξ is *negative* so that ψ is always $+ ve$.

The approximate solutions are

$$(1 - e^{2\xi})^{-\frac{1}{4}}.e^M \text{ and } (1 - e^{2\xi})^{-\frac{1}{4}}.e^{-M}$$

where
$$M = n \int^{\xi}(1 - e^{2\xi})^{\frac{1}{2}}d\xi$$
$$= \int^{\xi}(n^2 - x^2)^{\frac{1}{2}}.\frac{dx}{x} \qquad \left[\frac{x}{n} = e^{\xi}\right]$$
$$= -n(\theta - \tanh \theta)$$

where
$$\theta = \text{sech}^{-1}\frac{x}{n} = \log\left\{\frac{n}{x} + \left(\frac{n^2}{x^2} - 1\right)^{\frac{1}{2}}\right\}$$

Now
$$e^{-M} = e^{n(\theta - \tanh \theta)}$$
$$= e^{n\theta}.e^{-n \tanh \theta}$$
$$= \left\{\frac{n}{x} + \left(\frac{n^2}{x^2} - 1\right)^{\frac{1}{2}}\right\}^n e^{-\sqrt{(n^2 - x^2)}}.$$

Thus approximately the two solutions are

$$y_1 = \left(1 - \frac{x^2}{n^2}\right)^{-\frac{1}{4}}.x^n\left\{n + (n^2 - x^2)^{\frac{1}{2}}\right\}^{-n}.e^{\sqrt{(n^2 - x^2)}}$$

and
$$y_2 = \left(1 - \frac{x^2}{n^2}\right)^{-\frac{1}{4}}x^{-n}\left\{n + (n^2 - x^2)^{\frac{1}{2}}\right\}^n e^{-\sqrt{(n^2 - x^2)}}.$$

When $x > n$ the solutions are easily seen to be

$$(e^{2\xi} - 1)^{-\frac{1}{4}}.\cos L$$
and
$$(e^{2\xi} - 1)^{-\frac{1}{4}}.\sin L$$

Q

where
$$L = n \int_0^\xi (e^{2\xi} - 1)^{\frac{1}{2}} d\xi$$
$$= \int_n^x (x^2 - n^2)^{\frac{1}{2}} \frac{dx}{x}$$

Let
$$x = n \sec z$$

then
$$L = \int_0^z \tan^2 z \, dz = n(\tan z - z)$$

so that the first solution is given approximately by

$$\frac{1}{\sqrt{(\tan z)}} \cos \{n(\tan z - z)\}$$

and the second by

$$\frac{1}{\sqrt{(\tan z)}} \sin \{n(\tan z - z)\}$$

MISCELLANEOUS EXAMPLES

1. If a solution of the equation

$$\frac{d^2y}{dx^2} + (1 + e^{-x})y = 0$$

is such that when $x = 3$, $y = 0$ and $y' = 1$, find approximately where the maxima and minima of this solution lie, and where its zeros occur for values of x in the range $3 < x < \infty$.

2. Determine an approximate solution of the type $y = A \sin \lambda x$ to represent that solution of the equation

$$\frac{d^2y}{dx^2} + \frac{20 - \log x}{20 + \log x} y = 0,$$

which is such that $x = 1$, $y = 0$, $\dfrac{dy}{dx} = 1$.

The solution is to be valid for the range $2 > x > 1$.
State the accuracy of the solution.

3. Approximate by Jeffreys' Method to the solution of the equation

$$\frac{d^2y}{dx^2} + 10x^2y \sin x = 0,$$

where $x = 0$, $y = 0$, $\dfrac{dy}{dx} = 1$.

4. Find a tabulated solution of the equation

$$\frac{dy}{dx} + \sin \frac{\pi y}{4} = 0$$

where $x = 0$, $y = 1$ for the range $0 < x < 1 \cdot 0$, correct to four places of decimals.

Integrate the equation directly and verify your tabulated values from the integral obtained, viz.

$$\tan \frac{\pi y}{8} = (\sqrt{2} - 1)e^{-\pi x/4}.$$

5. If y satisfies the differential equation

$$\frac{d^2y}{dx^2} + \frac{y}{e^x + x^2} = 1,$$

subject to $x = 0$, $y = 0$, $x = \frac{1}{2}$, $y = \frac{1}{2}$; determine the values of y at intervals of $0 \cdot 05$ in the whole range correct to three significant figures.

6. The function y, tabulated below, satisfies the differential equation

$$\frac{d^2y}{dx^2} + P(x)y = 1;$$

determine $P(x)$.

x .	0	0·1	0·2	0·3	0·4	0·5	0·6	0·7	0·8	0·9	1·0
y .	1	0·9901	0·9608	0·9139	0·8521	0·7788	0·6977	0·6126	0·5273	0·4449	0·3679

7. The equation

$$P(x)\frac{d^2y}{dx^2} + x\frac{dy}{dx} = y$$

is satisfied by a function y, whose values for certain values of x are as follows :

x . .	1·5	1·6	1·7	1·8	1·9	2	2·1	2·2
y . .	5·2070	5·8124	6·4883	7·2427	8·0849	9·0250	10·0745	11·2459

Express $P(x)$ as a polynomial.

8. The equation

$$\frac{d^2y}{dx^2} = 4y(1 + 4x^2)$$

is satisfied by a function y, whose values, for the undermentioned values of x, are approximately as follows :

x .	0	0·2	0·4	0·6	0·8	1·0
y .	1	1·083	1·377	2·054	3·597	7·389

Tabulate the solution of the equation, which is such that

$$y(1) - y(0) = 6$$
$$y(0·6) = 2.$$

9. The differential equation

$$\frac{d^2y}{dx^2} + 3xy(2 - 3x^3) = 0$$

has the following solution :

x .	0	0·2	0·4	0·6	0·8	1·0
y .	1·00	0·990	0·937	0·806	0·599	0·368

Tabulate, at intervals of 0·2, the solution of the equation which satisfies the conditions

$$y(0) + y(1) = 2y(0·5)$$
$$y(0) - y(1) = 1.$$

10. Determine the values of y and $\dfrac{dy}{dx}$ at intervals of $0\cdot1$ in x for the range $1\cdot0 \leq x \leq 2\cdot0$ correct to four decimal places, given that y satisfies the equation

$$\frac{d^2y}{dx^2} + P\frac{dy}{dx} + Qy = 0,$$

subject to $y = 0$, $x = 1$, $\dfrac{dy}{dx} = 0$, where P and Q are functions of x tabulated below :

x . .	$1\cdot0$	$1\cdot1$	$1\cdot2$	$1\cdot3$	$1\cdot4$	$1\cdot5$
P . .	$-0\cdot5$	$-0\cdot45455$	$-0\cdot41667$	$-0\cdot38467$	$-0\cdot35715$	$-0\cdot33333$
Q . .	$0\cdot0$	$-0\cdot08678$	$-0\cdot15278$	$-0\cdot20414$	$-0\cdot24490$	$-0\cdot27778$

x . .	$1\cdot6$	$1\cdot7$	$1\cdot8$	$1\cdot9$	2	
P . .	$-0\cdot31250$	$-0\cdot29412$	$-0\cdot27778$	$-0\cdot26316$	$-0\cdot25$	
Q . .	$-0\cdot30469$	$-0\cdot32699$	$-0\cdot34568$	$-0\cdot36150$	$-0\cdot37500$	

11. Obtain the solution of the equation

$$\frac{d^2y}{dx^2} - (x^2 + 1)y = 0,$$

subject to $x = 0$, $y = 1$, $x = 1$, $y = 1\cdot6487$, correct to four decimal places at intervals of $0\cdot1$ in x.

12. If h is large, find an approximate solution to the equation :

$$(1 + x^2)y'' + 2xy'(1 + x^2) + (1 + x^2)^2y + h^2y = 0,$$

where $x = 0$, $y = 0$, $y' = 1$.

13. Sketch the system of integral curves of the differential equations :

    (i) $p^2 - 2pe^x = 4y - e^{2x} - 4e^x$.
    (ii) $(p - 1)^2 = 4(y - x)$.
    (iii) $(p - 1)^2 = 4(y^2 - x^2)$.
    (iv) $p^2 - 2yp + x^2 = 0$.

Examine in each case the nature of the approximation of the integral at the p-discriminant locus.

14. $\dfrac{dx}{dt} = x^2 - y + e^t$

                $\dfrac{dy}{dt} = x - y^2 - e^t$

$t = 0$, $x = 0$, $y = 1$.

Tabulate x and y over the range $0 \leq t \leq 1$ at intervals of $0\cdot1$ correct to three decimal places.

15.
$$\frac{d^2x}{dt^2} = x^2 - y + e^t$$
$$\frac{d^2y}{dt^2} = x - y^2 - e$$

$t = 0$, $x = 0$, $\frac{dx}{dt} = 0$, $y = 1$, $\frac{dy}{dt} = -2$.

16. If
$$\frac{d}{dt}\left(\frac{1}{t^2 + 1}\frac{dx}{dt}\right) + \lambda x = 0,$$

where $x = 0$ and $\frac{dx}{dt} = 1$ when $t = 0$, determine an expansion for x in ascending powers of λ, as far as λ^3.

17. If
$$\frac{d}{dt}\left(\frac{1}{t^2 + 1}\frac{dx}{dt}\right) + \lambda x = 0,$$

find the lowest value of λ which is such that x is zero at $t = 0$ and $t = 0.5$ but finite within the range.

18. Determine a lower bound to the range of x for which the sequence

$$y_{n+1} - \frac{\pi}{2} = \int_0^x x \sin y_n dx$$

is convergent, and show that in the limit it satisfies the relation

$$y = 2 \tan^{-1} e^{x^2/2}.$$

PURE MATHEMATICS

ANSCHAULICHE GEOMETRIE by D. Hilbert and S. Cohn-Vossen. Yellow (Grundlehren) Series. Text in German. English translation of table of contents. German-English glossary-index. 5-1/2 x 8-1/2. x + 314 pages. 330 illustrations. (Originally published at $10.00). $3.95

AUFGABEN UND LEHRSÄTZE AUS DER ANALYSIS by G. Pólya and G. Szegö. Two volume set. Text in German. English translation of table of contents. German-English glossary-index. 5-1/2 x 8-1/2. Volume I: xxvi + 342 pages. Volume II: xx + 412 pages. (Originally published at $14.40 for both volumes. Each Volume-- $3.95, The Set-- $7.90

A CONCISE HISTORY OF MATHEMATICS by Dirk J. Struik. Emphasizes ideas and continuity of mathematics rather than anecdotal aspects from Oriental beginnings through 19th century. "...rich in content, thoughtful in interpretation..."--U. S. Quarterly Book List. Two volume set. Dover Series in Mathematics and Physics. Bibliography. Index. 4-1/2 x 6-3/4. Volume I: xviii + 123 pages. Volume II: vi + 175 pages. 47 illustrations.   The Set-- $3.00

COURS D'ANALYSE INFINITESIMALE by Ch. J. de la Valle Poussin. Eighth revised edition. "The handling throughout is clear, elegant and concise..."--Bulletin of the American Mathematical Society. Two volume set. Text in French. 5-1/2 x 8-1/2. Volume I: xxi + 524 pages.Volume II: xii + 460 pages.   Each Volume-- $4.50, The Set-- $8.75

EINFUHRUNG IN DIE ALGEBRAISCHE GEOMETRIE by B. L. van der Waerden. "Clear, systematic exposition of an important new mathematical development."--Bulletin of the American Mathematical Society. Yellow (Grundlehren) Series. Text in German. 5-1/2 x 8-1/2. ix + 247 pages. 15 illustrations. (Originally published at $7.80). $3.95

EINLEITUNG IN DIE MENGENLEHRE by Adolf Fraenkel. Third revised edition. "The treatise by Fraenkel on the theory of aggregates is now one of the finest."--Bulletin of the American Mathematical Society. Yellow (Grundlehren) Series. Text in German. Bibliography. Index. 5-1/2 x 8-1/2. xiii + 424 pages. 13 figures. $4.00

ELEMENTARY MATHEMATICS FROM AN ADVANCED STANDPOINT by Felix Klein. Volume I: Arithmetic, Algebra, Analysis. Translated from the third German edition by E. R. Hedrick and C. A. Noble. "A very attractive introduction into some of the most modern developments of the theory of groups of finite order, with emphasis on its applications."--American Mathematical Monthly. Yellow (Grundlehren) Series. Index. 5-1/2 x 8-1/2. xiv + 274 pages. 125 illustrations. $3.75

ELEMENTARY MATHEMATICS FROM AN ADVANCED STANDPOINT by Felix Klein. Volume II: Geometry. Translated from the third German edition by E. R. Hedrick and C. A. Noble. "Required reading for anyone planning to teach high school geometry and...interesting and valuable to the experienced teacher."--School Science and Mathematics. Yellow (Grundlehren) Series. 5-1/2 x 8-1/2. ix + 214 pages. 141 illustrations. $2.95

GRUNDZÜGE DER THEORETISCHEN LOGIK by D Hilbert and W. Acker-
man. Second revised edition. Yellow (Grundlehren) Series. Text in German. Bibliography. Index. 5-1/2 x 8-1/2. xi + 133 pages. (Originally
published at $4.50). $3.00

MENGENLEHRE by F. Hausdorff. Third revised edition. Text in German.
Bibliography. Index. 5-1/2 x 8-1/2. v + 307 pages. 12 illustrations.
(Originally published at $10.00). $3.95

ORDINARY DIFFERENTIAL EQUATIONS by E. L. Ince. Fourth revised
edition. "Notable addition to the mathematical literature in English."
--Bulletin of the American Mathematical Society. 4 appendices. Index.
5-1/2 x 9. viii + 558 pages. 18 illustrations. (Originally published at
$12.00). $4.95

THEORIE DER DIFFERENTIALGLEICHUNGEN by Ludwig Bieberbach.
Third revised edition. Yellow (Grundlehren) Series. Text in German.
Index. 5-1/2 x 8-1/2. xvii + 399 pages. 22 illustrations. (Originally
published at $10.00). $3.95

DIE THEORIE DER GRUPPEN VON ENDLICHER ORDNUNG by Andreas
Speiser. Third revised edition. Yellow (Grundlehren) Series. Text in
German. Index. 5-1/2 x 8-1/2. x + 262 pages. 41 illustrations. (Orig-
inally published at $9.00). $3.95

THEORY OF FUNCTIONS by Konrad Knopp. Part I: Elements of the General Theory of Analytic Functions. Translated from the fifth German
edition by Frederick Bagemihl. "There is little doubt but that this is
the best monograph on functions of a complex variable yet written."
--American Mathematical Monthly. Bibliography. Index. 4-1/4 x 6-1/2.
xii + 146 pages. 4 illustrations. $1.50

THEORY OF FUNCTIONS by Konrad Knopp. Part II: Applications and
Further Development of the General Theory. Translated from the
fourth German edition by Frederick Bagemihl. Bibliography. Index.
4-1/4 x 6-1/2. x + 150 pages. 8 illustrations. $1.50

PROBLEM BOOK IN THE THEORY OF FUNCTIONS by Konrad Knopp.
Volume I: Problems in the Elementary Theory of Functions. Translated
by Lipman Bers. "The difficult task of selecting from the immense
material of the modern theory of functions the problems just within the
reach of the beginner is here masterfully accomplished."--Bulletin of
the American Mathematical Society. Dover Series in Mathematics and
Physics. 4-1/4 x 6-3/8. viii + 126 pages. $1.85

VORLESUNGEN UBER DIFFERENTIALGEOMETRIE by Wilhelm Blaschke.
Volume I: Elementare Differentialgeometrie. Third revised edition. Yellow (Grundlehren) Series. Text in German. English translation of table
of contents. German-English glossary-index. 5-1/2 x 8-1/2. xiv + 322
pages. 35 figures. (Originally published at $9.00). $3.95

APPLIED MATHEMATICS
AND MATHEMATICAL PHYSICS

APPLIED ELASTICITY by John Prescott. "... important contribution... old material presented in new and refreshing form... many original investigations."--Nature. 3 appendices. Index. 5-1/2 x 8-1/2. vi + 666 pages. (Originally published at $9.50). $3.95

BESSEL FUNCTIONS, Eleven and Fifteen-Place Tables of Bessel Functions of the First Kind to All Significant Orders by Enzo Cambi. The main tables give Jn (x) for x = 0 (0.01) 10.5 and n = 0 (1) 29 to 11 places. A supplementary table gives Jn (x) for x = 0 (0.001) 0.5 and n = 0 (1) 11 to 15 places. Bibliography. 8-1/2 x 10-3/4. Hard binding. vi + 160 pages. 2 graphs. $3.95

FOUNDATIONS OF NUCLEAR PHYSICS. Compiled by Robert T. Beyer. Facsimile reproductions with text in the original language of French, German or English of the 13 most important papers in atomic research by Chadwick, Cockcroft, Yukawa, Fermi, etc. 122 page bibliography with over 5,000 classified entries. 6-1/8 x 9-1/4. x = 272 pages. Illustrated. $2.95

HIGHER MATHEMATICS FOR STUDENTS OF CHEMISTRY AND PHYSICS by J. W. Mellor. Fourth revised edition. "... an eminently readable and thoroughly practical treatise."--Nature. 2 appendices. Index. 5-1/2 x 8-1/2. xxix + 641 pages. 189 figures. 18 tables. (Originally published at $7.00). $4.50

HYDRODYNAMICS by Sir Horace Lamb. Sixth revised edition. "Standard work... important theories (of the dynamics of liquids and gases), which underlie many present-day practical applications, are dealt with thoroughly and with mathematical rigour."--Engineering Societies Library. Index. 6 x 9. xviii + 738 pages. 83 illustrations. (Originally published at $13.75). $5.95

INTRODUCTION TO THE DIFFERENTIAL EQUATIONS OF PHYSICS by L. Hopf. Translated by Walter Nef. "There is a surprising amount of valuable material packed into this small book."--School Science and Mathematics. Dover Series in Mathematics and Physics. Index. 4-1/4 x 6-3/8. vi + 154 pages. 48 illustrations. $1.95

INTRODUCTION TO THE THEORY OF FOURIER'S SERIES AND INTE-GRALS by H. S. Carslaw. Third revised edition. "... needs little introduction... much new material has been introduced (in the present edition)... clearly and attractively written."--Nature. 2 appendices. Index. 5-3/8 x 8. xiii + 368 pages. 39 illustrations. $3.95

DIE MATHEMATISCHEN HILFSMITTEL DES PHYSIKERS by Erwin Madelung. Third revised edition. "Standard... collection of mathematical definitions and formulas and of laws and equations used in theoretical and applied physics."--Electronics Industries.Yellow (Grundlehren) Series. Text in German. German-English glossary. Bibliography. Index. 6 x 9. xvi + 384 pages. 25 illustrations. (Originally published at $12.00). $3.95

MICRO-WAVES AND WAVE GUIDES by H. M. Barlow. Up-to-date exposition which describes both the accomplishments and future possibilities in this increasingly important field. Glossary of symbols used. Bibliography. Index. 5-1/2 x 8-1/2. x + 122 pages. 70 illustrations. $1.95

PARTIAL DIFFERENTIAL EQUATIONS OF MATHEMATICAL PHYSICS by H. Bateman. First American edition with corrections. "The book must be in the hands of everyone who is interested in the boundary value problems of mathematical physics."--Bulletin of the American Mathematical Society. Appendix. Index. 6 x 9. xxii + 522 pages. 29 illustrations. (Originally published at $10.00). $4.95

PRACTICAL ANALYSIS (GRAPHICAL AND NUMERICAL METHODS) by Fr. A. Willers. Translated by Robert T. Beyer. Section on calculating machines rewritten by Tracy W. Simpson to reflect current methods with American-made calculators. "...is to be recommended as a convenient reference book."--Bulletin of the American Mathematical Society. Index. 6-1/8 x 9-1/4. x + 422 pages. 132 illustrations. $6.00

SPHERICAL HARMONICS, An Elementary Treatise on Harmonic Functions with Applications by T. M. MacRobert. Second revised edition. "...scholarly treatment of the type of problems arising in a great many branches of theoretical physics and the tools whereby such problems may be attacked."--Bulletin of the American Mathematical Society. Index. 5-1/2 x 8-1/2. vi + 372 pages. $4.50

THEORIE UND ANWENDUNG DER LAPLACE-TRANSFORMATION by Gustav Doetsch. Second revised edition. Yellow (Grundlehren) Series. Text in German. German-English glossary. Bibliography. Index. 6 x 9. xiv + 439 pages. 18 illustrations. Tables of Laplace transformations. (Originally published at $14.50). $3.95

THE THEORY OF SOUND by Lord Rayleigh. With an Historical Introduction by Robert Bruce Lindsay. Second revised edition. "...makes this outstanding treatise available again, and furthermore, at a popular price."--Review of Scientific Instruments. Appendix. Index. 5-1/2 x 8-1/2. Volume I: xlii + 408 pages. Volume II: xvi + 504 pages. (Originally published in two volumes at $8.00).

Unabridged One Volume Edition-- $5.95

A TREATISE ON THE ANALYTICAL DYNAMICS OF PARTICLES AND RIGID BODIES by E. T. Whittaker. Fourth revised edition. "...exhibits great mathematical power and attainments..."--Bulletin of the American Mathematical Society. Index. 6 x 9. xiv + 456 pages. (Originally published at $6.00). $4.50

A TREATISE ON THE MATHEMATICAL THEORY OF ELASTICITY by A. E. H. Love. Fourth revised edition. "...has been for years the standard treatise on elasticity...presents a picture of this extensive field in all its aspects in a single volume..."--American Mathematical Monthly. Index. 6 x 9. xxi + 643 pages. 76 illustrations. (Originally published at $10.50). $5.95

PHYSICS AND CHEMISTRY

ATOMIC SPECTRA AND ATOMIC STRUCTURE by Gerhard Herzberg. Translated with the cooperation of the author by J. W T. Spinks. Second revised edition. "...the vector model and the quantum mechanical view are skillfully blended together into a unified description of atomic processes..."--Nature. Bibliography. Index. 5-1/4 x 8-1/4. xv + 257 pages. 80 illustrations. 21 tables. (Originally published at $5.70). $3.95

BIOMETRICAL GENETICS, THE STUDY OF CONTINUOUS VARIATION by K. Mather. Based on the use of measurements, this work examines the pheno-type classes for which older methods of discontinuous variation are useless. 5-1/2 x 8-1/2. x + 158 pages. 16 diagrams. $3.50

COSMIC RADIATION. Edited by W. Heisenberg. Translated from the German by T. H. Johnson. 15 articles on recent accomplishments in the field written by eminent German physicists during World War II. Material well integrated with numerous cross references and consistent notation. Bibliography. Index. 6 x 9. xvi + 192 pages. 36 illustrations. 13 tables. $3.95

DESIGN OF CRYSTAL VIBRATING SYSTEMS by William J. Fry, John M. Taylor and Bertha W. Henvis. Second revised edition. Procedures for design of projectors involving a general set of curves based on fundamental piezoelectric relations. "Contains much valuable material released for the first time for general publication."--Electronic Engineering. 4 appendices. 6-1/8 x 9-1/4. viii + 182 pages. 126 graphs. $3.50

THE EVOLUTION OF SCIENTIFIC THOUGHT FROM NEWTON TO EINSTEIN by A. d'Abro. "...covers many more topics than any other popular book in English of which I know, and there are many admirable features in the presentation..."--Physical Review. 4 appendices. 5-3/8 x 8. 544 pages. $5.00

GAS DYNAMICS TABLES FOR AIR by Howard W. Emmons. "The precision of the computations makes the tables adequate for many special uses."--Review of Scientific Instruments. 6-1/8 x 9-1/4. Semi-stiff binding. 46 pages. 3 illustrations. 4 tables. 10 graphs. $1.75

HYDROLOGY. Edited by Oscar E. Meinzer. Chapters by 24 experts on precipitation, glaciers, soil moistures, runoff, droughts, hydrology of limestone and lava-rock terranes, etc. "Most up-to-date and most complete treatment of the subject..."--Bulletin of the American Association of Petroleum Geologists. Physics of the Earth Series. Bibliography. Index. 6-1/8 x 9-1/4. xi + 712 pages. 165 illustrations. 23 tables. (Originally published at $8.00). $4.95

MATHEMATICAL FOUNDATIONS OF STATISTICAL MECHANICS by A. I. Khinchin. Translated by G. Gamow. The most rigorous mathematical discussion available. Dover Series in Mathematics and Physics. Appendix. Notations. Index. 5 x 7-3/8. viii + 179 pages. $2.95

DOVER BOOKS ON SCIENCE

MATHEMATISCHE GRUNDLAGEN DER QUANTENMECHANIK by Johann von Neumann. Yellow (Grundlehren) Series. Text in German. German-English glossary. Index. 6 x 9. vi + 266 pages. 4 illustrations. (Originally published at $7.85). **$3.95**

MATTER AND LIGHT, THE NEW PHYSICS by Louis de Broglie. Translated by W. H. Johnston. 21 essays on present day physics, matter and electricity, light and radiation, wave mechanics and the philosophical implications of scientific achievement. 4-7/8 x 7-3/4. iv + 300 pages. (Originally published at $3.50). **$2.75**

THE NATURE OF PHYSICAL THEORY by P. W. Bridgman. "It can easily be read in about three hours, but it will then demand to be reread, parts of it several times over."--Review of Scientific Instruments. Index. 5-3/8 x 8. xi + 138 pages. **$2.25**

THE PHASE RULE AND ITS APPLICATIONS by Alexander Findlay. Eighth revised edition. "It has established itself as the standard work on the subject..."--Nature. Index. 5-1/2 x 8-1/2. xxxi + 313 pages. 163 illustrations. **$3.95**

POLAR MOLECULES by P. Debye. "This book not only brings together for the first time the accumulated information on electric dipoles, but also points out the gaps which still exist in theory and experiment." --Nature. Index. 5-1/2 x 8-1/2. iv + 172 pages. 33 illustrations. (Originally published at $8.00). **$3.50**

TABLES OF FUNCTIONS WITH FORMULAE AND CURVES (FUNKTION-ENTAFELN) by Eugene Jahnke and Fritz Emde. Fourth revised edition containing 400 corrections of errors and a supplementary bibliography of 43 titles. Text in German and English. Bibliography. Index. 5-1/2 x 8-1/2. xvi + 382 pages. 212 illustrations. (Originally published at $6.00). **$4.95**

LES TENSEURS EN MECANIQUE ET EN ELASTICITE by Leon Brillouin. "...first comprehensive treatise in any language on which the main emphasis is laid on the tensorial formulation of the classical (non-relativistic) laws of physics..."--Review of Scientific Instruments. Text in French. Index. 6 x 9. xx + 364 pages. 114 figures. **$3.95**

TERRESTRIAL MAGNETISM AND ELECTRICITY. Edited by J. A. Fleming. Chapters by 14 leading geophysicists. "An important and authoritative production...making available...the present state and fascinating and difficult problems of this branch of earth science."--Proceedings, Physical Society of London. Physics of the Earth Series. Bibliography with 1,523 entries. Index. 6-1/8 x 9-1/4. xii + 794 pages. 296 illustrations. (Originally published at $8.00). **$4.95**

TIME, KNOWLEDGE, AND THE NEBULAE by Martin Johnson. Foreword by Professor E. A. Milne. "...succinct and lucid summary of the new cosmology involved in Professor Milne's theory of relativity, of its physical background and of its possible philosophical significance." --London Times. Bibliography. Index. 5-1/2 x 8-1/2. iii + 189 pages. **$2.75**